MACMILLAN COLLEGE WORK OUT SE

Mechanics

Titles in this Series

MACMILLAN COLLEGE WORK OUT SERIES

Mechanics

Phil Dyke

MACMILLAN

First published 1995 by
MACMILLAN PRESS LTD
Houndmills, Basingstoke, Hampshire RG21 2XS
and London
Companies and representatives
throughout the world

ISBN 0–333–58522–4

A catalogue record for this book is available
from the British Library.

10 9   8   7   6   5   4   3   2   1
04 03 02 01 00 99 98 97 96 95

Printed in Malaysia

To my son Adrian

Contents

Preface

Since the time of Isaac Newton (1642–1727) and probably before, mechanics has played a central role in mathematics and physics. It is also essential for other subjects such as physical chemistry and civil, mechanical and aeronautical engineering.

Mathematics, and those subjects that use mathematics extensively, such as physics and engineering, are based on skill. In much the same way as sportsmen and sportswomen learn by doing, so do mathematicians and allied professionals learn by solving problems. Initially of course the golfer needs to know how to grip the club and how to stand, the pianist needs to know the rudiments of the keyboard and musical notation. Similarly, the student of mechanics needs to know the tools of the trade, in this case some algebra and calculus, a little geometry and trigonometry and some familiarity with vectors. After this, however, there is no substitute for doing problems. Many students have great difficulty getting started on a problem. One of the merits of this *Work Out* series is that the student learns precisely how to start by watching someone else (in this case me) doing problems. As I do the problems, I talk the reader through my thinking processes, so there should be no doubt why particular steps are being taken and why we are doing what we are doing at any particular stage. It has been said that of all skills-based subjects, mechanics stands out as being unique in benefitting students through exposing them to solved problems. I agree wholeheartedly with this. I learnt most of my mechanics by seeing others solve problems. The ones I have selected for this book include all my favourites. (I used to get so annoyed when the books I consulted never seemed to solve the hard problems. I sincerely hope that this criticism cannot be levelled here.) There are, at the end of each chapter, some exercises you should try for yourself. Outline solutions to all exercises are available at the very end of each set of exercises, but please resist the temptation to cheat!

Before running through the contents, some comments about student background and computer algebra are necessary. In the last ten years or so, the amount of algebraic manipulation required of schoolchildren in pre-16 mathematics has dramatically decreased. This has occurred in an environment when more assessment is in the form of course work rather than examination. It is much more difficult to assess skills such as algebraic manipulation (or spelling for that matter) outside the formal examination. In my view, the decrease in algebra skills has happened by default rather than by design. Parallel with this has been the loss of geometry at school level. Both of these have changed the kind of mechanics problems that can be tackled by the average student. I have taken this into account in selecting the problems. This brings me to computer algebra. I have, a little reluctantly, decided not to emphasise computer algebra. There are many packages available (Macsyma©, Derive©, Maple© and Mathematica© to name but a few). There are also many other excellent software packages, which will increasingly affect the education of mathematicians. (I have used Omnigraph© extensively in Chapter 12 for example). As yet there is no standard, and to base a problem-solving text such as this on just one computer algebra package would not be wise. Also, my colleagues and I can still find faults in most of these packages, in much the same way as no spell-checker is perfect in a word processor. The upshot of this is that I have included much of the algebraic manipulation in the solved problems. In mechanics, there is often an obvious point when all the mechanics has been done and the rest is calculus or algebra. Nevertheless, in order to get an answer, the solving of the equations is necessary. The reader thus has the choice of checking (following) the manipulations by hand or inputting the equations into the chosen package and executing the appropriate menu-driven instructions.

This *Work Out* assumes that the student is familiar with mechanics as presented to 17 to 19 year-olds. If you have zero knowledge or have had a very bad educational experience with regard to mechanics, my *Guide to Mechanics* (with Roger Whitworth) should cover the preliminary material. There is also some overlap (no bad thing, in my view). The organisation of material in a book such as this is never easy, and for mechanics this seems particularly so. Chapter 1 is a reprise of preliminary notions in mechanics. It is this chapter that should tell you if you need to see the *Guide* first. Chapters 2–10 cover material usually found in the first year of an undergraduate course in mechanics for mathematicians or physicists. It should also cover *all* the mechanics commonly found in engineering and technology courses. I have decided to include Lagrange's equations and Euler's equation (tops and gyroscopes) for completeness. This material usually occupies the second year of mathematics degrees and is absent from engineering degrees; however, it is a crucial precursor for theoretical physicists who wish to study quantum mechanics. It is also, incidently, a wonderfully systematic treatment of mechanics that often appears easy to those who complain at length of the *ad hoc* nature of earlier mechanics. Lagrange's equations almost seem like pure mathematics. Finally, Chapter 12 is a brief introduction to non-linear mechanics, which is a very fashionable area to study these days. Everyone seems to have heard of 'chaos', although few, I think, understand it.

In summary, therefore, you can expect to find the solved problems here representative of those in most undergraduate mechanics courses. In line with other *Work Out* texts, the material in this book can certainly be used in any order. There is very little cross-referencing, except perhaps for information. The 'fact sheet' at the beginning of each chapter is a brief summary of relevant formulae and results which is best used as a reference.

Phil Dyke
December 1993

Acknowledgements

I wish to thank all those who have taught me through my school and undergraduate years, particularly Harry Sefton, who stimulated my interest in mechanics. I should like to thank my colleagues at Plymouth for several discussions, particularly John Birch for useful input to one or two solutions, and Adrian Romilly for all those books. Thanks also to the University of London for permission to reproduce exam questions. However, all solutions and all mistakes are completely my responsibility.

Finally, special thanks to my wife Heather, who spent long hours word processing when there was so much else to do.

1 Revision of Preliminary Ideas

1.1 Fact Sheet

The Fundamental Process

1. Draw a diagram.
2. Choose a *fixed* origin.
3. Choose fixed axes, enough so that when each coordinate is frozen at a constant value, nothing can move.
4. Draw *all* the forces in the diagram.
5. Write down Newton's second law (in vector form, or in component form) for all particles or, equivalently, for the centres of mass of all rigid bodies. (If you are unfamiliar with rigid bodies, see Chapter 9.) Add to these equations that arise from experimental laws (e.g. Hooke's law for linear springs, laws for limiting friction) and the rotational equations for rigid bodies.
6. Write down the boundary conditions.

Then (hopefully) the problem can be solved – at least it now becomes one of solving differential equations.

Kinematics of a Particle

If $\mathbf{r}$ is the **displacement** of a particle from a fixed origin, $d\mathbf{r}/dt = \dot{\mathbf{r}}$ is its **velocity** and $d^2\mathbf{r}/dt^2 = d\mathbf{v}/dt = \ddot{\mathbf{r}}$ is its **acceleration**. In one dimension, displacement $= x$, velocity $= dx/dt = v$ and acceleration $= d^2x/dt^2 = dv/dt = v\,dv/dx$. The last expression is often very useful since it does not involve time explicitly.

Equilibrium

A particle is in equilibrium if the net force on the particle is zero.

Newton's Laws of Motion

1. Every body will remain at rest or continue to move with uniform velocity unless an external force is applied to it.
2. When an external force is applied to a body, the force produces an acceleration. This acceleration is directly proportional to the force. The constant of proportionality is the (constant) mass of the body. (See Chapter 5 for variable mass problems.) Mathematically:

$$\mathbf{F} = m\frac{d^2\mathbf{r}}{dt^2}$$

3. When a body A exerts a force on a body B, B exerts an equal and opposite force on A.

Resolution of Forces

Since force is a vector quantity, it can be resolved into three mutually perpendicular directions:

$$\mathbf{F} = (F_1, F_2, F_3) = F_1\mathbf{i} + F_2\mathbf{j} + F_3\mathbf{k}$$

1

(The two notations are used interchangeably; see Appendix A.) Thus Newton's second law, in component form, is

$$F_1 = m \frac{d^2x}{dt^2}, \; F_2 = m \frac{d^2y}{dt^2}, \; F_3 = m \frac{d^2z}{dt^2}$$

$$\mathbf{r} = (x,y,z) = x\mathbf{i} + y\mathbf{j} + z\mathbf{k}$$

A Rigid Body   A rigid body is a body such that any two points inside the body always remain the same distance apart, no matter what forces are acting. (See Chapter 9 for more about rigid bodies.)

Levers   Levers work using the **principle of moments** (a full discussion of which is left until Chapter 2). For equilibrium, the moment about any point of the forces acting on a rigid body must be zero. This principle can be used to calculate the minimum force required to move an object, but not to calculate the force on an object once it is moving.

1.2 Worked Examples

1.1   The acceleration of a body moving in one dimension is given by $a = 1 - x$. Determine the velocity v if $v = 2$ when $x = 1$ and hence show that the body always lies in the range $-1 \leq x \leq 3$. Determine x in terms of time t.

Solution   The acceleration is given in terms of x; hence we use $a = v \, dv/dx$ so that

$$v \frac{dv}{dx} = 1 - x$$

Integrating with respect to x gives

$$\frac{v^2}{2} = x - \frac{x^2}{2} + A$$

If $v = 2$ when $x = 1$, we obtain

$$\tfrac{1}{2} 4 = 1 - \tfrac{1}{2} + A$$

or

$$A = \tfrac{3}{2}$$

whence

$$\tfrac{1}{2} v^2 = x - \tfrac{1}{2} x^2 + \tfrac{3}{2}$$

or

$$v^2 = 3 + 2x - x^2$$
$$= (3 - x)(1 + x)$$

Since $v^2 \geq 0$, we must have either

$$3 - x \geq 0 \quad and \quad 1 + x \geq 0 \tag{1.1}$$

or

$$3 - x \leq 0 \quad and \quad 1 + x \leq 0 \tag{1.2}$$

Equation (1.1) gives $x \leq 3$ and $x \geq -1$, but Equation (1.2) gives $x \geq 3$ and $x \geq -1$ (which is impossible). Hence $-1 \leq x \leq 3$.

This type of motion occurs if masses are connected to springs. Writing $v = dx/dt$ we see that

$$\frac{dx}{dt} = [(3 - x)(1 + x)]^{1/2} = (3 + 2x - x^2)^{1/2} = [4 - (1 - x)^2]^{1/2}$$

$$\therefore \int \frac{dx}{[4 - (1 - x)^2]} = \int dt$$

Recall the standard integral

$$\int \frac{dx}{(a^2 - x^2)} = \sin^{-1}\left(\frac{x}{a}\right)$$

Hence

$$\sin^{-1}\left(\frac{1 - x}{2}\right) = t + \phi$$

or

$$1 - x = 2\sin(t + \phi)$$

i.e.

$$x = 1 - 2\sin(t + \phi)$$

where ϕ is an arbitrary constant (called the phase). We confirm from this that the maximum value of x is 3 ($t + \phi = -\pi/2$ plus any multiple of 2π), that the minimum value of x is -1 ($t + \phi = \pi/2$ plus any multiple of 2π), and that the body oscillates about $x = 1$, with amplitude 2. We shall have more to say about oscillations in Chapter 6.

1.2 The displacement of a particle from the origin is given by $x = 1/(1 + t)$, where t = time. Find the velocity and acceleration in terms of both x and t and hence describe the motion.

Solution Given that $x = 1/(1 + t)$, we differentiate to obtain

$$v = \frac{dx}{dt} = -\frac{1}{(1 + t)^2} = -x^2$$

Differentiating again gives

$$a = \frac{dv}{dt} = \frac{2}{(1 + t)^3} = 2x^3$$

We see that the particle starts from $x = 1$ with a velocity $v = -1$ (that is, directed towards the origin). As it approaches the origin, it slows and tends towards it but never reaches it. As $t \to \infty$, $x \to 0$, $v \to 0$ and $a \to 0$. Note that $a > 0$ (acceleration is positive), but $v < 0$, that is the particle moves in the negative x-direction, which means that the positive acceleration slows down the particle. Always be mindful of direction in mechanics.

1.3 The vector displacement of a particle is given by $\mathbf{r} = \hat{\mathbf{i}}t^2 - \hat{\mathbf{j}}t^{-2}$. Determine its velocity, speed and acceleration. At what time are the velocity and displacement at right angles?

Solution   Given that

$$\mathbf{r} = \hat{\mathbf{i}}t^2 + \hat{\mathbf{j}}t^{-2}$$

differentiate with respect to t to give the velocity:

$$\mathbf{v} = \frac{d\mathbf{r}}{dt} = 2t\hat{\mathbf{i}} - 2\hat{\mathbf{j}}t^{-3}$$

Take the modulus to obtain the speed:

$$|\mathbf{v}| = \left|\frac{d\mathbf{r}}{dt}\right| = 2(t^2 + t^{-6})^{1/2}$$

Finally, differentiate $\mathbf{v}$ to find the acceleration:

$$\mathbf{a} = \frac{d\mathbf{v}}{dt} = 2\hat{\mathbf{i}} + 6\hat{\mathbf{j}}t^{-4}$$

Thus, taking the scalar product, we obtain

$$\mathbf{v} \cdot \mathbf{r} = 2t^3 - 2t^{-5}$$

For $\mathbf{v}$ and $\mathbf{r}$ to be at right angles, $\mathbf{v} \cdot \mathbf{r} = 0$. This occurs only at $t = 1$. The path of the particle is found by eliminating t from $x = t^2$, $y = t^{-2}$, giving $xy = 1$, a rectangular hyperbola. At $t = 1$, the particle is at (1,1) and at this point the tangent is $x + y = 2$, which is at right angles to the position vector (1,1) (the line $y = x$).

1.4   Find the value of the forces X and Y shown in Fig. 1.1 such that all the forces are in equilibrium.

Solution   Resolving horizontally:

$$Y\sin 30° + X\cos 30° = 3$$

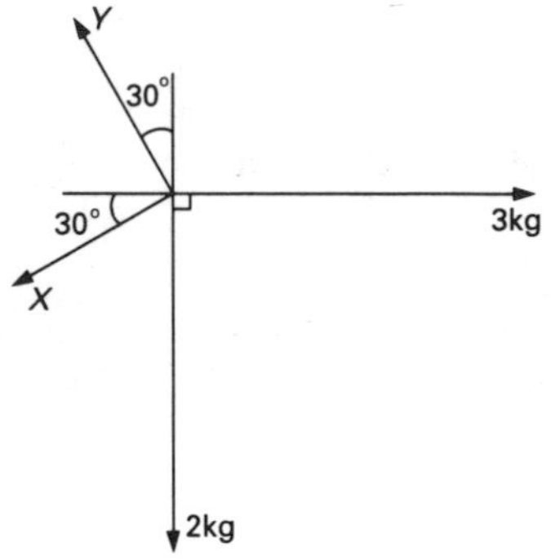

Resolving vertically:

$$-Y\cos 30° + X\sin 30° = -2$$

These equations are

$$\tfrac{1}{2}Y + \frac{\sqrt{3}}{2}X = 3 \tag{1.3}$$

and

$$-\frac{\sqrt{3}}{2}Y = \tfrac{1}{2}X = -2 \tag{1.4}$$

respectively. Manipulating as follows:

$$(1.3) \times \sqrt{3} + (1.2): \quad (\tfrac{3}{2} + \tfrac{1}{2})X = 3\sqrt{3} - 2$$

$$\therefore X = \tfrac{3}{2}\sqrt{3} - 1 \approx 1.6$$

$$(1.3) - (1.4) \times \sqrt{3}: \quad (\tfrac{1}{2} + \tfrac{3}{2})Y = 3 + 2\sqrt{3}$$

$$\therefore Y = \tfrac{3}{2} + \sqrt{3} \approx 3.2$$

These are the required values.

Figure 1.1

1.5 A neutrally buoyant jellyfish of mass 0.2 kg is travelling with a speed of 0.5 m s^{-1} in still water with negligible resistance.

(a) How far will it travel in 10 s if it does not use any propulsion?

(b) The jellyfish accelerates over the distance found in part (a). If the time of travel is now 5 s, find the acceleration and the force necessary to produce this acceleration.

(c) Estimate the speed of the jellyfish at the end of the 5 s. (You may assume that the jellyfish acts as a particle for this problem.)

Solution

(a) Time taken $= 10$ s, uniform speed $= 0.5$ m s^{-1}.
Newton's first law states that this uniform speed persists, hence distance travelled $= 10 \times 0.5 = 5$ m.

(b) Uniform acceleration of jellyfish $= a = dv/dt$. Integrating gives

$$v = at + A$$

At $t = 0$, $v = 0.5$; Hence $A = 0.5$, whence $v = at + 0.5$.

Also

$$v = \frac{dx}{dt} = at + 0.5$$

Integrating with respect to t gives

$$x = \tfrac{1}{2}at^2 + 0.5t + B$$

At $t = 0$, $x = 0$; thus $B = 0$.
After 5 s, the jellyfish has travelled 5 m. Inserting $x = 5$ and $t = 5$ gives

$$5 = \tfrac{1}{2}a(5)^2 + 0.5 \times 5$$

or

$$\frac{2.5 \times 2}{25} = a$$

$$\therefore a = 0.2 \text{ m s}^{-2}$$

The force necessary to produce this acceleration, using Newton's second law (force $=$ mass $\times$ acceleration) is

$$\text{Force} = 0.2 \times 0.2 = 0.04 \text{ N}$$

(c) From part (b) we have that

$$v = at + 0.5$$

Inserting $t = 5$ and $a = 0.2$ gives $v = 0.6$ m s^{-1}, the required speed.

1.6 It's Christmas time, and those lazy reindeer have overslept again! Father Christmas has to pull the sleigh himself. If the sleigh (laden with presents of course) weighs 150 kg and the (light) rope makes an angle of 15° to the ground, calculate the force Father Christmas needs to apply to move the sleigh at a constant speed, neglecting start up, if

(a) the ground is frictionless level ice;

(b) the ground is level packed snow with coefficient of dynamic friction 0.15;

(c) the ground is snow (coefficient of dynamic friction 0.15) with an upward slope of 1:10.

Assume $g = 9.81 \text{ m s}^{-2}$ and that $\sin\alpha = 0.1$ where α is the angle the ground makes with the horizontal for part (c).

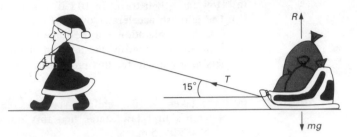

Figure 1.2

Solution   (a) Figure 1.2 displays the situation. Let T be the tension in the rope, R be the reaction and mg = the weight of the sleigh. (Note that $mg = 150 \times 9.81 = 1471.5 \text{ N}$.) Since the sleigh is moving at constant speed, by Newton's first law the net force on the sleigh must be zero. Resolving parallel and perpendicular to the ground gives the following equations:

$$\text{perpendicular to the ground:} \quad R + T\sin15° = mg$$
$$\text{parallel to the ground:} \quad T\cos15° = 0$$

Hence $T = 0$, and Father Christmas has to exert no force.

(b) The new situation is shown in Fig. 1.3. This time, a frictional force is added, and the equations are:

$$\text{perpendicular to the ground:} \quad R + T\sin15° = mg \qquad \textbf{(1.5)}$$
$$\text{parallel to the ground:} \quad T\cos15° = F \qquad \textbf{(1.6)}$$

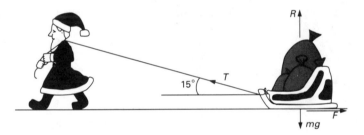

Figure 1.3

Also, since the sleigh is sliding, F is at its maximum value, given by $F = \mu R$, where $\mu = 0.15$ is the coefficient of dynamic friction. So we have a third equation

$$F = 0.15R \qquad \textbf{(1.7)}$$

We thus have three equations for three unknowns F, R and T. We wish to find T; hence we eliminate F and R. Combining Equations (1.6) and (1.7) gives

$$T\cos15° = 0.15R$$

whence

$$R = \frac{T\cos15°}{0.15}$$

Substituting this into Equation (1.5) gives

$$\frac{T\cos15°}{0.15} + T\sin15° = mg$$

Inserting the values $\cos15° = 0.966$, $\sin15° = 0.259$ and $mg = 1471.5 \text{ N}$ gives $T = 219.7 \text{ N}$. Hence Father Christmas has to exert a pull of 219.7 N.

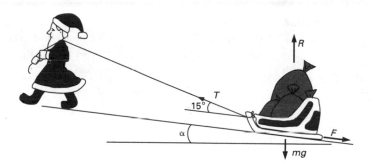

Figure 1.4

(c) Finally, the sleigh needs to be pulled up a slope α, where sinα = 0.1. Figure 1.4 shows the forces. We still resolve parallel and perpendicular to the ground. *R* is the *normal* reaction and Father Christmas's rope is still 15° to the ground (not the horizontal). With the angle α defined as drawn in Fig. 1.4 and with friction at its limiting value (0.15*R*), the equations are as follows:

$$\text{perpendicular to the ground:} \quad R + T\sin15° = mg\cos\alpha \qquad (1.8)$$
$$\text{parallel to the ground:} \quad F + mg\sin\alpha = T\cos15° \qquad (1.9)$$
$$\text{together with} \quad F = 0.15R \qquad (1.7)$$

Eliminating *F* between Equations (1.7) and (1.9) gives

$$0.15R + mg\sin\alpha = T\cos15°$$

Hence

$$R = \frac{T\cos15° - mg\sin\alpha}{0.15}$$

Substituting this into Equation (1.8) yields

$$\frac{T\cos15° - mg\sin\alpha}{0.15} + T\sin15° = mg\cos\alpha$$

Therefore

$$T = \frac{mg\sin\alpha + 0.15mg\cos\alpha}{\cos15° + 0.15\sin15°}$$

Substituting the values cosα = 0.995, sinα = 0.1, cos15° = 0.966 and sin15° = 0.259 gives *T* = 365 N. Hence poor Father Christmas has to pull with a force 365 N up the slope.

1.7 A force of 200 N is exerted on the handle of a claw hammer as it is used to extract a nail. The dimensions are shown in Fig. 1.5. What is the force that can be exerted on the nail?

Solution Since the point O is fixed, we can take moments to obtain the equation

$$0.05F = 0.2 \times 200 \text{ N}$$

Therefore

$$F = 40/0.05 = 800 \text{ N}$$

The next example looks at another class of lever.

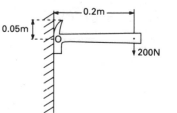

Figure 1.5

1.8 A force of 300 N is used to crack a Brazil nut. The dimensions are shown in Fig. 1.6. Calculate the force on the nut.

Solution As in the previous problem, we can take moments about O. The hinge at O is taken to be smooth, so that the force of 300 N on the upper and lower arms at B is related to the force F on the lower and upper jaws at A (respectively) by equating the moment on each arm. Either equation gives

$$0.02F = 0.1 \times 300$$

or

Figure 1.6

$$F = 1500 \text{ N}$$

Surely enough to crack any Brazil nut.

1.3 Exercises

1.1 The acceleration of a body is given by

$$a = x(4 - x^2)^{1/2}$$

where x represents the body's displacement from its starting position. Given that $v = 2 \text{ m s}^{-1}$ when $x = 0$, find:

(a) v in terms of x
(b) the value of x when $v = 0$
(c) the maximum value of v

1.2 On a flat visual display, the position of the cursor is given by the position vector $\mathbf{r} = 2t\hat{\mathbf{i}} - 2t^2\hat{\mathbf{j}}$.

(a) Determine the velocity and acceleration.
(b) Determine the equation of the path of the cursor.
(c) At what time (>0) is the velocity at right angles to the position vector?

1.3 A bee of mass 0.002 kg flies along the line $\mathbf{l} = 3\hat{\mathbf{i}} + 2\hat{\mathbf{j}}$ with constant speed $\frac{1}{2}\sqrt{13} \text{ ms}^{-1}$, where $\hat{\mathbf{i}}$ is due east and $\mathbf{j}$ is due north. A west wind springs up, and lasts for 40 s. This wind subjects the insect to a constant force of 10^{-4} N. What velocity is the insect flying at:

(a) after 10 s?
(b) after 30 s?
(c) when there is no longer any wind?

1.4 Find the resultants of the following sets of forces:

(a) $\mathbf{F}_1 = 3\hat{\mathbf{i}} + 2\hat{\mathbf{j}}$, $\mathbf{F}_2 = -4\hat{\mathbf{j}}$, $\mathbf{F}_3 = -2\hat{\mathbf{i}} + 5\hat{\mathbf{j}}$

(b) $\mathbf{F}_1 = 3\hat{\mathbf{i}} + 4\hat{\mathbf{j}} - 5\hat{\mathbf{k}}$, $\mathbf{F}_2 = 2\hat{\mathbf{i}} + \hat{\mathbf{j}} + \hat{\mathbf{k}}$, $\mathbf{F}_3 = \hat{\mathbf{i}} + \hat{\mathbf{j}} + \hat{\mathbf{k}}$

(c) $\mathbf{F}_1 = 3\sin^2\theta\hat{\mathbf{i}} - 4.\cos^2\theta\hat{\mathbf{j}}$

$\mathbf{F}_2 = 2\cos^2\theta\hat{\mathbf{i}} - 4\sin^2\theta\hat{\mathbf{j}} + \hat{\mathbf{k}}$

$\mathbf{F}_3 = \cos^2\theta\hat{\mathbf{i}} + 2\hat{\mathbf{k}}$

1.5 Find the components of the following vectors:

(a) a force of magnitude 10 N in the x–y plane, at an angle of 30° to the positive x-axis;
(b) a wind blowing up an incline of 1 in 5 from a south-west direction, of magnitude 30 km h^{-1} ($\hat{\mathbf{i}}$ = east, $\hat{\mathbf{j}}$ = north, $\hat{\mathbf{k}}$ = up)

1.6 A helicopter whose speed is U in still air flies horizontally due north from A to B in a wind blowing with speed w from a direction θ east of north. If the distance between A and B is d, find the time taken for the helicopter to travel.

1.7 A large rock of mass 1000 kg blocks the front entrance of a grotto. What force, F, has to be exerted at the end of a strong stick AB (see Fig. 1.7) in order to move it? The dimensions are shown in Fig. 1.7.

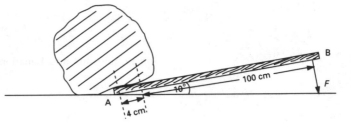

Figure 1.7

1.8 A balloon of total mass M has a downward acceleration f_1. How much ballast must be ejected so that (a) the balloon is neutrally buoyant, or (b) the balloon rises with an acceleration of f_2?

1.9 A woman walks her dog along the x-axis with a constant speed of 1.5 m s^{-1}. At the point where $x = 30$ m, the dog sees a sleeping cat at the point $x = 30$, $y = 30$ and runs directly at it, accelerating at 5 m s^{-2}. The cat continues to sleep. Find:

(a) the angle the lead makes with the y-direction, and
(b) the tension on the lead when the dog is halted, if the dog is stopped after 2 s and its mass is 10 kg.

1.4 Outline Solutions to Exercises

1.1 (a) Since $a = \mathrm{d}v/\mathrm{d}x$, we need to solve

$$v\frac{\mathrm{d}v}{\mathrm{d}x} = x(4 - x^2)^{1/2}$$

which integrates to give

$$\tfrac{1}{2}v^2 = C - \tfrac{1}{3}(4 - x^2)^{3/2} \qquad \textbf{(1.10)}$$

$v = 2$ when $x = 0$, giving $C = 14/3$.

(b) Putting $v = 0$ in Equation (1.10) gives

$$4 - x^2 = 5.81$$

Hence v is never zero.

(c) From Equation (1.10), the maximum value of v occurs at $x = 2$, which gives $v = \sqrt{28/3} = 3.1$ m s^{-1}.

1.2 (a) Since $\mathbf{r} = 2t\hat{\mathbf{i}} - 2t^2\hat{\mathbf{j}}$:

$$\mathbf{v} = \frac{d\mathbf{r}}{dt} = 2\hat{\mathbf{i}} - 4t\hat{\mathbf{j}}$$

and

$$\mathbf{a} = \frac{d\mathbf{v}}{dt} = -4\hat{\mathbf{j}}$$

(b) $x = 2t$ and $y = -2t^2$, hence

$$y = -2\left(\frac{x}{2}\right)^2 = -\tfrac{1}{2}x^2,$$

which is a parabola.

(c) $\mathbf{r} \cdot \mathbf{v} = 0$ if $\mathbf{r}$ is perpendicular to $\mathbf{v}$:

$$\mathbf{r} \cdot \mathbf{v} = 4t - 8t^3$$

whence $\mathbf{r} \cdot \mathbf{v} = 0$ when $t = 1\sqrt{2} = 0.7071$.

1.3 Before the wind starts, the velocity of the bee is $\mathbf{U} = \tfrac{1}{2}(3\hat{\mathbf{i}} + 2\hat{\mathbf{j}})$ m s^{-1} (in the direction of $\mathbf{l}$, magnitude $\tfrac{1}{2}\sqrt{13}$). The force due to the wind is $10^{-4}\hat{\mathbf{i}}$ N (*from* the west is in the $\hat{\mathbf{i}}$ direction). Hence

$$10^{-4}\hat{\mathbf{i}} = 2 \times 10^{-3}\frac{d^2\mathbf{r}}{dt^2}$$

(by Newton's second law), which gives, on integrating:

$$\frac{d\mathbf{r}}{dt} = 0.05t\hat{\mathbf{i}} + \mathbf{U} \qquad\qquad (1.11)$$

where $\mathbf{U} = \tfrac{1}{2}(3\hat{\mathbf{i}} + 2\hat{\mathbf{j}})$.

Hence Equation (1.11) is an expression giving the velocity of the bee at any time t.

(a) $t = 10$ gives

$$\frac{d\mathbf{r}}{dt} = 2\hat{\mathbf{i}} + \hat{\mathbf{j}} \text{ m s}^{-1}$$

(b) $t = 30$ gives

$$\frac{d\mathbf{r}}{dt} = 3\hat{\mathbf{i}} + \hat{\mathbf{j}} \text{ m s}^{-1}$$

(c) When there is no longer any wind, the velocity of the bee remains at $3\hat{\mathbf{i}} + \hat{\mathbf{j}}$ m s^{-1}.

1.4 Simply add the components to give the following resultants:
(a) $\hat{\mathbf{i}} + 3\hat{\mathbf{j}}$ (b) $6\hat{\mathbf{i}} + 6\hat{\mathbf{j}} - 3\hat{\mathbf{k}}$ (c) $3\hat{\mathbf{i}} - 4\hat{\mathbf{j}} + 3\hat{\mathbf{k}}$

1.5 (a) The components are $10\cos30°$ and $10\sin30°$, giving $\mathbf{F} = 5\sqrt{3}\hat{\mathbf{i}} + 5\hat{\mathbf{j}}$ N.

(b) Staying in km h^{-1}, a 1 in 5 slope leads to a $5,1,\sqrt{26}$ triangle, hence giving a wind of 30 km h^{-1} in component form of

$$30\left(\frac{5}{\sqrt{52}}\hat{\mathbf{i}} + \frac{5}{\sqrt{52}}\hat{\mathbf{j}} + \frac{1}{\sqrt{26}}\hat{\mathbf{k}}\right) = 20.8\hat{\mathbf{i}} + 20.8\hat{\mathbf{j}} + 5.88\hat{\mathbf{k}}$$

1.6 If u is the northwards speed of the helicopter, its net northwards speed is thus $u - w\cos\theta$. The helicopter needs to fly $w\sin\theta$ east too. Its speed is U, hence

$$w^2 \sin^2\theta + u^2 = U^2$$

So the northwards speed is $(U^2 - w^2 \sin^2\theta)^{1/2} - w\cos\theta$.

The time to travel distance d is given by

$$t = \frac{d}{(U^2 - w^2 \sin^2\theta)^{1/2} - w\cos\theta}$$
$$= \frac{d}{(U^2 - w^2)}\left[(U^2 - w^2 \sin^2\theta)^{1/2} - w\cos\theta\right]$$

1.7 We follow Example 1.7 (hammer and nail) and use the moment equation

$$100F = 4 \times 1000 \times 9.81 \text{ N}$$

$$F = 40 \times 9.81 = 392.4 \text{ N}$$

assuming the stick is virtually horizontal.

1.8 If B is the buoyancy of the balloon, taking the up direction as positive,

$$B - Mg = -Mf_1$$

(a) If m_1 is the ballast ejected for neutral buoyancy, then $B - (M - m_1)g = 0$, so that $m_1 = Mf_1/g$.

(b) If m_2 is the ballast ejected for an upward acceleration of f_2, then $B - (M - m_2)g = (M - m_2)f_2$ from which

$$m_2 = \frac{M(f_1 + f_2)}{g + f_2}$$

1.9 Acceleration $= 5\hat{\mathbf{j}}$, velocity $= 5t\hat{\mathbf{j}}$, $y = \tfrac{5}{2}t^2$, $x = 1.5t$. After 2 s, $x = 3$, $y = 10$.

(a) Angle with y-direction is $\tan^{-1}(3/10) = \theta$.

(b) Tension = force on lead = mass × acceleration $= 50\cos\theta = 47.89$ N. (The dog continues to move at right angles to the lead with acceleration $5\sin\theta = 1.44$ m s^{-2}.)

2 Statics

2.1 Fact Sheet

Moment of a force

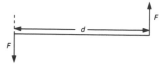

Figure 2.1

A force **F** acts at a point of a body that has position vector **r** with respect to an origin O. The *moment* of **F** about O is the quantity **r** × **F**. Its magnitude is the magnitude of the force, F, multiplied by the perpendicular distance of the line of action of **F** from the origin O. This is a more useful definition for two-dimensional problems.

If forces exhibit the arrangement shown in Fig. 2.1, then the common magnitude of the force F and the distance separating their lines of action, d, constitutes a **couple** of magnitude Fd. The *direction* of this couple is *out* of the paper (the direction of a right-handed screw). Fd is the moment of this arrangement of forces about any point of the plane whatsoever.

Any system of forces can be reduced to a single force (the resultant) together with a couple.

Equilibrium

In order for a rigid body to be in equilibrium, the resultant of all the forces acting on the body must be zero. In addition, the moment of the forces about any point must also be zero. In a truly three-dimensional problem, this leads to six conditions (three components in each of two vector equations). In problems in two dimensions, that is where there is a fixed axis of rotation (which is more often than not the case), the condition for equilibrium leads to three equations: two arising from zero force, and one arising from zero moment.

Friction

When a body is in equilibrium on an inclined plane, the weight of the body has a component acting down the plane. The equilibrium is maintained by **friction**, which is equal and opposite in direction to this component down the plane. If the plane continues to be tilted until the body is just about to slip, then the frictional force, F, and the **normal reaction** of the plane on the body, N, are related by

$$F = \mu N$$

where μ is called the coefficient of static friction and is determined experimentally. It is, for example, obviously dependent on the properties of the two surfaces in contact.

Centre of Gravity

The weight of a rigid body acts as if the mass of the body were concentrated at one point called the centre of mass or centre of gravity. These quantities are synonymous for bodies of constant density. We shall deal only with such bodies; hence the phrases 'centre of mass' and 'centre of gravity' will be used interchangeably. The centre of gravity is independent of the orientation of the body. If the body occupies a volume V and has density ρ, then the position vector of the centre of mass $\bar{\mathbf{r}}$ is given by

$$\bar{\mathbf{r}} = \frac{\int_V \rho \mathbf{r} \, dV}{\int_V \rho \, dV}$$

The denominator is the mass of the body. The volume intergrals are usually evaluated using the techniques of multiple integration.

2.2 Worked Examples

2.1 A light rod AB of length $2a$ is smoothly hinged at A. It is supported in a horizontal position by an inextensible string attached to the wall vertically above A and to the rod at B, so that the string makes an angle of 30° with the horizontal. The mechanism is used to support two lamps, each of weight W, as illustrated in Fig. 2.2.

Calculate (a) the tension in the string, (b) the reaction at the hinge.

Solution   Since the rod is light, only the two lamps, each of weight W, and the tension of the string T act on the rod AB. At A, a reaction with horizontal component X and vertical component Y has to be included.

Since the rod is to be in equilibrium, there are three equations to be solved:

Vertically:

$$Y + T\sin30° = 2W$$

Horizontally:

$$X = T\cos30°$$

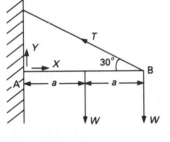

Figure 2.2

Taking moments about A:

$$Wa + W2a = T\sin30°2a$$
$$\therefore 3Wa = Ta$$
$$\therefore T = 3W$$

which answers part (a).

The first two equations then give

$$Y = 2W - T\sin30°$$
$$= 2W - 3W/2 = W/2$$

and

$$X = T\cos30° = 3W\sqrt{3}/2$$

The magnitude of the reaction is thus

$$(X^2 + Y^2)^{1/2} = \left(\frac{1}{4}W^2 + \frac{27}{4}W^2\right)^{1/2} = W\sqrt{7}$$

in the direction $\tan^{-1}(3\sqrt{3})$ to the vertical.

2.2 A beam ABCDE whose mass is negligible is supported in a horizontal position by two trestles at B and D. A boy whose mass is 40 kg sits on the beam at C. AB = DE = 2 m, BC = CD = 3 m. A woman sits on the end A. How heavy can she be before she tips up the beam?

Solution   Figure 2.3 displays the situation. Since the whole is to remain in equilibrium, resolving vertically we have that

$$Mg + 40g = R_1 + R_2$$

where M is the mass of the woman. Now, taking moments about B gives

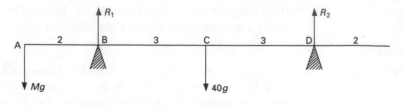

Figure 2.3

$$Mg \times 2 \quad - \quad 40g \times 3 \quad + \quad 6 \times R_2 \quad = 0$$
$$\text{(anticlockwise)} \quad \text{(clockwise)} \quad \text{(anticlockwise)}$$

If the beam is balancing, at the limiting position R_2 is zero; hence the maximum value of Mg is

$$Mg = 40g \times 3/2 = 60g$$

That is, the maximum mass that the woman can be is 60 kg.

2.3 A Catherine wheel has been manufactured so that, when lit, equal forces act along the edges of a regular hexagon. However, there has been a fault and two adjacent edges have anti-clockwise forces. If the magnitude of the force on one edge is F, and the length of the edge is $2a$, determine the resultant force and couple on the pin through the centre of the hexagon.

Determine the resultant and couple if the Catherine wheel was correctly manufactured (all forces clockwise).

Solution

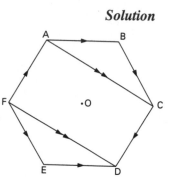

Figure 2.4

Figure 2.4 shows the faulty Catherine wheel together with the forces. The hexagon has been labelled ABCDEF in a clockwise fashion. By the geometry of the regular hexagon, the forces AB and BC are equivalent to AC, which has magnitude $2F\sqrt{3}$. Similarly forces FE and ED are equivalent to FD with magnitude $2F\sqrt{3}$. The rectangle AFCD has forces $2F\sqrt{3}$ acting on the parallel sides AC and FD, leading to a resultant in the same direction of magnitude $4F\sqrt{3}$. The forces acting on the sides AF and DC are equal in magnitude but opposite in direction, and are of magnitude F. Since AC is of length $2a\sqrt{3}$, this leads to a couple $2Fa\sqrt{3}$, clockwise. Hence the resultant force on the hexagon is of magnitude $4F\sqrt{3}$ acting in the direction of AC, and the couple is clockwise, of magnitude $2Fa\sqrt{3}$.

If all the forces are clockwise, the sum of the forces gives a pure couple of magnitude $6Fa\sqrt{3}$. There is no net force on O and the Catherine wheel spins freely on the central pin.

2.4 Two fixed planes, one vertical and the other inclined to it such that they intersect at an angle α, intersect in a horizontal line. A uniform heavy rod is placed at right angles to the inclined plane, with one end on it and the other against the vertical plane. If the vertical plane is smooth, show that, if the rod is about to slip on the inclined plane, the coefficient of friction between rod and plane is $\tan\alpha/(2\tan^2 \alpha + 1)$.

Solution

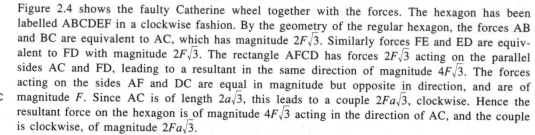

Figure 2.5

Figure 2.5 shows the rod resting against the two planes, the angle α and all the forces acting. We have labelled the rod AB. In total, four equations are available to us in this problem. They are the horizontal and vertical equilibrium equations obtained by equating the force components to zero, one moment equation and $F = \mu R_2$, where R_2 is the normal reaction, F the frictional force and μ the coefficient of friction. These equations are given below.

Vertically:

$$R_2\sin\alpha - mg + F\cos\alpha = 0 \qquad (2.1)$$

Horizontally:

$$R_1 - R_2 \cos\alpha + F\sin\alpha = 0 \qquad (2.2)$$

Taking moments about A:

$$lR_1 \sin\alpha = l \tfrac{1}{2} mg \qquad (2.3)$$

12

(l = length AB, but this cancels at once) and

$$F = \mu R_2 \tag{2.4}$$

From Equation (2.3) we have an expression for R_1, which we insert into Equation (2.2) to give

$$\tfrac{1}{2} mg \cot\alpha - R_2 \cos\alpha + F \sin\alpha = 0$$

from which we obtain

$$R_2 \sin\alpha = \tfrac{1}{2} mg + F \sin\alpha \tan\alpha \tag{2.5}$$

on multiplication by $\tan\alpha$. Rearranging Equation (2.1) now gives an expression for F:

$$\tfrac{1}{2} mg + \frac{F\sin^2\alpha}{\cos\alpha} - mg + F\cos\alpha = 0$$

so

$$F = \tfrac{1}{2} mg\cos\alpha$$

whence, from Equation (2.5)

$$R_2 = \tfrac{1}{2} mg\operatorname{cosec}\alpha + \tfrac{1}{2} mg\sin\alpha$$
$$= mg\,(1 + \sin^2\alpha)/2\sin\alpha$$

Equation (2.4) then gives

$$\tfrac{1}{2} \cos\alpha = \frac{\mu(1 + \sin^2\alpha)}{2\sin\alpha}$$

or

$$\mu = \frac{\cos\alpha\sin\alpha}{1 + \sin^2\alpha}$$
$$= \frac{\tan\alpha}{\sec^2\alpha + \tan^2\alpha} \quad \text{(dividing top and bottom by } \cos^2\alpha\text{)}$$
$$= \frac{\tan\alpha}{2\tan^2\alpha + 1} \quad \text{(using } \sec^2\alpha = 1 + \tan^2\alpha\text{)}$$

which is the required value. Quite typically, the manipulation of the four equations takes more of our attention than the application of the mechanics from which Equations (2.1)–(2.4) arise. These days, this manipulation can be done using computer algebra.

2.5 A uniform rod rests in limiting equilibrium with one end A in contact with rough horizontal ground and the other end B in contact with a rough sloping bank which meets the ground at a point C. The rod is in a vertical plane perpendicular to the bank. The angle BAC is α, and the angle BCA is $\beta + \pi/2$, as shown in Fig. 2.6. If μ is the coefficient of friction at each end of the rod, prove that

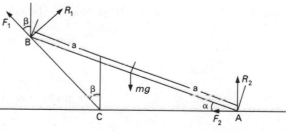

Figure 2.6

$$(1 + \mu^2)\cos\alpha\cos\beta = 2\mu\sin(\alpha + \beta) + 2\mu^2 \cos(\alpha + \beta)$$

Solution   Resolving vertically:

$$R_2 + F_1 \cos\beta + R_1 \sin\beta = mg \tag{2.6}$$

Resolving horizontally:

$$F_1 \sin\beta + F_2 = R_1 \cos\beta \tag{2.7}$$

The limiting friction laws give

$$F_1 = \mu R_1$$

and

$$F_2 = \mu R_2$$

Taking moments about B gives

$$mg\cos\alpha = 2R_2 \cos\alpha - 2F_2 \sin\alpha \tag{2.8}$$

Substituting for F_1 in Equation (2.6) and F_2 in Equation (2.7) gives

$$R_2 + R_1\mu \cos\beta + R_1 \sin\beta = mg \tag{2.9}$$

and, from Equation (2.7)

$$\mu R_1 \sin\beta + \mu R_2 = R_1 \cos\beta$$

Hence, rearranging:

$$\mu R_2 = R_1 \cos\beta - \mu R_1 \sin\beta$$

Multiplying Equation (2.9) by $\mu\cos\alpha$ yields

$$\mu R_2 \cos\alpha + R_1\mu^2 \cos\alpha \cos\beta + R_1\mu \cos\alpha \sin\beta = mg\mu \cos\alpha = 2\mu R_2 \cos\alpha - 2\mu^2 R_2 \sin\alpha$$

(using Equation (2.8)).

Eliminating R_1 and R_2, further manipulation yields

$$(\cos\beta - \mu \sin\beta) \cos\alpha + \mu^2 \cos\alpha \cos\beta + \mu \cos\alpha \sin\beta = (2 \cos\alpha - 2\mu \sin\alpha)(\cos\beta - \mu \sin\beta)$$

i.e.

$$\mu^2 \cos\alpha \cos\beta + \mu \cos\alpha \sin\beta = (\cos\beta - \mu \sin\beta)(\cos\alpha - 2\mu \sin\alpha)$$
$$= \cos\alpha \cos\beta - \mu \cos\alpha \sin\beta - 2\mu \sin\alpha \cos\beta + 2\mu^2 \sin\alpha \sin\beta$$

so that

$$(-1 + \mu^2) \cos\alpha \cos\beta = -2\mu \cos\alpha \sin\beta - 2\mu \sin\alpha \cos\beta + 2\mu^2 \sin\alpha \sin\beta$$

the right-hand side of which is the same as

$$-2\mu \sin(\alpha + \beta) - 2\mu^2 \cos(\alpha + \beta) + 2\mu^2 \cos\alpha \cos\beta$$

Hence

$$(1 + \mu^2) \cos\alpha \cos\beta = 2\mu \sin(\alpha + \beta) + 2\mu^2 \cos(\alpha + \beta)$$

as required. This is another example heavy on manipulation which could yield to computer algebra.

2.6 A light cylinder, radius a, contains two spheres, each of radius b ($2a>2b>a$). Show that the whole is in equilibrium on an inclined plane, angle α, provided

$$\frac{(b-a)}{(2ab-a^2)^{1/2}} \leq \tan\alpha \leq \frac{a}{b+(2ab-a^2)^{1/2}}$$

You may assume that frictional effects are negligibly small.

Solution Since the spheres are equal, the centre of mass of the whole is at Q. Thus when OQ is vertical we have limiting equilibrium. When α exceeds this angle, the cylinder will topple. Figure 2.7 shows the situation.

The solution follows immediately from the application of trigonometry. We see that $b(1 + \sin\beta) = a$. Considering the triangle OQP with OP $= a$, angle OQP $= \alpha$, and QP $= b\cos\beta + b$, then

$$\tan\alpha = \frac{a}{b + b\cos\beta} = \frac{1 + \sin\beta}{1 + \cos\beta}$$

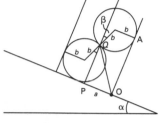

Figure 2.7

Since

$$\sin\beta = \frac{a - b}{b}$$

we have

$$\cos^2\beta = 1 - \left(\frac{a-b}{b}\right)^2 = \frac{2ab - a^2}{b^2}$$

Therefore

$$\tan\alpha = \frac{a}{b + (2ab - a^2)^{1/2}}$$

when OQ is vertical, which is the limiting position. Hence for equilibrium:

$$\tan\alpha < \frac{a}{b + (2ab - a^2)^{1/2}}$$

If the plane tilts in the other direction, Fig. 2.8 shows the situation. As before, the limiting condition occurs when O'Q is vertical, that is, when $\alpha = -\beta$ (bearing in mind the change in sense of the angle).

Thus

$$\sin\alpha = \frac{b - a}{a}$$

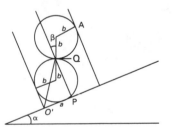

Figure 2.8

so that

$$\cos\alpha = \frac{(2ab - a^2)^{1/2}}{b}$$

giving

$$\tan\alpha = \frac{b - a}{(2ab - a^2)^{1/2}}$$

Of course for this case $\alpha > 0$, and thus $\tan\alpha$ lies between the values given by

$$\frac{(b-a)}{(2ab-a^2)^{1/2}} \le \tan\alpha \le \frac{a}{b+(2ab-a^2)}$$

2.7 A uniform rod AB, of length $2a$ and weight W, is in equilibrium with the upper end B resting against a smooth vertical wall and the end A attached by a light inextensible string to a point C vertically above B.

(a) If in equilibrium AB makes an angle 60° with the vertical, determine the length of the string.

(b) When a particle, of weight nW, is attached at B to the rod, it is found that the rod can rest in equilibrium at an angle 30° with the vertical. Prove that $n = 1/\sqrt{2}$.

Solution (a) See Fig. 2.9. Since the rod AB is in equilibrium we have that

$$T\cos\theta = W$$

and

$$T\sin\theta = R$$

Taking moments about A gives

$$aR = W\frac{a\sqrt{3}}{2} = T\sin\theta$$

whence

$$\tan\theta = \frac{\sqrt{3}}{2}$$

Therefore

$$AC^2 = 4a^2 + 3a^2 = 7a^2$$

so

$$AC = a\sqrt{7}$$

and the length of the string is $a\sqrt{7}$.

(b) See Fig. 2.10. For the new situation:

$$T\cos\phi = nW + W$$

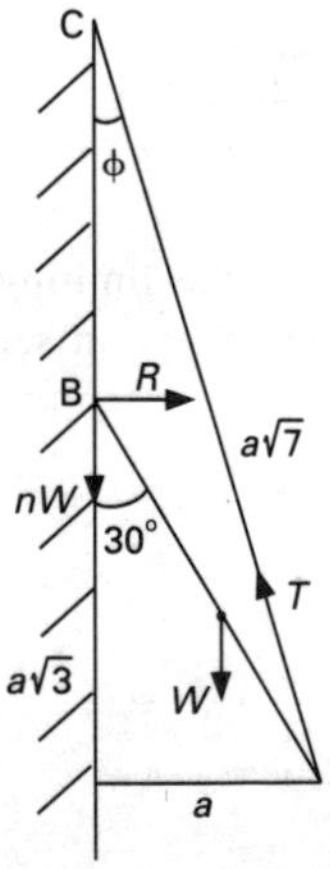

and

$$R = T\sin\phi$$

Taking moments about A yields

$$nWa + Wa/2 = Ra\sqrt{3}$$

Now, we derived in (a) that

$$AC = a\sqrt{7}$$

Therefore

$$\sin\phi = \frac{a}{a\sqrt{7}} = \frac{1}{\sqrt{7}}$$

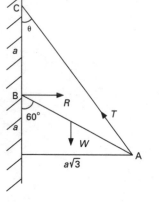

Figure 2.9

Figure 2.10

so that

$$\cos^2\phi = 1 - \tfrac{1}{7} = \tfrac{6}{7}$$

$$\cos\phi = \sqrt{\frac{6}{7}}$$

whence

$$nWa + \frac{W}{2}a = T\frac{1}{\sqrt{7}}a\sqrt{3} = \frac{nW + W}{\sqrt{\frac{6}{7}}}\frac{a\sqrt{3}}{\sqrt{7}}$$

$$= \frac{W(n + 1)a}{\sqrt{2}}$$

Cancelling Wa gives the following equation for n:

$$n + \tfrac{1}{2} = \frac{1}{\sqrt{2}}(n + 1)$$

Rearranging gives

$$n = \frac{2 - \sqrt{2}}{2(\sqrt{2} - 1)} = \frac{\sqrt{2}}{2} = \frac{1}{\sqrt{2}}$$

2.8 A cylinder of density ρ_1, internal radius a, height h_1 and thickness d stands on level ground. It is partially filled with liquid of density ρ_2 to a height h_2. If $d\rho_1 = a\rho_2$, and d is small enough for its square to be neglected, show that the centre of mass of the partially filled cylinder is closest to the ground when

$$h_2 = h_1(\sqrt{6} - 2)$$

and determine the height of the centre of mass in this case.

Solution Figure 2.11 displays the situation. The mass m of the (hollow) cylinder is exactly

$$m = \pi[(a + d)^2 - a^2]\rho_1 h_1$$

$$= \pi(2ad + d^2)\rho_1 h_1$$

which is approximately $2\pi ad\rho_1 h_1$, since d^2 can be neglected. The mass of the liquid in the cylinder is that of a cylinder of height h_2. That is, it is equal to $\pi a^2 h_2\rho_2$.

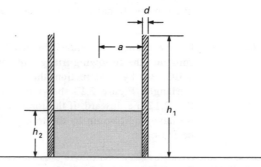

Figure 2.11

The heights of the centres of mass of the hollow cylinder and its contents are $\tfrac{1}{2}h_1$ and $\tfrac{1}{2}h_2$ respectively above the ground. Hence if $\bar{h}$ denotes the height of the centre of mass of cylinder + contents, then, by definition

$$\bar{h} = \frac{\frac{1}{2}h_1 \, 2\pi a d\rho_1 h_1 + \frac{1}{2}h_2 \, \pi a^2 h_2 \rho_2}{2\pi a d\rho_1 h_1 + \pi a^2 h_2 \rho_2}$$

Hence

$$\bar{h} = \frac{2h_1^2 + h_2^2}{4h_1 + 2h_2}$$

upon some cancellation. This can be written

$$\bar{h} = \frac{2 + x^2}{4 + 2x}$$

by writing $x = h_2/h_1$. For an extreme value $d\bar{h}/dx = 0$; hence

$$\frac{d}{dx}\left(\frac{2 + x^2}{4 + 2x}\right) = 0$$

or

$$(4 + 2x)2x - (2 + x^2)2 = 0$$

whence

$$x^2 + 4x - 2 = 0$$

or

$$x = \sqrt{6} - 2$$

(rejecting the negative value). Testing $\bar{h}$ reveals this indeed to be a minimum; thus $h_2 = h_1(\sqrt{6} - 2)$, as required.

Substituting this into the expression for $\bar{h}$ yields

$$\bar{h} = \frac{2h_1^2 + h_1^2 (\sqrt{6} - 2)^2}{4h_1 + 2h_1(\sqrt{6} - 2)}$$

$$= h_1\left(\frac{2 + 6 - 4\sqrt{6} + 4}{4 + 2\sqrt{6} - 4}\right)$$

$$= h_1(\sqrt{6} - 2) \cong 0.45h_1$$

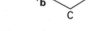

Figure 2.12

Thus the cylinder is at its most stable when 0.45 full.

2.9 Forces act at the middle points of the sides of a triangle at right angles to the sides and respectively proportional to them. Show that if they all act inwards, or outwards, they are in equilibrium.

Solution Let the triangle be denoted by ABC, and the vectors be **a**, **b** and **c** as shown in Fig. 2.12. We can construct the following triangle of forces diagram, since we know that |**c**| = AB, |**b**| = AC and |**a**| = BC. But by construction, this triangle of forces (Fig. 2.13) is congruent to ABC and thus forms a triangle. Figure 2.13 shows that the directions of the forces are the same as those depicted in Fig. 2.12, i.e. inward. If the forces are all reversed then the arrows would be reversed. In each case we have equilibrium by the triangle law. If *one* or *two* arrows were reversed, this would no longer be the case.

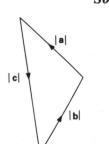

Figure 2.13

2.10 A uniform cube, of side d, stands on a rough plane. A uniform circular cylinder of diameter d and length d rests with its curved surface in contact with the plane and with one of the vertical sides of the cube. The plane is gradually tilted. If the densities of the cube and cylinder are the same, and the coefficient of friction for every contact is μ, show that if $\mu < 1$ equilibrium is broken by the cube sliding down the plane and that the angle of the plane is then

$$\tan^{-1}\left(\frac{4\mu}{4 + (1 - \mu)\pi}\right)$$

Solution Figure 2.14 displays the situation. If m_1 is the mass of the cube and m_2 is the mass of the cylinder, then

$$m_1 = \rho d^3 \quad \text{and} \quad m_2 = \frac{\pi}{4}\rho d^3$$

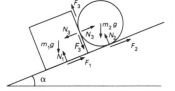

Figure 2.14

The forces are shown in Fig. 2.14. Note the use of Newton's third law at the point of contact between the cube and the cylinder. The number of forces may be a little bewildering; however taking moments about the centre of the cylinder immediately implies that $F_2 = F_3 = F$ (say). (The lack of point contact between plane and cube means that we cannot do the same simple calculation to relate F_1 and F.)

Resolving along and perpendicular to the plane for the cube gives

$$m_1 g\sin\alpha + N_3 - F_1 = 0$$

and

$$m_1 g\cos\alpha - N_1 + F = 0$$

Doing the same for the cylinder gives

$$m_2 g\sin\alpha - N_3 - F = 0$$

and

$$m_2 g\cos\alpha - N_2 - F = 0$$

These last two equations give

$$N_2 = m_2 g \cos\alpha - F$$

and

$$N_3 = m_2 g \sin\alpha - F$$

Now, since $\tan\alpha < 1$ (the plane is being tilted from the horizontal), then $\sin\alpha < \cos\alpha$; hence $N_3 < N_2$ and so, since μ is the same for all contacts, the inequality

$$\frac{F}{N_2} < \frac{F}{N_3}$$

implies that slipping will occur between cylinder and plane before it occurs between cylinder and cube.

If the cylinder is assumed to slip (and $\tan\alpha < 1$), then

$$F_1 = \mu N_1$$

and

$$F = \mu N_3 = \mu(m_2 g\sin\alpha - F)$$

so that

$$F = \frac{\mu}{1 + \mu} m_2 g\sin\alpha$$

19

and

$$N_3 = \frac{m_2 g \sin\alpha}{1 + \mu}$$

We can eliminate N_3 and F from

$$m_1 g \sin\alpha + N_3 = F_1 = \mu N_1 = \mu(m_1 g \cos\alpha + F)$$

to give

$$m_1 g \sin\alpha + \frac{m_2 g \sin\alpha}{1 + \mu} = \mu m_1 g \cos\alpha + \frac{\mu^2}{1 + \mu} m_2 g \sin\alpha$$

from which

$$\tan\alpha = \frac{\mu m_1}{m_1 + (1 - \mu)m_2}$$

Using $m_1 = \rho d^3$ and $m_2 = (\pi/4)\rho d^3$, we obtain

$$\tan\alpha = \frac{4\mu}{4 + (1 - \mu)\pi}$$

so that

$$\alpha = \tan^{-1}\left(\frac{4\mu}{4 + (1 - \mu)\pi} \right)$$

as required.

The problem is not quite completely solved, for it might be possible for the cube to tilt about its corner furthest down the plane. If tilting is on the point of occurring, then the moment of N_1 about this leading edge will be zero. Taking moments about this corner then gives

$$\tfrac{1}{2} dN_3 - dF - \tfrac{1}{2} dm_1 g \cos\alpha + \tfrac{1}{2} dm_1 g \sin\alpha = 0$$

Cancelling d, and substituting

$$F = \frac{\mu m_2 g \sin\alpha}{1 + \mu}$$

and

$$N_3 = \frac{m_2 g \sin\alpha}{1 + \mu}$$

gives

$$m_1 g(\cos\alpha - \sin\alpha) - \left(\frac{1 - 2\mu}{1 + \mu} \right) m_2 g \sin\alpha = 0$$

which on rearrangement is

$$\tan\alpha = \frac{(1 + \mu)m_1}{(1 + \mu)m_1 + (1 - 2\mu)m_2}$$

Now, if this value of α is *greater* than that obtained by assuming slippage between cube and plane, we have

$$\frac{(1 + \mu)m_1}{(1 + \mu)m_1 + (1 - 2\mu)m_2} > \frac{\mu_1 m_1}{m_1 + (1 + \mu)m_2}$$

or

$$\frac{\mu(1 - 2\mu)}{1 - \mu^2} < 1 + \frac{m_1}{m_2} = 1 + \frac{4}{\pi}$$

since $0 \le \mu \le 1$. We need to show that the LHS is always smaller than $1 + (4/\pi)$. Let

$$f(\mu) = \frac{\mu - 2\mu^2}{1 - \mu^2}$$

then

$$\frac{df}{d\mu} = \frac{(1 - \mu^2)(1 - 4\mu) + 2\mu(\mu - 2\mu^2)}{(1 - \mu^2)^2} = 0$$

for a maximum. This implies

$$(1 - \mu^2)(1 - 4\mu) + 2\mu(\mu - 2\mu) = 0$$
$$1 - \mu^2 - 4\mu + 4\mu^3 + 2\mu^2 - 4\mu^3 = 0$$
$$\mu^2 - 4\mu + 1 = 0$$

so that

$$\mu = \frac{4 \pm \sqrt{16 - 4}}{2}$$
$$= 2 - \sqrt{3} \qquad (\mu < 1)$$

At this value

$$\frac{\mu - 2\mu^2}{1 - \mu^2} < 1$$

so slippage always occurs before tilting.

2.3 Exercises

2.1 The jack illustrated in Fig. 2.15 is a screw type which is used for the raising of cars. The screw at B provides enough resistance to allow large loads to be supported. The rods AB, BC, CD, AD and the screw are light compared with the load W that the jack supports at A. When all rods make an angle of $30°$ with the horizontal, find, by considering all the forces acting at A and then B, the forces in each rod and the screw.

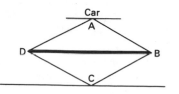

Figure 2.15

2.2 Equal forces F_1 act on the edges of an equilateral octagon, of side $2a$, ABCDEFGH (labelled clockwise).
(a) Find the couple if all the forces turn the octagon clockwise.
(b) Find the reaction at the centre if the forces along AB and GH are reversed.

2.3 A bicycle has both wheels of the same radius and there is no friction between either wheel and its axle. When the bicycle stands on level ground the perpendicular from its centre of mass to the ground is of length h and bisects the distance, $2l$, between the centres of the wheels. If the bicycle stands in equilibrium on a rough plane inclined at an angle α to the horizontal, where $\tan\alpha < l/h$ and faces down the plane with the rear wheel locked and the front wheel free, prove that the coefficient of friction between the wheels and the plane must be at least

$$\frac{2l\sin\alpha}{l\cos\alpha - h\sin\alpha}.$$

Find the corresponding result when the front wheel is locked and the rear wheel is free.

2.4 Establish Pappus' theorem: let there be a plane curve C, and a line L in the same plane as C but not crossing it. Suppose the curve C is a (thin) wire of uniform density with a centre of mass which is a distance d from L. If S is the surface area generated by rotating C about L, and l is the length of C, then show that

$$2\pi dl = S$$

2.5 A leaning tower of n equal coins is constructed on a horizontal table so that the centres of gravity of all the coins lie in a straight line: find the greatest inclination of this line to the vertical.

2.6 A plane regular hexagon, side a, is formed from uniform wire. One of its sides is removed. What is the distance of the centre of mass of the new body from the centre of the hexagon?

2.7 A circular cylinder C of radius R is fixed with axis horizontal. Two uniform circular cylinders C_1 and C_2, of the same radius a and the same mass, rest inside C in contact with it and with each other, their axes being parallel to the axis of C. When a third cylinder C_3, equal in all respects to C_1 and C_2, is placed on C_1 and C_2 with its axis parallel to the other axes, C_1 and C_2 do not separate. Show that $R < a(2\sqrt{7} + 1)$, where C_3 is assumed not to touch C. Friction can be neglected for this problem.

2.8 A ladder of length $2l$ and weight W, which may be assumed uniform, rests over a smooth vertical wall. The ladder is perpendicular to the top edge of the wall and is inclined at 60° to the horizontal. The lower end of the ladder rests on a rough horizontal plane and is at a horizontal distance of $2l/3$ from the wall. Show that the coefficient of friction must be at least $3\sqrt{3}/13$.

A man of weight $2W$ stands on the ladder at the top of the wall. What is the new minimum value of the coefficient of friction?

2.9 A uniform solid hemisphere of weight W rests with its curved surface on a smooth horizontal plane. A weight of $W/4$ is placed on the rim of the hemisphere. Find the angle between the plane and the plane face of the hemisphere at equilibrium.

2.10 An equilateral cone (slant height = base diameter) rests on a horizontal table on its curved side. A cut is made parallel to the base, and the vertex portion is removed, leaving the frustrum. If this frustrum is to remain stable resting on its curved side, show that the ratio of the length of the curved side to the radius of the base must exceed 0.5437, to four significant figures.

2.4 Outline Solutions to Exercises

2.1 Figure 2.16 shows that B and C are in equilibrium. A and D are also in equilibrium, but the weight (W) at D gives rise to

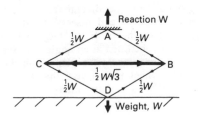

Figure 2.16

the (distributed) reaction along DC and DB, and the reaction of the jack at A is due to the (distributed) weight along AC and AB.

2.2 (a) Figure 2.17 shows that the forces on the octagon consist of four equal couples. If F_1 is the magnitude of the force on each side, one couple will have magnitude $F_1\,2a\cot(\pi/8)$. Hence the total couple will be $8\cot(\pi/8)\,aF_1 = 19.3aF_1$.

(b) If AB and GH are reversed, then there is a net force of $2F_1$ in the $-\hat{\mathbf{j}}$ direction due to the forces on sides HG and CD, and another force of magnitude $2F_1$ in the $-\hat{\mathbf{i}}$ direction due to the forces on the sides BA and EF. Hence the net force is $2\sqrt{2}F_1$ in the $-\hat{\mathbf{i}}-\hat{\mathbf{j}}$ direction.

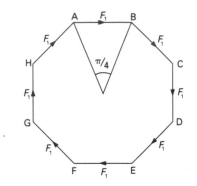

Figure 2.17

2.3 The bicycle is shown (schematically) in Fig. 2.18. Resolving perpendicular and parallel to the plane gives

$$R_1 + R_2 = mg\cos\alpha$$

$$F_1 + F_2 = mg\sin\alpha$$

Taking moments about the foot of the front wheel (the restriction $\tan\alpha < l/h$ ensures that the line of action is always between the wheels) gives

$$mgl\cos\alpha = R_2\,2l + mgh\sin\alpha$$

If the front wheel is free, with zero inertia, this is equivalent to assuming that $F_1 = 0$. The condition that $\mu \geq F_2/R_2$ gives the least value $2l\sin\alpha/(l\cos\alpha - h\sin\alpha)$ as required.

If the back wheel is free, this is (similarly) equivalent to assuming that $F_2 = 0$. The condition that $\mu \geq F_1/R_1$ leads to a least value of μ of $2l\sin\alpha/(l\cos\alpha + h\sin\alpha)$.

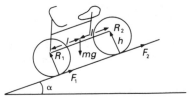

Figure 2.18

2.4 Take axis x along L, and let s be the arc length of the curve. Hence, by the definition of the centre of mass,

$$d = \frac{1}{l}\int_C y\,ds$$

Also we have, by construction,

$$S = \int_C 2\pi y \, ds = 2\pi dl$$

as required.

2.5 Figure 2.19 shows three stacked coins. Their thickness is b, and their combined centre of mass is at the centre of mass of the centre coin. For n coins, it is not difficult to see that the centre of mass is $\frac{1}{2}(n-1)b$ above the centre of mass of the bottom coin.

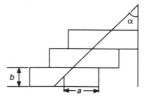

Figure 2.19

If this centre of mass is greater than a horizontal distance a away from the centre of mass of the bottom coin then the tower will topple. Hence, if α is the vertical angle, for stability we require that

$$\tan\alpha < \frac{a}{\frac{1}{2}b(n-1)} = \frac{2a}{b(n-1)}$$

The greatest inclination is thus

$$\tan^{-1}\left(\frac{2a}{b(n-1)}\right)$$

2.6 Suppose the centres of the six sides of the hexagon are labelled A, B, C, D, E, F, and F is the side that is removed. If x is the required distance, then the perpendicular distances of the five sides from O are $a\sqrt{3}/4$, $a\sqrt{3}/4$ on one side, and $a\sqrt{3}/4$, $a\sqrt{3}/4$ and $a\sqrt{3}/2$ on the other. Taking moments gives the equation

$$\frac{a\sqrt{3}}{2} - x + 2\left(\frac{a\sqrt{3}}{4} - x\right) = 2\left(\frac{a\sqrt{3}}{4} + x\right)$$

from which

$$x = \frac{a\sqrt{3}}{10}$$

2.7 Figure 2.20 shows the three cylinders. In the limit, there will be no forces between C_1 and C_2. If α is the angle the re-

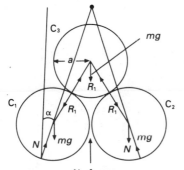

No forces

Figure 2.20

action of C_1 with C makes with the vertical, then

$$\sin\alpha = \frac{a}{R-a}.$$

Equilibrium of the whole system gives

$$2N\cos\alpha = 3mg$$

Equilibrium of C_3 gives

$$2R_1\cos\frac{\pi}{3} = mg$$

Equilibrium of C_1 gives

$$N\sin\alpha = R_1\cos\frac{\pi}{6} \quad \text{(horizontally).}$$

From these equations,

$$\tan\alpha = \frac{1}{3\sqrt{3}}$$

whence

$$(R-a)^2 = 28a^2$$

or

$$R = a + 2a\sqrt{7}$$

Hence, for the cylinders C_1 and C_2 not to separate:

$$\tan\alpha > \frac{1}{3\sqrt{3}}$$

hence

$$R < a + 2a\sqrt{7}$$

as required.

2.8 Figure 2.21 shows the geometry of the problem and the notation used. For equilibrium:

$$R_1\cos\frac{\pi}{6} = F$$

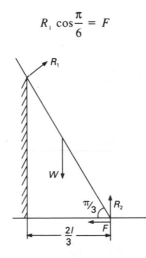

Figure 2.21

and

$$R_2 + R_1 \sin\frac{\pi}{6} = W$$

Taking moments about the foot of the ladder:

$$R_1\frac{4l}{3} = Wl\cos\frac{\pi}{3}$$

Solving:

$$R^2 = \frac{13W}{16}, \qquad F = \frac{3\sqrt{3}}{16}W \Rightarrow \mu = \frac{3\sqrt{3}}{13}$$

as required.

With the man on the ladder, the equations are now

$$3W = R_2 + R_1\sin\frac{\pi}{6}$$

$$F = R_1\cos\frac{\pi}{6}$$

$$R_1\frac{4l}{3} = W\frac{l}{2} + 2W\frac{2l}{3}$$

Solving gives

$$R_2 = \frac{37W}{16}, \qquad F = \frac{11W\sqrt{3}}{16}$$

Thus the new minimum value of the coefficient is $11\sqrt{3}/37$.

2.9 See Fig. 2.22. Let OX denote the vertical line at equilibrium. Triangles ODA and OCD are similar. AD = x, BC = y.

Taking moments, $Wx = Wy/4$, so that $y = 4x$. OB = a and OA = $3a/8$ (centre of mass of a hemisphere). If $\widehat{OBC} = a = \widehat{AOD}$, $\cos\alpha = y/a$ and

$$\sin\alpha = \frac{x}{\frac{3}{8}a} = \frac{8x}{3a}$$

Hence

$$\tan\alpha = \frac{8x}{3y} = \frac{2}{3}$$

Thus $\alpha = \tan^{-1}(\frac{2}{3})$ is the required angle.

2.10 Let the original cone have slant height $2a$, and the removed cone slant height $2h$ (see Fig. 2.23). Let A be the apex, G_2 the centre of mass of the original cone, G_1 the centre of mass of the removed cone and G_3 the centre of mass of the frustrum. Let D, B and C be the feet of the respective perpendiculars from the three centres of mass on the horizontal table. In the limiting case, C coincides with the corner of the frustrum as shown. From the geometry of the triangle,

$$AG_1 = \frac{2h\sqrt{3}}{3}, \qquad AG_2 = \frac{2a\sqrt{3}}{3}$$

so that AB = h, AC = 2h and AD = a. Taking moments in this limiting case gives

$$\tfrac{1}{3}\pi\sqrt{3}(a^3 - h^3)2h = a\tfrac{1}{3}\pi a^3\sqrt{3} - h\tfrac{1}{3}\pi h^3\sqrt{3}$$

which on rearranging is

$$\left(\frac{h}{a}\right)^3 + \left(\frac{h}{a}\right)^2 + \left(\frac{h}{a}\right) - 1 = 0$$

The positive real root of this is $h/a = 0.5437$ to four significant figures.

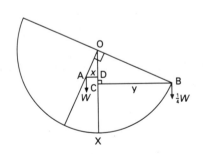

Figure 2.22

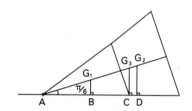

Figure 2.23

Topic Guide

Projectiles in the Vertical
Projectiles with Resistance
Parabolic Paths with Impact
Constrained Motion under
  Gravity

3 Motion Under Gravity

3.1 Fact Sheet

Projectiles

Projectiles are particles that move under the influence of the Earth's gravity. The vertical axis is taken as pointing vertically upward, so that the Earth's acceleration $= -g\hat{\mathbf{k}}$, where g is the magnitude of the acceleration due to gravity, usually taken as 9.81 m s^{-2} (or sometimes 10 m s^{-2} for arithmetical convenience). Thus the force on a particle of mass m due solely to the Earth's gravitational pull is $-mg\hat{\mathbf{k}}$. Newton's law takes the form

$$-mg\hat{\mathbf{k}} + \mathbf{R} = m\ddot{\mathbf{r}}$$

where $\mathbf{R}$ is the drag or resistance force on the particle.

In the absence of resistance

$$\ddot{\mathbf{r}} = -g\hat{\mathbf{k}}$$

and the motion is a (plane) parabola. (In reality of course, g is not a constant, but this will not be considered until Chapter 8.)

Resistance will be proportional to velocity (fast particles) or proportional to the square of velocity (strictly $v|v|$) for slower particles, corresponding to form drag. Although of course particles, having zero volume, have no 'form' as such, resistance can be included to mimic its effects.

Other Motion Under Gravity

Constrained motion under gravity includes motion of particles on inclined planes and on other surfaces. Many of these problems are postponed until we consider energy (Chapter 10), but using the Frenet apparatus of a curve (that is tangent $\hat{\mathbf{T}}$, normal $\hat{\mathbf{N}}$ and binormal $\hat{\mathbf{B}}$ of a curve $\mathbf{r} = \mathbf{r}(s)$) the acceleration of a particle $\ddot{\mathbf{r}}$ can be written $\ddot{s}\,\hat{\mathbf{T}} + \dot{s}^2\hat{\mathbf{N}} / \rho$, where ρ is the curvature of the path.

3.2 Worked Examples

3.1 A stone is dropped from rest in a well and the impact is heard after a time T. Find the depth of the well and show that it is approximately

$$\tfrac{1}{2}gT^2 - \tfrac{1}{2}g^2T^3 / U$$

where U is the speed of sound.

If $T = 1.5 \text{ s}$ and $U = 332 \text{ m s}^{-1}$ find the percentage error in the depth caused by assuming that U is infinite.

Solution Since the stone is dropped from rest, we can quickly derive the following:

$$\frac{\mathrm{d}^2 x}{\mathrm{d}t^2} = -g$$

$$\frac{dx}{dt} = -gt \qquad \text{(initial velocity is zero)}$$

$$x = -\tfrac{1}{2}gt^2 \qquad (x = 0 \text{ when } t = 0)$$

Actual time is thus T, where

$$-h = -\tfrac{1}{2}gT^2,$$

i.e.

$$T = \left(\frac{2h}{g}\right)^{1/2}.$$

Now, the sound travels with uniform speed U, so it takes a time h/U to reach the top of the well. So the measured time T is the actual time T with this extra h/U added. Thus,

$$T = \left(\frac{2h}{g}\right)^{1/2} + \frac{h}{U}$$

or

$$\left(T - \frac{h}{U}\right)^2 = \frac{2h}{g}$$

U is large, hence

$$\left(T - \frac{h}{U}\right)^2 \cong T^2 - \frac{2Th}{U} = \frac{2h}{g}$$

$$\therefore \quad h\left(\frac{2T}{U} - \frac{2}{g}\right) = T^2$$

$$h = T^2\left(\frac{2T}{U} + \frac{2}{g}\right)^{-1}$$

i.e.

$$h = \frac{gT^2}{2}\left(1 + \frac{gT}{U}\right)^{-1}$$

$$= \frac{gT^2}{2}\left(1 - \frac{gT}{U} + \ldots\right)$$

using the binomial expansion. So

$$h = \frac{gT^2}{2} - \frac{g^2T^3}{2U}$$

retaining only two terms.

The value of h taking U as infinite is $h_1 = gT^2/2$, where we have called this h_1. Taking the ratio,

$$\frac{h}{h_1} = 1 - \frac{g^2T^3}{2U}\frac{2}{gT^2}$$

$$= 1 - \frac{gT}{U}$$

and inserting the values $g = 9.81$, $T = 1.5$, $U = 332$ gives $h/h_1 = 1 - 0.044$, and hence a 4.4% error.

3.2 A ball is thrown vertically upwards with initial velocity u m s^{-1} in air, which causes a retardation of kv m s^{-2} when the velocity of the ball is v m s^{-1}, k being a constant. If Y m is the maximum height reached above the point of projection, and T s is the time to the summit, prove that

$$u = kY + gT$$

If $k = \frac{1}{4}$ and $u = 200$ m s^{-1}, find T and Y. (Take g as 10 m s^{-2}.)

Solution We have that

$$\ddot{y} = -g - kv$$

from Newton's second law. Integrating gives

$$\dot{y} = -gt - ky + A$$

We are given that $y = 0$, $\dot{y} = u$, $t = 0$. This implies $A = u$, so that

$$\dot{y} = -gt - ky + u$$

At the top, $\dot{y} = 0$, $t = T$, $y = Y$, giving $u = gT + kY$. Now,

$$\dot{y} + ky = -gt + u$$

Multiplying by the integrating factor e^{kt} gives

$$\frac{\mathrm{d}}{\mathrm{d}t}(ye^{kt}) = -yte^{kt} + ue^{kt}.$$

Integrating:

$$ye^{kt} = -g\int(te^{kt} + ue^{kt})\mathrm{d}t$$

$$= \left(\frac{-g}{k}te^{kt} + \frac{g}{k^2}e^{kt} + \frac{u}{k}e^{kt} + B\right)$$

when $t = 0$, $y = 0$. Therefore

$$0 = 0 + \frac{g}{k^2} + \frac{u}{k} + B$$

or

$$B = -\left(\frac{g}{k^2} + \frac{u}{k}\right)$$

so that

$$y = -\frac{gt}{k} + \frac{g}{k^2} + \frac{u}{k} - \left(\frac{g}{k^2} + \frac{u}{k}\right)e^{-kt}$$

Now $y = Y$ when $t = T$; Hence

$$Y = -\frac{gT}{k} + \frac{g}{k^2} + \frac{u}{k} - \left(\frac{g}{k^2} + \frac{u}{k}\right)e^{-kT}$$

or

$$kY + gT = \frac{g}{k} + u - \left(\frac{g}{k^2} + \frac{u}{k}\right)e^{-kT}.$$

We have already shown that $u = kY + gT$. Eliminating Y gives the following equation:

$$\frac{g}{k} = \left(\frac{g}{k^2} + \frac{u}{k}\right)e^{-kT}$$

Inserting the numerical values $u = 200 \text{ m s}^{-1}$, $g = 10 \text{ m s}^{-2}$ yields

$$40 = (1600 + 800)e^{-kT} = 960e^{-kT}.$$

so that

$$T = 4\ln\left(\frac{96}{4}\right) = 12.7 \text{ s}$$

and

$$200 = 127 + \tfrac{1}{4}Y \Rightarrow Y = 292 \text{ m}$$

3.3 A particle is projected from the foot of a smooth inclined plane up the line of greatest slope. It hits the plane at right angles and bounces twice before returning precisely to the starting point. Find the coefficient of restitution. (See Chapter 4 for more about restitution.)

Solution Suppose the plane makes an angle α with the horizontal. Let the x-axis be along the plane, and the y-axis be perpendicular to it, with the starting point as the origin. Figure 3.1 shows the path of the particle. Let v be the velocity in the y-direction, and u the velocity in the x-direction. The components of gravity are $-g\sin\alpha$ and $-g\cos\alpha$ in the x- and y-directions, respectively. Hence the equations of motion are:

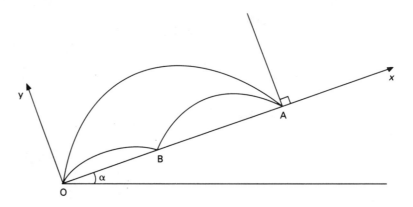

Figure 3.1

$$\frac{dv}{dt} = -g\cos\alpha$$

and

$$\frac{du}{dt} = -g\sin\alpha$$

Integrating these with $(u, v) = (u_0, v_0)$ at O gives $v = v_0 - gt\cos\alpha$, so that $y = v_0t - \tfrac{1}{2}gt^2\cos\alpha$, and $u = u_0 - gt\sin\alpha$, so that $x = u_0t - \tfrac{1}{2}gt^2\sin\alpha$.

At A, $y = 0$, so $t = 2v_0/(g\cos\alpha)$. Also, $u = 0$ (it hits at right angles), so

$$0 = u_0 - \frac{2v_0}{g\cos\alpha}\, g\sin\alpha \Rightarrow u_0 = 2v_0\tan\alpha \tag{3.1}$$

The distance OA is thus given by

$$OA = u_0 \frac{2v_0}{g\cos\alpha} - \tfrac{1}{2}g\left(\frac{2v_0}{g\cos\alpha}\right)^2 \sin\alpha$$

$$= \frac{2u_0v_0}{g\cos\alpha} - \frac{2v_0^2\sin\alpha}{g\cos^2\alpha}$$

or, substituting for u_0 from Equation (3.1),

$$OA = \frac{4v_0^2\tan\alpha}{g\cos\alpha} - \frac{2v_0^2\tan\alpha}{g\cos\alpha} = \frac{2v_0^2\tan\alpha}{g\cos\alpha}$$

Also at A,

$$v = v_0 - g\left(\frac{2v_0}{g\cos\alpha}\right)\cos\alpha = -v_0$$

After the first bounce, $v = ev_0$ (by the definition of restitution e), and $u = 0$. We start the clock again ($t = 0$) for convenience. Once again

$$\frac{dv}{dt} = -g\cos\alpha$$

and

$$\frac{du}{dt} = -g\sin\alpha$$

which integrate to $v = -gt\cos\alpha + ev_0$ and $u = -gt\sin\alpha$, respectively, so that

$$y = -\tfrac{1}{2}gt^2\cos\alpha + ev_0t$$

and

$$x = AO - \tfrac{1}{2}gt^2\sin\alpha$$

At B, $y = 0$, so that $t = 2ev_0/(g\cos\alpha)$. Substituting for this value of t and for OA in the expression for x gives

$$OB = \frac{2v_0^2\tan\alpha}{g\cos\alpha} - \frac{2e^2v_0^2\tan\alpha}{g\cos\alpha} \tag{3.2}$$

Also, at B,

$$v = -g\frac{2ev_0\cos\alpha}{g\cos\alpha} + ev_0 = -ev_0$$

and

$$u = -g\frac{2ev_0\sin\alpha}{g\cos\alpha} + -2ev_0\tan\alpha$$

After the second bounce, $v = e^2v_0$, with $u = -2ev_0\tan\alpha$ remaining true. For convenience, we start the clock again ($t = 0$), with

$$\frac{dv}{dt} = -g\cos\alpha$$

and

$$\frac{du}{dt} = -g\sin\alpha$$

Integrating gives $v = -gt\cos\alpha + e^2v_0$ and $u = -gt\sin\alpha - 2ev_0\tan\alpha$, so that

$$y = -\tfrac{1}{2}gt^2\cos\alpha + e^2tv_0$$

and

$$x = \text{OB} -\tfrac{1}{2}gt^2\sin\alpha - 2ev_0t\tan\alpha \qquad (3.3)$$

The ball bounces again when $y = 0$, i.e. $t = 2e^2v_0/(g\cos\alpha)$. At this value of t, the ball has returned to the starting point, i.e. $x = 0$. So substituting for t and OB from Equation (3.2) into Equation (3.3) gives

$$0 = \frac{2v_0^2\tan\alpha}{g\cos\alpha} - \frac{2e^2v_0^2\tan\alpha}{g\cos\alpha} - \tfrac{1}{2}g\left(\frac{2e^2v_0}{g\cos\alpha}\right)^2\sin\alpha - 2ev_0\left(\frac{2e^2v_0}{g\cos\alpha}\right)$$

or

$$0 = \frac{2v_0^2\tan\alpha}{g\cos\alpha} - \frac{2e^2v_0^2}{g\cos\alpha} - \frac{2e^4v_0^2\tan\alpha}{g\cos\alpha} - \frac{4e^3v_0^2\tan\alpha}{g\cos\alpha}$$

Cancelling the factor $2v_0^2\tan\alpha/g\cos\alpha$ gives the quartic for e:

$$e^4 + 2e^3 + e^2 - 1 = 0$$

or

$$e^2(e^2 + 2e + 1) - 1 = 0$$

so that

$$e^2(e + 1)^2 - 1 = 0$$

which factorises to

$$[e(e + 1) - 1][e(e + 1) + 1] = 0$$

i.e.

$$(e^2 + e - 1)(e^2 + e + 1) = 0$$

The first quadratic has real roots, only one of which is positive. The second quadratic has complex roots and can be discarded. The only positive root, $e = \tfrac{1}{2}(\sqrt{5} - 1)$, is the required value of e.

This seems quite a hard problem, but exemplifies the virtue of persistence. Some of the algebra can be done using software.

3.4 A heavy perfectly elastic particle is dropped from a point P on the inside surface of a smooth sphere. Prove that the second point of impact will be in the same horizontal plane as the first if the angle subtended at the centre of the sphere by P and the topmost point of the sphere is

$$\cos^{-1}[(2^{1/2} + 1)^{1/2}/2]$$

Solution This question requires knowledge of projectiles, elastic impact and a certain amount of geometry. Figure 3.2 shows the situation; in particular, the question requires us to find α.

P$\hat{\text{Q}}$R is a right angle, and the particle hits the sphere first at Q, then at R. Also, since the particle is perfectly elastic, P$\hat{\text{Q}}$O = O$\hat{\text{Q}}$L = α. We now look at the dynamics of the particle. Since it is dropped from rest, by integrating

$$\frac{dv}{dt} = v\frac{dv}{dy} = +g$$

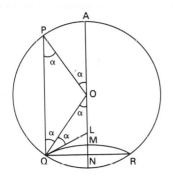

Figure 3.2

we obtain $v^2 = 2g\text{PQ} = 2g2a\cos\alpha = 4ag\cos\alpha$, where v is the velocity of the particle as it reaches Q. v is therefore also the launch velocity of the projectile as it bounces towards R. Taking $x = y = 0$ at point Q,

$$\frac{d^2y}{dt^2} = -g$$

and

$$\frac{d^2x}{dt^2} = 0$$

Integrating gives

$$\frac{dy}{dt} = v\sin\beta - gt$$

and

$$\frac{dx}{dt} = v\cos\beta$$

so that, at M,

$$\frac{dy}{dt} = 0$$

or

$$t = \frac{v}{g}\sin\beta$$

Also

$$\frac{dx}{dt} = v\cos\beta$$

gives

$$x = vt\cos\beta = \frac{v^2\sin\beta\cos\beta}{g} \qquad \text{(at M)}$$

This value of x is, of course, half the range. The dynamics is now all solved. In order to find the value of α, we need to use some geometry and trigonometry. First of all, since $v^2 = 4ag\cos\alpha$, the formula

$$x = \frac{v^2\sin\beta\cos\beta}{g}$$

becomes

$$x = \frac{4ag\cos\alpha \sin\beta \cos\beta}{g} = 4a\cos\alpha \sin\beta \cos\beta$$

Also, QN $= a\sin\alpha$ (triangle OQN). Hence

$$a\sin\alpha = 4a\cos\alpha \cos\beta \sin\beta$$

or

$$\tan\alpha = 4\cos\beta\sin\beta \qquad\qquad (3.4)$$

Since PQO is $\pi/2$, we have that

$$2\alpha + \beta = \pi/2$$

so that

$$\cos(2\alpha + \beta) = 0$$

i.e.

$$\cos 2\alpha\cos\beta - \sin 2\alpha\sin\beta = 0$$

or

$$\tan 2\alpha\tan\beta = 1$$

i.e.

$$\frac{2\tan\alpha\tan\beta}{1 - \tan^2\alpha} = 1$$

Substituting for $\tan\alpha$ from Equation (3.4) gives

$$\frac{8\cos\beta\,\sin\beta\,\tan\beta}{1 - 16\cos^2\beta\sin^2\beta} = 1$$

Rearranging in terms of $\sin^2\beta$ gives

$$8\sin^2\beta = 1 - 16\sin^2\beta(1 - \sin^2\beta)$$
$$(4\sin^2\beta)^2 - 6(4\sin^2\beta)^2 + 1 = 0$$

or

$$4\sin^2\beta = 3 \pm 2\sqrt{2}$$
$$= 3 - 2\sqrt{2} \qquad (\text{since } \sin\beta \le 1)$$

so that

$$4\cos^2\beta = 4 - (3 - 2\sqrt{2}) = 1 + 2\sqrt{2}$$

We can now use Equation (3.4) to find α, but first we square it!

$$\tan^2\alpha = 16\cos^2\beta\sin^2\beta = (3 - 2\sqrt{2})(1 + 2\sqrt{2})$$
$$= 3 - 2\sqrt{2} + 6\sqrt{2} - 8$$

so

$$\tan^2\alpha = 4\sqrt{2} - 5$$

Hence

$$\sec^2\alpha = 1 + \tan^2\alpha = 4\sqrt{2} - 4 = 4(2\sqrt{2} - 1)$$

so that

$$\cos^2\alpha = \frac{1}{\sec^2\alpha} = \frac{1}{4(\sqrt{2} - 1)} = \frac{1}{4}(\sqrt{2} + 1)$$

i.e.

$$\cos\alpha = \tfrac{1}{2}(\sqrt{2} + 1)^{1/2}$$

and

$$\alpha = \cos^{-1}[(2^{1/2} + 1)^{1/2}/2]$$

as required.

This kind of manipulation problem is well solved by modern computer algebra packages. The dynamics stopped at the expression for dx/dt.

3.5   A particle is projected with speed V from a point O. Show that its subsequent path must lie wholly within a paraboloid with O as focus. Find the equation of this paraboloid.

Solution   If we take x as horizontal, y vertical, then for angle of launch θ, the equations of motion are

$$\ddot{x} = 0, \qquad \ddot{y} = -g$$

which integrate to

$$x = V\cos\theta\, t$$

and

$$y = V\sin\theta\, t - \tfrac{1}{2}gt^2$$

(see fact sheet).

We can eliminate t to obtain the equation of the parabola. Inserting

$$t = \frac{x}{V\cos\theta}$$

into the second equation gives

$$y = x\tan\theta - \tfrac{1}{2}g\left(\frac{x}{V\cos\theta}\right)^2$$

$$= x\tan\theta - \frac{gx^2}{2V^2}(1 + \tan^2\theta)$$

where we have used $1/\cos^2\theta = \sec^2\theta = 1 + \tan^2\theta$ to get the parabola in terms of $\tan\theta$ alone. Now the equation

$$y = x\tan\theta - \frac{gx^2}{2V^2}(1 + \tan^2\theta) \tag{3.5}$$

is the equation of *any* parabolic path with θ any angle of projection. The quantity $\tan\theta$ describes the slope of the parabolic path, and in general there will be *two* angles which pass through a chosen point. Only if this point is on the bounding curve will *one* angle of trajectory provide a path such that the particle will reach it (see Fig. 3.3).

Rewriting Equation (3.5) as a quadratic in $\tan\theta$, we obtain

$$\frac{gx^2}{2V^2}\tan^2\theta - x\tan\theta + \left(y + \frac{gx^2}{2V^2}\right) = 0$$

The condition for this equation to have real roots is

$$x^2 \geq \frac{2gx^2}{V^2}\left(y + \frac{gx^2}{2V^2}\right)$$

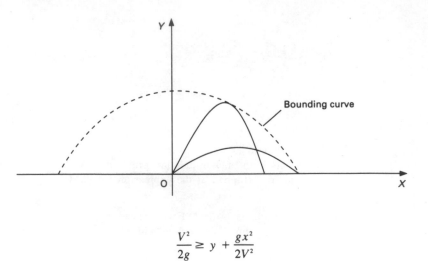

Figure 3.3

or

$$\frac{V^2}{2g} \geq y + \frac{gx^2}{2V^2}$$

Equality is the case for a single root, i.e. one value of tanθ. It is thus the equation of the bounding curve

$$\frac{V^2}{2g} = y + \frac{gx^2}{2V^2}$$

This is a parabola. However, if we allow the particle to be thrown out of the x–y plane, it is easy to see that this generalises to

$$\frac{V^2}{2g} = y + \frac{g}{2V^2}(x^2 + z^2)$$

which is a paraboloid with O as the focus.

3.6 A particle of mass m, moving in a medium offering resistance mkv^2, where v is the speed, is projected vertically upward with velocity U. If it comes to rest after a distance h, find the velocity on returning to the point of projection.

Solution If the particle is travelling upwards, Newton's second law gives

$$-mg - mkv^2 = mv\frac{dv}{dx}$$

which is integrated as follows:

$$\int dx = -\int \frac{v\,dv}{g + kv^2}$$

$$x = A - \frac{1}{2k}\ln(g + kv^2)$$

$v = U$ at $x = 0$ implies

$$0 = A - \frac{1}{2k}\ln(g + kU^2)$$

$$\therefore x = \frac{1}{2k}\ln\left(\frac{g + kU^2}{g + kv^2}\right)$$

Now, $v = 0$ at $x = h$ implies

$$h = \frac{1}{2k}\ln\left(1 + \frac{kU^2}{g}\right)$$

This is the height reached by the particle.

Travelling downwards, notice that the sign of mkv^2 changes, as it must always oppose the motion. Newton's second law is thus

$$-mg - mkv^2 = mv\frac{dv}{dx}$$

Integrating as before leads to

$$\int dx = -\int \frac{v\,dv}{-g + kv^2}$$

so

$$x = B + \frac{1}{2k}U\ln|g - kv^2|$$

(The modulus sign is there to ensure that we do not try to take natural logarithms of negative quantities. These are complex numbers.) To evaluate the arbitrary constant B we note that when

$$x = \frac{1}{2k}\ln\left(1 + \frac{kU^2}{g}\right),$$

$v = 0$. Hence

$$\frac{1}{2k}\ln\left(1 + \frac{kU^2}{g}\right) = B + \frac{1}{2k}\ln g$$

$$\therefore \quad B = \frac{1}{2k}\left[\ln\left(1 + \frac{kU^2}{g}\right) - \ln g\right]$$

so that

$$B = \frac{1}{2k}\ln\left[\frac{1}{g}\left(1 + \frac{kU^2}{g}\right)\right]$$

At $x = 0$, we must have

$$0 = \frac{1}{2k}\ln\left[\frac{1}{g}\left(1 + \frac{kU^2}{g}\right)\right] + \frac{1}{2k}\ln(g - kv^2)$$

$$= \frac{1}{2k}\ln\left[\left(1 + \frac{kU^2}{g}\right)\left(1 - \frac{kv^2}{g}\right)\right]$$

Taking the exponential gives

$$1 = \left(1 + \frac{kU^2}{g}\right)\left(1 - \frac{kv^2}{g}\right)$$

(sometimes called the 'antilog'). Thus

$$1 - \frac{kv^2}{g} = \frac{1}{1 + (kU^2/g)}$$

$$\therefore \quad \frac{kv^2}{g} = 1 - \frac{1}{1 + (kU^2/g)}$$

$$= \frac{kU^2}{g + kU^2}$$

This gives the return velocity v as satisfying

$$v^2 = \frac{g}{k}\frac{kU^2}{g + kU^2} = \frac{gU^2}{g + kU^2}$$

so

$$v = U\left(1 + \frac{kU^2}{g}\right)^{-1/2}$$

3.7 Determine general expressions for the velocity **v** and the acceleration **a** in terms of the Frenet formulae of a curve, *viz*: $\hat{\mathbf{T}}$ the tangent vector, $\hat{\mathbf{N}}$ the principal normal vector, $\hat{\mathbf{B}}$ the binormal vector, κ the curvature and τ the torsion.

Solution The Frenet formulae of a curve $\mathbf{r} = \mathbf{r}(s)$ (where s is the arc length) give rise to the following equations:

$$\frac{d\hat{\mathbf{T}}}{ds} = \kappa\hat{\mathbf{N}}$$

$$\frac{d\hat{\mathbf{N}}}{ds} = -\kappa\hat{\mathbf{T}} + \tau\hat{\mathbf{B}}$$

and

$$\frac{d\hat{\mathbf{B}}}{ds} = -\tau\hat{\mathbf{N}}$$

However, only the first of these is used in this example. Now, $\mathbf{r} = \mathbf{r}(s)$; hence

$$v = \frac{d\mathbf{r}}{dt} = \frac{d\mathbf{r}}{ds}\frac{ds}{dt} = \dot{s}\hat{\mathbf{T}}$$

(since $\hat{\mathbf{T}} = d\mathbf{r}/ds$). Differentiating again gives

$$\mathbf{a} = \frac{d\mathbf{v}}{dt} = \frac{d}{dt}(\dot{s}\hat{\mathbf{T}})$$

$$= \ddot{s}\hat{\mathbf{T}} + \dot{s}\frac{d\hat{\mathbf{T}}}{dt}$$

$$= \ddot{s}\hat{\mathbf{T}} + \dot{s}^2\frac{d\hat{\mathbf{T}}}{ds}$$

$$= \ddot{s}\hat{\mathbf{T}} + \dot{s}^2\kappa\hat{\mathbf{N}}$$

using the first equation of the Frenet apparatus. Hence

$$\mathbf{v} = \dot{s}\hat{\mathbf{T}}$$

and

$$\mathbf{a} = \ddot{s}\hat{\mathbf{T}} + \dot{s}^2\kappa\hat{\mathbf{N}}$$

are the required expressions. Sometimes κ is written $1/\rho$, where ρ is the radius of curvature.

3.8 A smooth narrow tube has the form

$$x = ae^\theta \cos\theta, \qquad y = ae^\theta \sin\theta, \qquad z = \sqrt{2}a(e^\theta - 1)$$

where a is a constant and the z-axis is vertically downwards. A particle of mass m inside the tube is released from rest at a point for which $\theta = 0$, and slides down the tube under gravity. Prove that at the point for which $\theta = \pi$ the reaction of the tube has magnitude.

$$mg[\tfrac{1}{2} + (1 - e^{-\pi})^2]^{1/2}$$

Solution From the given expressions for x, y and z in terms of θ,

$$\frac{d\mathbf{r}}{d\theta} = (ae^{\theta}(\cos\theta - \sin\theta),\ ae^{\theta}(\sin\theta + \cos\theta),\ \sqrt{2}ae^{\theta})$$

Hence

$$\frac{ds}{d\theta} = \left|\frac{d\mathbf{r}}{d\theta}\right| = 2ae^{\theta}$$

Thus the tangent vector

$$\hat{\mathbf{T}} = \frac{d\mathbf{r}}{ds} = (\tfrac{1}{2}(\cos\theta - \sin\theta),\ \tfrac{1}{2}(\sin\theta + \cos\theta),\ 1/\sqrt{2})$$

Differentiating with respect to θ gives

$$\frac{d\hat{\mathbf{T}}}{d\theta} = (-\tfrac{1}{2}(\sin\theta + \cos\theta),\ \tfrac{1}{2}(\cos\theta - \sin\theta),\ 0)$$

Hence

$$\frac{d\hat{\mathbf{T}}}{ds} = \frac{1}{2ae^{\theta}}\frac{d\hat{\mathbf{T}}}{d\theta} = \frac{e^{-\theta}}{4a}(-\sin\theta - \cos\theta,\ \cos\theta - \sin\theta,\ 0)$$

Since

$$\kappa\hat{\mathbf{N}} = \frac{d\hat{\mathbf{T}}}{ds}$$

we have that

$$\kappa = \frac{\sqrt{2}e^{-\theta}}{4a}$$

Hence

$$\hat{\mathbf{N}} = \frac{1}{\kappa}\frac{d\hat{\mathbf{T}}}{ds} = \frac{1}{\sqrt{2}}(-\sin\theta - \cos\theta,\ \cos\theta - \sin\theta,\ 0)$$

Finally, we find $\hat{\mathbf{B}}$ using $\hat{\mathbf{B}} = \hat{\mathbf{T}} \times \hat{\mathbf{N}}$ so that

$$\hat{\mathbf{B}} = \begin{vmatrix} \hat{\mathbf{i}} & \hat{\mathbf{j}} & \hat{\mathbf{k}} \\ \tfrac{1}{2}(c - s) & \tfrac{1}{2}(c + s) & 1/\sqrt{2} \\ \tfrac{1}{2}(-c - s) & \tfrac{1}{2}(c - s) & 0 \end{vmatrix}$$

where $c = \cos\theta$, $s = \sin\theta$. Hence

$$\hat{\mathbf{B}} = (\tfrac{1}{2}(\sin\theta - \cos\theta),\ \tfrac{1}{2}(-\cos\theta - \sin\theta),\ 1/\sqrt{2})$$

We now use Newton's laws, resolved in the $\hat{\mathbf{T}}$, $\hat{\mathbf{N}}$ and $\hat{\mathbf{B}}$ directions. From Example 3.7, the acceleration is given by $\mathbf{a} = \ddot{s}\hat{\mathbf{T}} + \dot{s}^2\kappa\hat{\mathbf{N}}$. Thus

$$m(\ddot{s}\hat{\mathbf{T}} + \dot{s}^2\kappa\hat{\mathbf{N}}) = \mathbf{R} - mg\hat{\mathbf{k}}$$

Resolving in the $\hat{\mathbf{T}}$, $\hat{\mathbf{N}}$ and $\hat{\mathbf{B}}$ directions gives

$$m(\ddot{s}\hat{\mathbf{T}} + \dot{s}^2\kappa\hat{\mathbf{N}}) = R_N\hat{\mathbf{N}} + R_B\hat{\mathbf{B}} - mg\left(\frac{\hat{\mathbf{T}}}{\sqrt{2}} + \frac{\hat{\mathbf{B}}}{\sqrt{2}}\right)$$

since

$$\hat{\mathbf{k}} = \frac{1}{\sqrt{2}}(\hat{\mathbf{T}} + \hat{\mathbf{B}})$$

and where we have written $\mathbf{R} = R_N\hat{\mathbf{N}} + R_B\hat{\mathbf{B}}$. In component form,

$$\ddot{s} = -\frac{g}{\sqrt{2}} \tag{3.6}$$

$$m\kappa\dot{s}^2 = R_N \tag{3.7}$$

and

$$0 = R_B - \frac{mg}{\sqrt{2}} \tag{3.8}$$

The remainder of the solution is devoted to finding $|\mathbf{R}| = (R_N^2 + R_B^2)^{1/2}$ in terms of θ. We then put $\theta = \pi$. From Equation (3.6), integrating once with respect to t leads to

$$\frac{\mathrm{d}s}{\mathrm{d}t} = -\frac{gt}{\sqrt{2}}$$

given $\dot{s} = 0$ when $t = 0$. Hence

$$\frac{\mathrm{d}\theta}{\mathrm{d}t} = \frac{\mathrm{d}s}{\mathrm{d}t} \bigg/ \frac{\mathrm{d}s}{\mathrm{d}\theta}$$

$$= -\frac{gt}{\sqrt{2}} \bigg/ 2ae^\theta$$

so that

$$2ae^\theta \mathrm{d}\theta = -\frac{gt\,\mathrm{d}t}{\sqrt{2}}$$

whence

$$2\sqrt{2}ae^\theta = -\frac{gt^2}{2} + \text{constant}$$

The constant is $2a\sqrt{2}$, since $\theta = 0$ when $t = 0$, and hence

$$2\sqrt{2}ae^\theta = 2\sqrt{2}a - \frac{gt^2}{2} \tag{3.9}$$

Now, from Equation (3.7):

$$R_N = m\kappa\dot{s}^2$$

$$= m\frac{\sqrt{2}e^{-\theta}}{4a}\frac{g^2t^2}{2}$$

and substituting from Equation (3.9) for t^2 gives

$$R_N = m\frac{\sqrt{2}e^{-\theta}}{4a}\frac{g^2}{2}\frac{4\sqrt{2}a}{g}(1 - e^{\theta})$$

$$= -mg(1 - e^{-\theta})$$

Hence

$$|\mathbf{R}| = (R_N^2 + R_B^2)^{1/2}$$

$$= mg[(1 - e^{-\theta})^2 + \tfrac{1}{2}]^{1/2}$$

When $\theta = \pi$ we obtain the given value of $|\mathbf{R}|$.

3.3 Exercises

3.1 A particle is projected with a velocity of $40\,\text{m s}^{-1}$ at an angle of $30°$ to an inclined plane in a plane containing its line of greatest slope. The plane makes an angle of $30°$ to the horizontal. Calculate

(a) the range of the particle along the plane, and
(b) the angle that the path of the projectile makes with the plane at impact.

(Take $g = 10\,\text{m s}^{-2}$.)

3.2 (Generalising the above example) A particle is launched at an angle β to the plane, which is at an angle α to the horizontal. The particle is launched up the line of greatest slope of the plane. Show that, if the particle is to strike the plane at right angles, then

$$2\tan\alpha \tan\beta = 1$$

3.3 A rotary lawn sprinkler operates on the side of a hill. If the lawn is flat and the force of the water is the same in all directions, show that

$$\frac{1}{R} = \frac{g}{V^2}(1 + \sin\alpha)$$

where R is the furthest distance on the lawn that the water travels from the sprinkler, α is the slope of the hill and V is the 'launch' speed of the water. Deduce the shape of the wetted area.

3.4 A ball is dropped from a height h and bounces to a height $\tfrac{2}{3}h$. Find the coefficient of restitution and the time elapsed before the bouncing stops.

3.5 Determine the equation of the path of a projectile in a medium where the resistance $\mathbf{R} = -mk\mathbf{v}$, given a launch angle α and initial velocity $\mathbf{u}$.

3.6 A particle of mass m is projected with velocity U at an angle of elevation α in a medium in which resistance is horizontal and equal to mkv, where v is the horizontal component of the velocity of the particle. Show that the range on the horizontal plane through the point of projection is

$$\frac{U\cos\alpha}{k}(1 - e^{-kz})$$

where

$$z = \frac{2U\sin\alpha}{g}$$

If this range is denoted by x_R, show that the horizontal distance travelled by the particle before reaching the highest point of the path is greater than $\tfrac{1}{2}x_R$.

3.7 A bead of mass m slides down a smooth wire which takes the form of a helix:

$$\mathbf{r} = (a\cos\theta, a\sin\theta, b\theta).$$

If it starts from rest at the point corresponding to the point $\theta = 0$, show that, at any subsequent point, the reaction of the wire on the bead will have magnitude

$$\frac{mga}{a^2 + b^2}[a^2 + b^2(1 + 4\theta^2)]^{1/2}$$

3.4 Outline Solutions to Exercises

3.1 Using y vertical, x horizontal, the equation of the path is

$$y = x\sqrt{3} - \frac{x^2}{80}$$

The equation of the plane's line of greatest slope is

$$y = \frac{x}{\sqrt{3}}$$

The range up the slope is the intersection, which is $160/\sqrt{3}$ m. The slope of the parabola is given by

$$\frac{dy}{dx} = \sqrt{3} - \frac{x}{40}$$

$$= -\frac{1}{\sqrt{3}}$$

at the maximum range. This gives an angle of $60°$ below the horizontal. Hence (a) range $= (160/3)\sqrt{3}$; (b) $-60°$.

3.2 Figure 3.4 shows the axes and notation. The equation of the parabola is

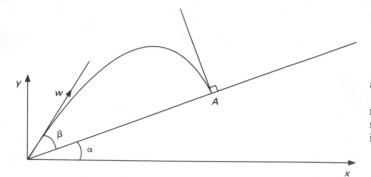

Figure 3.4

$$y = x\tan(\alpha + \beta) - \frac{gx^2}{2w^2}\sec^2(\alpha + \beta)$$

The equation of the plane is

$$y = x\tan\alpha$$

Point A is thus given by

$$\frac{gx}{2w^2}\sec^2(\alpha + \beta) = \tan(\alpha + \beta) - \tan\alpha \qquad \textbf{(3.10)}$$

The gradient of the parabola is given by

$$\frac{dy}{dx} = \tan(\alpha + \beta) - \frac{gx}{w^2}\sec^2(\alpha + \beta)$$

and at A this must be $-1/\tan\alpha$, so that

$$\tan(\alpha + \beta) - \frac{gx}{w^2}\sec^2(\alpha + \beta) = -\frac{1}{\tan\alpha} \qquad \textbf{(3.11)}$$

Eliminating $(gx/w^2)\sec^2(\alpha + \beta)$ between Equations (3.10) and (3.11) gives

$$[2\tan\alpha - \tan(\alpha + \beta)]\tan\alpha = -1$$

or, writing $t = \tan\alpha$ and using the addition formula for $\tan(\alpha + \beta)$,

$$(t^2 + 1)(1 - 2t\tan\beta) = 0$$

or $2\tan\alpha\tan\beta = 1$, as required. (This problem can be solved purely geometrically using the properties of a parabola.)

3.3 If we use the same notation as Fig. 3.4 in the answer to Exercise 3.2, then the equation of the path is

$$y = x\tan(\alpha + \beta) - \frac{gx^2}{2V^2}\sec^2(\alpha + \beta)$$

The point where this intersects $y = x\tan\alpha$ is

$$x = \frac{2V^2}{g}[\tan(\alpha + \beta) - \tan\alpha]\cos^2(\alpha + \beta)$$

We next set $dx/d\beta = 0$ to find the value of β for which x is a maximum. Since $R = x\sec\alpha$, this will also be a maximum for R. After some algebra, we obtain

$$\beta = \frac{\pi}{4} - \frac{1}{2}\alpha$$

whence

$$R = \frac{V^2}{g(1 + \sin\alpha)}$$

as required.

If the plan view of the hill is as in Fig. 3.5, then $\theta = 0$ corresponds to the maximum value of α (say α_0) (line of greatest slope). $\theta = \pi/2$ corresponds to $\alpha = 0$. The intersection of an inclined plane and a paraboloid is an ellipse.

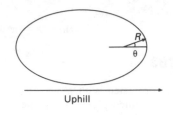

Uphill

Figure 3.5

3.4 Since $v^2 = 2gh$, where v is the speed on impact, and $V^2 = 2g(2h/3)$, where V is the speed after one bounce, this gives $e = \sqrt{\frac{2}{3}} = \frac{1}{3}\sqrt{6}$, the value of the coefficient of restitution.

The time to subsequent bounces is t, where

$$0 = Vt - \tfrac{1}{2}gt^2$$

or

$$t = \frac{2V}{g}$$

The total number of bounces is infinite, but, using the formula for the sum of a geometric progression, the time is

$$\frac{2v}{g} + \frac{2ev}{g} + \frac{2e^2v}{g} + \ldots = \frac{2v}{g}(1 - e)^{-1}$$

$$= \frac{2v}{g}\frac{1}{1 - \tfrac{1}{3}\sqrt{6}}$$

$$= \frac{2v}{g}(3 + \sqrt{6})$$

$$= 2\sqrt{\frac{2h}{g}}(3 + \sqrt{6})$$

3.5 Newton's second law gives, in vector form,

$$\frac{d^2\mathbf{r}}{dt^2} = \mathbf{g} - k\frac{d\mathbf{r}}{dt}$$

Integrating:

$$\frac{d\mathbf{r}}{dt} = \frac{\mathbf{g}}{k} + \left(\mathbf{u} - \frac{\mathbf{g}}{k}\right)e^{-kt}$$

from which

$$\mathbf{r} = \frac{\mathbf{g}t}{k} + \frac{1}{k}\left(\mathbf{u} - \frac{\mathbf{g}}{k}\right)(1 - e^{-kt})$$

In component form, with x horizontal and y vertical, we obtain

$$x = \frac{u\cos\alpha}{k}(1 - e^{-kt})$$

$$y = -\frac{gt}{k} + \frac{1}{k^2}(ku\sin\alpha + g)(1 - e^{-kt})$$

Eliminating t gives the equation of the path:

$$y = \frac{g}{k^2}\ln\left(1 - \frac{kx}{u\cos\alpha}\right) + x\left(\tan\alpha + \frac{g}{ku\cos\alpha}\right)$$

3.6 Figure 3.6 shows the particle's path. The equations of motion give

$$\ddot{x} = -k\dot{x}$$
$$\ddot{y} = -g$$

which integrate to give

$$x = \frac{U\cos\alpha}{k}(1 - e^{-kt})$$
$$y = Ut\sin\alpha - \tfrac{1}{2}gt^2$$

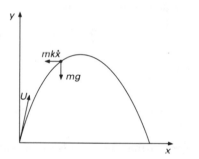

Figure 3.6

Thus $y = 0$ when $t = 0$ or $2U\sin\alpha/g$. Hence

$$x_R = \frac{U\cos\alpha}{k}(1 - e^{-kT})$$

where

$$T = \frac{2U\sin\alpha}{g}$$

At the highest point $t = T/2$, at which time

$$x = x_T = \frac{U\cos\alpha}{k}(1 - e^{-kT/2})$$

$$2x_T - x_R = \frac{U\cos\alpha}{k}(1 - 2e^{-kT/2} + e^{-kT})$$

$$= \frac{U\cos\alpha}{k}(1 - e^{-kT/2})^2 > 0$$

Thus $x_T > \frac{1}{2}x_R$.

3.7 From $\mathbf{r} = (a\cos\theta, a\sin\theta, b\theta)$ we obtain

$$\hat{\mathbf{T}} = \frac{a}{(a^2 + b^2)^{1/2}}\left(-\sin\theta, \cos\theta, \frac{b}{a}\right)$$
$$\hat{\mathbf{N}} = (-\cos\theta, -\sin\theta, 0)$$

and

$$\hat{\mathbf{B}} = \frac{a}{(a^2 + b^2)^{1/2}}\left(\frac{b}{a}\sin\theta, -\frac{b}{a}\cos\theta, 1\right)$$

Newton's laws then give

$$\ddot{s} = -\frac{gb}{(a^2 + b^2)^{1/2}}$$
$$m\kappa\dot{s}^2 = R_N$$
$$0 = R_B - \frac{mga}{(a^2 + b^2)^{1/2}}$$

where s = arc length = $\theta(a^2 + b^2)^{1/2}$, κ = curvature = $a/(a^2 + b^2)$ and

$$\mathbf{R} = R_N\hat{\mathbf{N}} + R_B\hat{\mathbf{B}}$$

Integrating the first of these equations twice and then substituting into the second gives

$$\kappa\dot{s}^2 = -\frac{2gab\theta}{a^2 + b^2}$$

from which

$$R_N = -\frac{2mgab\theta}{a^2 + b^2}$$

With

$$R_B = \frac{mga}{(a^2 + b^2)^{1/2}}$$

we obtain the desired result.

4 Linear Momentum

4.1 Fact Sheet

Momentum The linear momentum of a particle, usually abbreviated to just momentum, is defined as the particle's mass times its velocity $= m\mathbf{v}$. It is a vector in the same direction as velocity.

Impulse Impulse is defined as the application of a force integrated over the interval of time over which it acts. From integrating Newton's second law.

$$\text{Impulse} = \int_{t_1}^{t_2} \mathbf{F}\,dt = \int_{t_1}^{t_2} \frac{d}{dt}(m\mathbf{v})dt = [m\mathbf{v}]_{t_2} - [m\mathbf{v}]_{t_1}$$

that is: impulse = change in momentum.

Since $t_2 - t_1$, the time over which the force acts, is often extremely small (it is often called δt), we also have

$$\text{Impulse} = \mathbf{F}\delta t$$

($\mathbf{F}$ is almost always correspondingly very large, so that the impulse is a reasonable magnitude). The direction of the impulse is the same as the force that creates it.

Collisions When particles collide, the momentum before impact is equal to the momentum after impact. This is a vector equation.

If two particles are connected by a string, then the relation *impulse = change in momentum* can be used to calculate the impulse in the string. If no information is required about the impulse in the string, and the string is light and inextensible, then the fact that momentum is still conserved over the whole system is often useful.

Restitution If a particle hits a fixed object (for example a ball hitting the floor) then the ratio

$$e = \frac{\text{speed after impact}}{\text{speed before impact}}$$

is called the coefficient of restitution (we have already met this in Chapter 3, Example 3.3). Since the component of velocity in the direction of movement reverses, a negative sign occurs in the formula:

$$v_2\hat{\mathbf{n}} = -ev_1\hat{\mathbf{n}}$$

where $v_1\hat{\mathbf{n}}$ is the velocity before impact and $-v_2\hat{\mathbf{n}}$ the velocity after impact.

Energy The kinetic energy of a particle of mass m and velocity $\mathbf{v}$ is given by $\frac{1}{2}m|\mathbf{v}|^2$. Although problems involving energy conservation are postponed until Chapter 10, this expression is useful in the context of collisions between particles.

4.2 Worked Examples

4.1 A bullet of mass 1 g is fired into a block of ice of mass 1 kg which can slide freely. If the bullet is fired with speed 2000 m s^{-1} and comes to rest embedded in the ice, what is the final speed of the ice (and bullet)?

Solution The conservation of momentum applied to this problem is

$$m_1 v_1 + m_2 v_2 = (m_1 + m_2)v$$

where

$$m_1 = 0.001, \ v_1 = 2000, \ m_2 = 1.0 \ \text{and} \ v_2 = 0$$

so that $0.001 \times 2000 = 1.001v$, where v is the final speed of the ice block plus bullet. Hence $v = 1.998$ m s^{-1}.

4.2 A ball of mass m is dropped on to a plane inclined at an angle α to the horizontal. If the ball rebounds so that its motion is initially horizontal, calculate the coefficient of restitution.

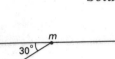

Solution The ball will hit the plane at a speed V (say). Momentum is conserved parallel to the plane (see Fig. 4.1). Hence $mv\sin\alpha = mv\cos\alpha$, where V is the speed of the ball before impact, and v is the speed after impact. The law of restitution gives

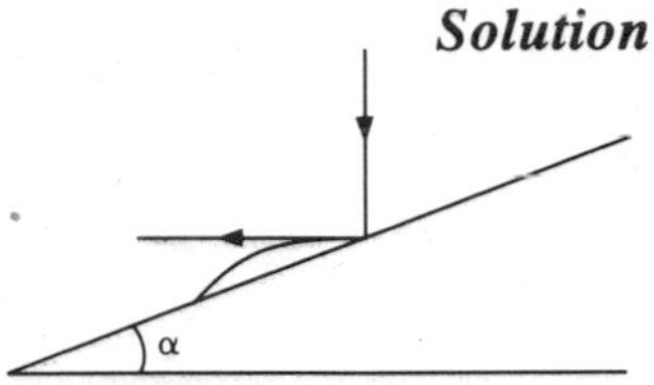

$$eV\cos\alpha = v\sin\alpha$$

These two equations give the restitution $e = \tan^2\alpha$.

Figure 4.1

4.3 Three particles of mass m lie on a level, smooth table and are connected by two light inextensible strings. Initially all the strings are slack. One of the end particles is given a speed u. When the second string goes taut, the situation is as in Fig. 4.2. Determine the final speeds of the three masses.

Solution Let the final speeds of the masses be as indicated in Fig. 4.3. By the conservation of momentum, the total momentum in the x direction is mu, and the total momentum in the y-direction remains zero. Thus

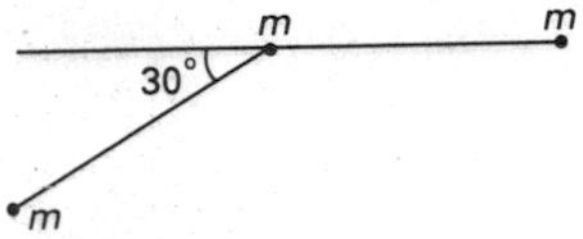

$$mu_1 + mu_1 + mu_3 \cos 30° = mu \tag{4.1}$$

and

$$mu_2 - mu_3 \sin 30° = 0 \tag{4.2}$$

Figure 4.2

Inextensibility of the second string gives

$$u_3 = u_1 \cos 30° - u_2 \sin 30° \tag{4.3}$$

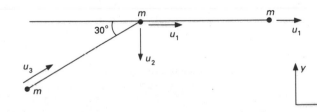

Figure 4.3

Equation (4.2) implies

$$u_2 = u_3 \sin 30° = \tfrac{1}{2} u_3$$

and Equation (4.3) implies

$$u_1 \cos 30° = u_3 + u_2 \sin 30°$$

so

$$\frac{u_1\sqrt{3}}{2} = u_3 + \tfrac{1}{2} u_2 = u_3 + \tfrac{1}{4} u_3 = \frac{5u_3}{4}$$

$$\therefore \qquad u_1 = \frac{10u_3}{4\sqrt{3}} = \frac{5u_3}{2\sqrt{3}}$$

or

$$u_3 = \frac{2\sqrt{3}}{5} u_1$$

Now Equation (4.1) implies

$$2u_1 + u_3 \cos 30° = u$$

so that substituting for u_3 gives

$$2u_1 + \frac{2\sqrt{3}}{5} \frac{\sqrt{3}}{2} u_1 = u$$

or

$$(2 + \tfrac{3}{5}) u_1 = u$$

$$\therefore \qquad u_1 = \frac{5u}{13}$$

Hence

$$u_3 = \frac{2\sqrt{3}}{5} u_1 = \frac{2\sqrt{3}}{13} u$$

giving

$$u_2 = \tfrac{1}{2} u_3 = \frac{\sqrt{3}}{13} u$$

Finally, the speed of the middle particle is given by

$$(u_1^2 + u_2^2)^{1/2} = (25 + 3)^{1/2} \frac{u}{13}$$

$$= \frac{2\sqrt{7}}{13} u$$

Hence the speeds are

$$\frac{5u}{13}; \qquad \frac{2\sqrt{7}}{13} u; \qquad \frac{2\sqrt{3}}{13} u$$

In this example, Equations (4.1), (4.2) and (4.3) contain all the mechanics. The rest is algebra which can be solved by software if necessary.

4.4 Three equal masses lie at the vertices of an isosceles triangle ABC. There are light taut inelastic strings connecting AB and BC, and the angle ABC is θ. The mass at A is given a velocity **v** in the direction $\overrightarrow{CB}$. Determine the velocity of the mass at C immediately the string AB is once again taut.

Solution The string becomes taut again when the geometry is as displayed in Fig. 4.4. There is an impulsive tension T_1 in A'B and an impulsive tension T_2 in BC. Let the velocities be as displayed in Fig. 4.4. We have already used the fact that BC is inextensible, and momentum is automatically conserved perpendicular to AA' by choice of u_2 for the 'transverse' speeds of the masses at A' and B. We write down the conservation of momentum in the AA' direction:

$$mv = mu_1 + 2mu_3 \tag{4.4}$$

The inextensibility of A'B leads to

$$u_1 \cos\theta - u_2 \sin\theta = u_3\cos\theta + u_2 \sin\theta$$

whence

$$2u_2 \sin\theta = (u_1 - u_3) \cos\theta \tag{4.5}$$

The relationship *impulse = change in momentum* for A' is

$$T_1 = mv\cos\theta - m(u_1 \cos\theta - u_2\sin\theta) \tag{4.6}$$

and for string BA' at B is

$$T_1 - T_2\cos\theta = mu_3\cos\theta + mu_2\sin\theta \tag{4.7}$$

and for string BC at B is

$$T_1\cos\theta - T_2 = mu_3 \tag{4.8}$$

and finally for string BC at C is

$$T_2 = mu_3 \tag{4.9}$$

The remainder of the question is concerned with algebraic manipulation (which can be done using an appropriate software package). From Equations (4.8) and (4.9):

$$T_1 \cos\theta = 2T_2 \tag{4.10}$$

Substituting for T_2 into Equation (4.7), at the same time eliminating u_2 from Equation (4.5), yields

$$T_1(1 - \tfrac{1}{2} \cos^2\theta) = \tfrac{1}{2} m(u_1 + u_3)\cos\theta$$

Now, Equation (4.6) is (eliminating u_2 again using Equation (4.5))

$$T_1 = mv\cos\theta - \tfrac{1}{2} m(u_1 + u_3)\cos\theta$$

Hence, eliminating $(u_1 + u_3) \cos\theta$ from these last two equations gives

$$T_1 = \frac{2mv\cos\theta}{4 - \cos^2\theta}$$

whence

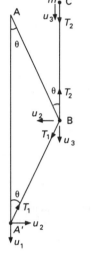

Figure 4.4

$$T_2 = \frac{mv\cos^2\theta}{4 - \cos^2\theta}$$

so that

$$u_3 = \frac{T_2}{m} = \frac{v\cos^2\theta}{4 - \cos^2\theta}$$

Expressing u_3 terms of $\tan\theta$, using

$$\cos^2\theta = \frac{1}{\sec^2\theta} = \frac{1}{1 + \tan^2\theta}$$

gives

$$u_3 = \frac{v}{3 + 4\tan^2\theta}$$

Also, substituting back,

$$u_2 = \frac{2v\tan\theta}{3 + 4\tan^2\theta}$$

$$u_1 = \frac{v(1 + 4\tan^2\theta)}{3 + 4\tan^2\theta}$$

Several points are worthy of note here. First of all, not all the equations are independent, but we chose the convenient ones to solve. The limiting cases $\theta \to 0$ and $\theta \to \pi/2$ are instructive. As $\theta \to 0$ all three masses are (virtually) collinear: $u_1 \approx u_3 \approx \frac{1}{3} v$, $u_2 \approx 0$; hence all masses have the initial momentum (mv) evenly distributed amongst them. As $\theta \to \pi/2$, the string AB is extremely long and AA' is very short, hence $u_1 \approx v$, $u_2 \approx u_3 \approx 0$ and virtually nothing happens to hinder the initial progress of the mass at A.

For an equilateral triangle, $\theta = \pi/3$, giving $u_3 = v/15$, $u_2 = (2v\sqrt{3})/15$ and $u_1 = 13v/15$.

4.5 Four particles of equal mass are attached to a light inextensible string at points A, B, C, D, where AB = BC = CD, and placed with the three parts of the string taut and forming three sides of a regular hexagon. An impulse is given to the particle at A so that it moves in the direction BA with speed u. Prove that the particle at D begins to move with speed $u/13$.

Solution In this example, we are given that 'an impulse' sets off the motion. Let this impulse be I and let the various velocities be as shown in Fig. 4.5. Sometimes it is sufficient to use the conservation of momentum in two directions, followed by the inextensibility condition of the strings. However, the inextensibility of AB and CD is already assured by the labelling of u and v_2, and although we can use conservation of momentum perpendicular to AB, parallel to AB we must also use

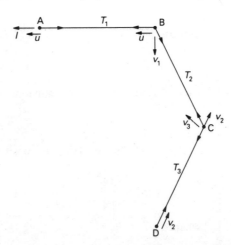

Figure 4.5

impulse = change in momentum in this example. Since the momentum before the impulse I was applied is zero, we have the equations:

$$I = m(u + u - v_2\cos60° + v_3\cos30° - v_2\cos60°)$$
$$\quad\;\; A \quad B \qquad\qquad C \qquad\qquad\quad D$$

and

$$0 = m(v_1 - v_3 \sin 30° - v_2 \sin 60° - v_2 \sin 60°)$$

and the inextensibility of BC yields

$$u \cos60° - v_1\cos30° = v_3\cos30° + v_2 \cos60°$$

These three equations simplify to:

$$I = m\left(2u - v_2 + \frac{v_3\sqrt{3}}{2}\right) \tag{4.11}$$

$$0 = v_1 - \tfrac{1}{2}v_3 - v_2\sqrt{3} \tag{4.12}$$

and

$$\tfrac{1}{2}u - \frac{v_1\sqrt{3}}{2} = \frac{v_3\sqrt{3}}{2} + \tfrac{1}{2}v_2 \tag{4.13}$$

respectively.

As you can now see, we do not have enough information here to eliminate I, v_1 and v_3 to obtain v_2 in terms of u, as the question demands. We must introduce the three impulsive tensions in the strings: T_1 in AB, T_2 in BC and T_3 in CD. These are labelled in Fig. 4.5. Using *impulse = change in momentum* at A, B, C and D leads to the four equations:

$$I - T_1 = mu \qquad\qquad\text{for A}$$

$$T_1 - T_2 \cos60° = mu \qquad\qquad\text{for B}$$

$$T_2 - T_3 \cos60° = m(v_3\cos30° + v_2\cos60°) \qquad\text{for C}$$

and

$$T_3 = mv_2 \qquad\qquad\text{for D}$$

These simplify to

$$I - T_1 = mu \tag{4.14}$$

$$T_1 - \tfrac{1}{2}T_2 = mu \tag{4.15}$$

$$T_2 - \tfrac{1}{2}T_3 = m\left(v_3\frac{\sqrt{3}}{2} + \tfrac{1}{2}v_2\right) \tag{4.16}$$

and

$$T_3 = mv_2 \tag{4.17}$$

respectively.

Successive elimination of T_1, T_2 and T_3 is achieved as follows: adding Equations (4.14) and (4.15) gives

$$I - \tfrac{1}{2}T_2 = 2mu$$

Adding this to half of Equation (4.16) gives

$$I - \frac{1}{4} T_3 = 2mu + \frac{1}{2} m \left(v_3 \frac{\sqrt{3}}{2} + \frac{1}{2} v_2 \right)$$

Eliminating T_3 using Equation (4.17) gives

$$I = \frac{1}{4} m v_2 + 2mu + \frac{1}{2} m \left(v_3 \frac{\sqrt{3}}{2} + \frac{1}{2} v_2 \right)$$

$$= m \left(2u + v_3 \frac{\sqrt{3}}{4} + \frac{1}{2} v_2 \right) \tag{4.18}$$

We can now use Equations (4.11) and (4.18), which imply that

$$2u - v_2 + \frac{1}{2} v_2 \sqrt{3} = 2u + v_3 \frac{\sqrt{3}}{4} + \frac{1}{2} v_2$$

or

$$v_3 = 2\sqrt{3} v_2$$

Equation (4.12) is

$$v_1 = \frac{1}{2} v_3 + v_2 \sqrt{3} = 2\sqrt{3} v_2$$

Substituting for v_1 and v_3 in Equation (4.13) thus gives

$$u = v_1 \sqrt{3} + v_3 \sqrt{3} + v_2$$

$$= (2\sqrt{3} \sqrt{3} + 2\sqrt{3} \sqrt{3} + 1) v_2$$

$$= 13 v_2$$

giving $v_2 = u/13$, as required.

Notice that the explicit use of impulse is required to solve this problem. Again the algebra could be done using a computer algebra system.

4.6   Two particles of masses M and m are connected by an elastic string of natural length l and modulus λ. They are at rest on a smooth table and the distance between them is l. The particle of mass M receives an instantaneous impulse of magnitude J in a direction away from the other particle. Show that the greatest extension of the string in the subsequent motion is $J(ml/\lambda M(M + m))^{1/2}$.

Solution   See Fig. 4.6. Let the tension in the string $= T$. Define the position of A to be x, and the position of B to be y. The extension of the string e is thus $y - x - l$.

Newton's law for A is $m\ddot{x} = T$, and for B is $M\ddot{y} = -T$. The definition of Young's modulus, λ, leads to the following equation for the tension, T:

$$T = \frac{\lambda}{l} (y - x - l)$$

Substituting for T gives

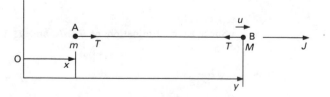

Figure 4.6

48

$$m\ddot{x} = \frac{\lambda}{l} (y - x - l) \qquad \textbf{(4.19)}$$

or

$$M\ddot{y} = -\frac{\lambda}{l} (y - x - l) \qquad \textbf{(4.20)}$$

It turns out that this can be written in terms of $x - y \, (= \varepsilon$ say). To facilitate this, perform the following operation:

$$\text{Equation (4.19)} \times M - \text{Equation (4.20)} \times m$$

$$mM(\ddot{x} - \ddot{y}) = \frac{\lambda}{l} (M + m)(y - x - l)$$

or, writing in terms of ε,

$$\ddot{\varepsilon}mM + \varepsilon \, \frac{\lambda}{l} (M + m) = 0$$

To integrate this, multiply by $\dot{\varepsilon}$ first, and then perform the integration, to obtain

$$\dot{\varepsilon}^2 mM + \varepsilon^2 \frac{\lambda}{l} (M + m) = k \qquad \textbf{(4.21)}$$

where k is an arbitrary constant.

Initially B is given an impulse $J = Mu$. Now $\dot{\varepsilon} = \dot{x} - \dot{y} = u - v = J/M$ at time $t = 0$, when also $\varepsilon = 0$. Hence from Equation (4.21),

$$\frac{J^2}{M^2} mM + 0 = k \Rightarrow k = J^2 m/M$$

Substituting back into Equation (4.21):

$$\dot{\varepsilon}^2 mM + \varepsilon^2 \frac{\lambda}{l} (m + M) = \frac{J^2 m}{M}$$

Now we set $\dot{\varepsilon} = 0$ in order to find the maximum extension. Thus

$$\varepsilon^2 = \frac{J^2 lm}{\lambda M(m + M)}$$

or

$$\varepsilon = J \left(\frac{ml}{\lambda M(m + M)} \right)^{1/2}$$

as required.

4.7 A and B are fixed points in a horizontal plane and are separated by a distance $2R$. Initially, two spherical balls, S_1 and S_2, each of mass m and of radius R, hang vertically from A and B by means of identical light inextensible strings AC and BD. The ball S_1 is then raised so that the string AC is taut and is turned through an angle $\pi/2$ radians in the vertical plane through A and B. It is released from rest. The ball S_2 rises after the collision until the string BD has turned through an angle α. Show that the coefficient of restitution between the balls is $2(1 - \cos\alpha)^{1/2} - 1$.

Solution Let a be the distance from A to the centre of S_1 (and from B to the centre of S_2). The initial potential energy (PE) of S_1 is mga, which must equal the kinetic energy (KE) of S_1 just before impact, which is $\frac{1}{2}mu_1^2$, where u_1 is the speed of S_1 on impact. After impact, let the speed of S_2 be v and the speed of S_1 be u_2 (Fig. 4.7). Applying the conservation of momentum gives

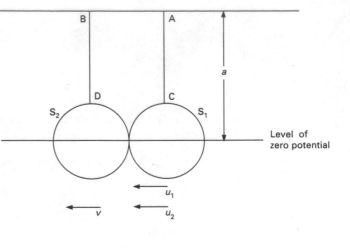

Figure 4.7

$$mu_1 + m \, 0 = mu_2 + mv$$

$\therefore$
$$u_1 = u_2 + v \qquad\qquad (4.22)$$

Newton's law of restitution gives

$$v - u_2 = eu_1$$

whence

$$eu_1 = v - u_2 \qquad\qquad (4.23)$$

Adding Equations (4.22) and (4.23) gives

$$2v = (1 + e)u_1 \qquad\qquad (4.24)$$

Again using energy, since S_2 turns through an angle α, equating the potential energy when S_2 finally stops to its kinetic energy immediately after impact gives the equation

$$amg(1 - \cos\alpha) = \tfrac{1}{2} mv^2$$

so that

$$v^2 = 2ag(1 - \cos\alpha)$$

We also have that

$$u_1^2 = 2ag$$

Substituting for v and u_1 into Equation (4.24) implies

$$2[2ag(1 - \cos\alpha)]^{1/2} = (1 + e)(2ga)^{1/2}$$

Hence

$$e = 2(1 - \cos\alpha)^{1/2} - 1$$

as required.

4.8 On a snooker table, the cue ball strikes a red, identical in every other way, which is stationary. If the coefficient of restitution between the balls is e, determine the maximum angle through which the path of the cue ball can be deflected. Find this angle if $e = \tfrac{1}{2}$, and comment on the cases $e = 0$ and $e = 1$.

Solution   Figure 4.8 displays the situation. Let the initial speed of the cue ball be u directed at an angle α to the line joining the centres of the balls. Call this line $0x$. Let the second ball be given a speed v, and the components of the cue ball after collision, along and perpendicular to $0x$, be u_2 and u_3, respectively. The following equations express the conservation of momentum along and perpendicular to $0x$. Parallel to $0x$:

$$u \cos\alpha = u_2 + v \qquad \text{(cancelling the mass)}$$

perpendicular to $0x$:

$$u \sin\alpha = u_3 \qquad \text{(cancelling the mass)}$$

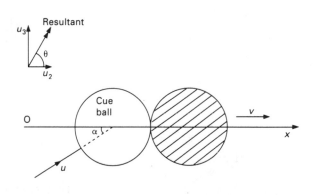

Figure 4.8

Newton's law of restitution is that $e \times$ (relative velocity before impact) = relative velocity after impact, where we note that the relative velocity is taken in the $0x$ direction (along the line between the centres), and that the minus sign arises from the fact that before impact, the cue ball's component in the $0x$ direction exceeds the second ball's component, whereas after impact the reverse is true.

We thus obtain the equation:

$$e(u\cos\alpha - 0) = -(u_2 - v)$$

or

$$eu\cos\alpha = v - u_2$$

Eliminating v from the first and last equations by subtraction gives

$$(1 - e)u \cos\alpha = 2u_2$$

Also

$$u \sin\alpha = u_3$$

Dividing to eliminate u gives

$$\frac{1}{1 - e} \tan\alpha = \frac{u_3}{2u_2}$$

But $\bar{u}_3/u_2 = \tan\theta$, where θ is the direction made by the cue ball with $0x$ after collision. Hence

$$\tan\theta = \frac{2}{1 - e} \tan\alpha.$$

If β denotes the angle turned through by the cue ball, then $\beta = \theta - \alpha$, so that

$$\tan\beta = \tan(\theta - \alpha) = \frac{\tan\theta - \tan\alpha}{1 + \tan\theta \tan\alpha}$$

$$= \frac{[2\tan\alpha/(1 - e)] - \tan\alpha}{1 + 2\tan^2\alpha/(1 - e)}$$

$$= \frac{(1 + e)\tan\alpha}{1 - e + 2\tan^2\alpha}$$

Writing $t = \tan\alpha$, for an extreme value $(d/dt)(\tan\beta) = 0$, or

$$\frac{d}{dt}\left(\frac{(1 + e)t}{1 - e + 2t^2}\right) = 0$$

giving

$$\frac{(1 - e + 2t^2)(1 + e) - (1 + e)t\, 4t}{(1 - e + 2t^2)^2} = 0$$

$$\therefore \qquad 1 - e + 2t^2 - 4t^2 = 0,$$

so

$$t^2 = \tfrac{1}{2}(1 - e)$$

Hence

$$\tan\beta = \frac{(1 + e)[\tfrac{1}{2}(1 - e)]^{1/2}}{1 - e + 2\tfrac{1}{2}(1 - e)} = \frac{1 + e}{2[2(1 - e)]^{1/2}}$$

If $e = 1/2$,

$$\tan\beta = \frac{1 + \tfrac{1}{2}}{2[2(1 - \tfrac{1}{2})]^{1/2}} = \tfrac{3}{4}$$

$$\therefore \qquad \beta = 37°$$

Also, since $t^2 = (1 - e)/2$, then $t = \tfrac{1}{2}$ and $\alpha = 27°$ here.

If $e = 0$, the impact is perfectly inelastic and

$$u_2 = v$$

so the balls adhere. In this case

$$\tan\beta = \frac{1}{2\sqrt{2}}$$

so that $\beta = 19°$. (Also $t = 1/\sqrt{2}$, giving $\alpha = 35°$.)

If $e = 1$, the impact is perfectly elastic. Reverting to the three original equations, we see that $u_2 = 0$ and $\theta = 90°$, so that $\beta = 90 - \alpha$. Hence β can get very close to $90°$. Of course, if $\alpha = 0$ then the cue ball stops at impact (having given all of its momentum to the second ball); hence $\beta = 90°$ cannot actually be achieved.

4.9 A woman of mass m is standing in a lift of mass M, which is descending with velocity V. The lift is a simple mechanical one with a counterpoise weight of mass $M + m$. Suddenly the woman jumps with an impulse which would raise her to a height h if she were jumping from the ground. Calculate the speeds of the woman and lift immediately after the impulse, and their subsequent accelerations. Deduce that the height in the lift to which the woman jumps is

$$(M + m)h/(M + m/2)$$

Solution

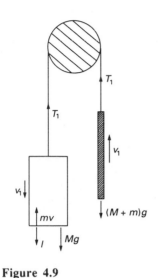

Figure 4.9

This kind of problem needs to be tackled in stages. As the woman jumps, she exerts an impulse I on the floor of the lift. This, in turn, gives an impulse T_1 to the lift cable which is translated to the counterpoise weight. Figure 4.9 shows this situation. Suppose that the impulse gives rise to a velocity v_1 in the lift. The letter v denotes the velocity of the woman. Consider first the impulse of the woman of the floor of the lift. Using *impulse* = *change in momentum*, applied to the lift, gives

$$I - T_1 = M(v_1 - V)$$

Applied to the counterpoise weight, we have

$$T_1 = (M + m)(v_1 - V)$$

Thus, on addition to eliminate T_1 we obtain

$$I = (2M + m)(v_1 - V)$$

However, also $I = mv$ and $v^2 = 2gh$, where h is the height the woman would have reached jumping from the ground. Thus

$$m\sqrt{2gh} = (2M + m)(v_1 - V)$$

or

$$v_1 = V + \frac{m\sqrt{2gh}}{2M + m}$$

is the new speed of descent of the lift at the point the woman becomes airborne. Now we need to calculate how the lift moves subsequently. To do this, see Fig. 4.10: we define x as the downwards coordinate, $x = 0$ denoting the position of the lift at the moment she jumps.

Newton's second law applied to the lift and the counterpoise weight gives

$$Mg - T = M\ddot{x}$$

and

$$(M + m)g - T = -(M + m)\ddot{x}$$

respectively, whence

$$\ddot{x} = -\frac{mg}{(2M + m)}$$

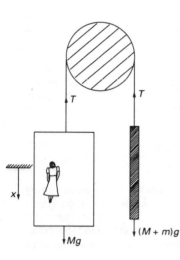

Figure 4.10

is the acceleration (in fact a retardation) of the lift.

Integrating with respect to time, noting that $\dot{x} = v_1$ at time $t = 0$, gives

$$\dot{x} = v_1 - \frac{mgt}{(2M + m)}$$

so that

$$\dot{x} = V + \frac{m\sqrt{2gh}}{(2M + m)} - \frac{mgt}{(2M + m)}$$

Integrating again, noting that $x = 0$ when $t = 0$, gives

$$x = Vt + \frac{mt\sqrt{2gh}}{(2M + m)} - \frac{mgt^2}{2(2M + m)}$$

We now need to remember two things. First of all, we are interested in how far the woman jumps *inside the lift*, so although we add h to the amount that x is at the time she has taken to jump this height, we must subtract Vt because both she and the lift started with a downward speed of V. Secondly, we need to calculate the time taken (t_0) to jump a height h from the ground. Since $v = gt_0$,

$$t_0 = \sqrt{\frac{2h}{g}}$$

Thus the height reached inside the lift is

$$x_0 + h - Vt_0 = h + \frac{m\sqrt{2h/g}\,\sqrt{2gh}}{2M + m} - \frac{mg(2h/g)}{2(2M + m)}$$

$$= h + \frac{m}{2M + m}\,h$$

$$= \frac{M + m}{M + \frac{1}{2}m}\,h$$

as required. The speeds of woman and lift immediately after the impulse are

$$V - \sqrt{2gh}, \qquad V + \frac{m\sqrt{2gh}}{2M + m}$$

respectively. Their subsequent accelerations are g and $-mg/(2M + m)$ respectively. (The woman in mid-air is, of course, only subject to gravity.)

4.3. Exercises

4.1 A harpoon of mass 40 g is launched at a fish of mass 100 g. Assuming that all motion occurs at the same horizontal level, what is the final speed of harpoon and fish if the harpoon was launched at $50 \, \mathrm{m \, s^{-1}}$ and the fish was stationary?

4.2 A large smooth circular table has a rim about its edge. A puck is projected from the edge so that it hits the edge twice before returning to its original position. If the angle between the radius and the line of projection is α, and the coefficient of restitution is e, show that $\cot^2 \alpha = e(1 + e + e^2)$.

4.3 Particles m_1, m_2 moving with velocities u_1, u_2 respectively ($u_1 > u_2$) in the same line impinge. Show that:

(a) the impulse between them is

$$\frac{m_1 m_2}{m_1 + m_2}\,(u_1 - u_2)(1 + e)\,,$$

where e is the coefficient of restitution,
(b) if $m_1 = m_2$ and $e = 1$ they exchange velocities,
(c) the kinetic energy lost is

$$\frac{1}{2}\frac{m_1 m_2}{m_1 + m_2}\,(u_1 - u_2)^2(1 - e^2)$$

4.4 Three perfectly elastic masses lie in a straight line on a smooth table. In order, their masses are M, m and M ($M > m$). The middle mass is propelled towards one of the larger masses with a constant speed. Two collisions take place. Show that a third will not take place provided $M < (2 + \sqrt{5})m$.

4.5 Three particles A, B, C of equal mass, connected by light inextensible strings AB and BC, lie on a smooth horizontal table. C is struck and moves off with a velocity u. When AB goes taut, the angle A$\hat{B}$C $= \pi - \theta$. Determine the velocities of all three particles at this instant.

4.6 Show that if a smooth sphere of mass m collides with another sphere of mass M at rest, and is deflected through an angle θ from its former path, the sphere of mass M being set in motion in a direction ϕ with the former path of m, then provided both spheres are perfectly elastic:

$$\tan\theta = \frac{M\sin 2\phi}{m - M\cos 2\phi}$$

4.7 Two particles of mass m are connected by an elastic string of natural length l and elastic modulus λ; they lie a distance l apart on a smooth horizontal table. Each is given an impulse J along the line of the string away from its centre. Find the greatest extension of the string and the time taken to attain this greatest extension.

4.8 Two identical blocks of mass m are attached by a light inextensible string over a frictionless pulley and are in perfect balance. A object of mass M is dropped on to one of the masses from a height h above it and is brought to rest by the impact. The mass takes the impact, but the string then breaks on the same side of the pulley. Show that the other mass reaches its initial position once more after a time

$$\frac{M}{m}\sqrt{\frac{2h}{g}}$$

4.9 Two smooth spheres A and B, of equal mass, collide obliquely and B is brought to rest by the impact.
(a) If A's kinetic energy is unchanged by the impact, prove that $e = 1/3$.

(b) If $e = 1/2$, prove that the increase in kinetic energy of A is one third of B's original kinetic energy.

4.4 Outline Solutions to Exercises

4.1 Conservation of momentum gives $0.04 \times 50 = 0.14v$ so that $v = 2/0.14 = 14.3 \text{ m s}^{-1}$.

4.2 The table is shown in Fig. 4.11. The puck is launched at A, hits the table again at B and C before returning to A. With β and γ angles as shown,

$$\alpha + \beta + \gamma = \pi/2$$

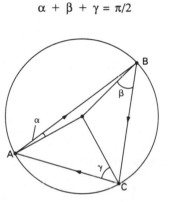

Figure 4.11

Using the restitution law at B and C gives

$$e\tan\alpha = \tan\beta$$

and

$$e\tan\beta = \tan\gamma$$

Thus

$$e\tan\beta = \tan(\tfrac{1}{2}\pi - \alpha - \beta) = \cot(\alpha + \beta)$$

$$= \frac{1 - \tan\alpha \, \tan\beta}{\tan\alpha + \tan\beta},$$

Substituting for $\tan\beta$ gives

$$e^2\tan\alpha = \frac{1 - e\tan^2\alpha}{\tan\alpha + e\tan\alpha}$$

from which the result follows.

4.3 The equations valid for the collision are:

$$m_1 u_1 + m_2 u_2 = m_1 v_1 + m_2 v_2 \qquad \textbf{(4.25)}$$

where v_1 and v_2 are the new velocities of m_1 and m_2 after collision. The restitution law gives

$$e(u_1 - u_2) = v_2 - v_1 \qquad \textbf{(4.26)}$$

(a) Eliminating v_1 between Equations (4.25) and (4.26) gives

$$m_1 u_1 + m_2 u_2 - m_2 e(u_1 - u_2) = (m_1 + m_2)v_1$$

Impulse = change in momentum for mass m_1 gives:

$$I = m_1(u_1 - v_1)$$
$$= m_1 u_1 - m_1 \left(\frac{m_1 u_1 + m_2 u_2 - m_2 e(u_1 - u_2)}{m_1 + m_2} \right)$$
$$= \frac{m_1 m_2 (u_1 - u_2)(1 + e)}{m_1 + m_2}$$

as required.

(b) If $m_1 = m_2$ and $e = 1$, Equations (4.25) and (4.26) simplify to

$$u_1 + u_2 = v_1 + v_2$$

$$u_1 - u_2 = v_2 - v_1$$

whence $u_1 = v_2$ and $u_2 = v_1$. Thus the particles exchange velocities.

(c) The kinetic energy lost is

$$K = \tfrac{1}{2} m_1(u_1^2 - v_1^2) + \tfrac{1}{2} m_2(u_2^2 - v_2^2)$$

Now

$$\tfrac{1}{2} m_1(u_1^2 - v_1^2) = \tfrac{1}{2} m_1(u_1 - v_1)(u_1 + v_1)$$

and

$$m_1(u_1 - v_1) = \frac{m_1 m_2}{m_1 + m_2} (u_1 - u_2)(1 + e)$$

from part (a). Similarly,

$$\tfrac{1}{2} m_2(u_2^2 - v_2^2) = \tfrac{1}{2} m^2(u_2 - v_2)(u_2 + v_2)$$

and

$$m_2(u_2 - v_2) = - \frac{m_1 m_2}{m_1 + m_2} (u_1 - u_2)(1 + e)$$

either by direct calculation, or by Newton's third law. Hence

$$K = \frac{m_1 m_2}{m_1 + m_2}(u_1 - u_2)(1 + e)(u_1 + v_1 - u_2 - v_2)$$

which, using Equation (4.26), gives the result.

4.4 Figure 4.12 shows the collisions and the notation. Momentum conservation gives

$$mu = - mu_1 + Mu_2$$

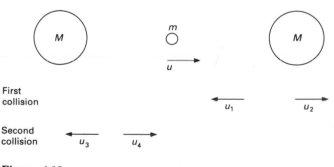

First collision

Second collision

Figure 4.12

and

$$mu_1 = -mu_4 + Mu_3$$

Perfectly elastic collisions imply

$$u = u_2 + u_1$$

and

$$u_1 = u_3 + u_4$$

These equations give

$$u_2 = \frac{2mu}{M + m}, \qquad u_1 = \frac{M - m}{M + m}\, u$$

$$u_3 = \frac{2m(M - m)}{M + m}, \qquad u_4 = \left(\frac{M - m}{M + m}\right)^2 u$$

For a third collision not to take place, $u_2 > u_4$, or

$$\frac{2m}{M + m} > \left(\frac{M - m}{M + m}\right)^2$$

which reduces to

$$\left(\frac{M}{m}\right)^2 - 4\left(\frac{M}{m}\right) - 1 < 0$$

whence $M < (2 + \sqrt{5})m$, as required.

4.5 Adopting the notation of Fig. 4.13, the equations are

$$2v_2\cos\theta + v_3\sin\theta + v_1 = u$$

$$2v_2\sin\theta = v_3\cos\theta$$

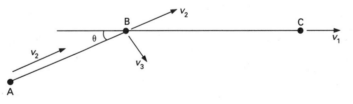

Figure 4.13

and

$$v_1 = v_2\cos\theta + v_3\sin\theta$$

Solving for v_1, v_2 and v_3 yields

$$v_1 = \frac{u(1 + \sin^2\theta)}{3 + \sin^2\theta}$$

$$v_2 = \frac{u\cos\theta}{3 + \sin^2\theta}$$

and

$$v_3 = \frac{2u\sin\theta}{3 + \sin^2\theta}$$

giving the speeds of A, B and C as, respectively,

$$\frac{u(1 + \sin^2\theta)}{3 + \sin^2\theta}, \qquad \frac{u(3\sin^2\theta + 1)}{3 + \sin^2\theta}, \qquad \frac{u\cos\theta}{3 + \sin^2\theta}$$

4.6 The notation is as in Fig. 4.14. Conservation of momentum leads to

$$mu = mv_1\cos\theta + Mv_2\cos\phi$$

and

$$mv_1\sin\theta = Mv_2\sin\phi$$

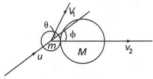

Figure 4.14

The perfectly elastic collision implies

$$u\cos\phi = v_2 - v_1\cos(\theta + \phi)$$

Elimination of u by division of the first equation by the last and some manipulation gives

$$v_2(m - M\cos^2\phi) = v_1(2M\cos\theta\cos\phi - M\sin\theta\sin\phi)$$

The second equation is

$$v_2 M\sin\phi = v_1 m\sin\theta$$

Division to eliminate v_2 and v_1 gives

$$m\sin\theta - M\sin\theta\cos^2\phi = 2M\cos\theta\sin\phi\cos\phi - M\sin\theta\sin^2\phi$$

or

$$m\sin\theta - M\sin\theta\cos2\phi = M\cos\theta\sin2\phi$$

so that

$$\tan\theta = \frac{M\sin2\phi}{m - M\cos2\phi}$$

as required.

4.7 Initially, the particles move with speed v, where $J = mv$. Choose the mid-point of the string as origin (see Fig. 4.15). By symmetry, identical dynamics happen to each particle, and

$$T = \frac{\lambda}{l}\,(2x - l)$$

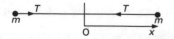

Figure 4.15

For the right-hand mass,

$$m\ddot{x} = -T = -\frac{\lambda}{l}\,(2x - l)$$

This integrates to

$$\tfrac{1}{2}m\dot{x}^2 = -\frac{\lambda x^2}{l} + \lambda x + c$$

and using $\dot{x} = v$ at $x = \tfrac{1}{2}l$ gives

$$c = \frac{J^2}{2m} - \frac{\lambda l}{4}$$

Hence

$$\frac{2J^2}{\lambda ml} = \left(2\,\frac{x}{l} - 1\right)^2$$

so that

$$x = \frac{l}{2} + \frac{Jl}{(2\lambda ml)^{1/2}}$$

This gives the greatest extension as $J(2l/\lambda m)^{1/2}$.

The period is $2\pi/\omega$ where $\omega^2 = 2\lambda/ml$. The maximum extension is attained in a quarter period

$$\frac{\pi}{2\omega} = \pi\,\frac{(ml)^{1/2}}{8\lambda}$$

4.8 At impact the mass M has speed $(2gh)^{1/2}$. If the block is given a speed v by the impact due to the impulse I, an impulsive tension T is induced in the string. Using *impulse = change in momentum* on both blocks leads to

$$I - T = mv$$

and

$$T = mv$$

This gives $T = mv$, $I = 2mv$. However, $I = M\,(2gh)^{1/2}$; thus

$$v = \frac{M(2gh)^{1/2}}{2m}$$

Developing the usual equations for free fall, the displacement of the second block (B) is given by

$$x = vt - \tfrac{1}{2}\,gt^2$$

whence $x = 0$ at $t = 0$ (start) and

$$t = \frac{2v}{g} = \frac{2}{g}\,\frac{M(2gh)^{1/2}}{2m}$$

$$= \frac{M}{m}\left(\frac{2h}{g}\right)^{1/2}$$

as required.

4.9 Since B is brought to rest by the impact, the situation must be as in Fig. 4.16. Conservation of momentum leads to the two equations

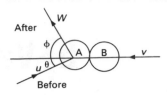

Figure 4.16

$$u\cos\theta - v = -w\cos\phi \qquad (4.27)$$

$$u\sin\theta = w\sin\phi \qquad (4.28)$$

Restitution gives

$$e(v + u\cos\theta) = w\cos\phi \qquad (4.29)$$

(a) If the kinetic energy of A is unchanged, then $u = w$ and hence $\theta = \phi$. Thus Equations (4.27) and (4.29) become

$$u\cos\theta - v = -u\cos\theta$$

$$e(v + u\cos\theta) = u\cos\theta$$

giving

$$v = 2u\cos\theta$$

and

$$v = \frac{1 - e}{e}\,u\cos\theta$$

from which

$$\frac{1 - e}{e} = 2 \text{ or } e = \tfrac{1}{3}$$

as required.

(b) With $e = \tfrac{1}{2}$, Equation (4.29) is

$$v + u\cos\theta = 2w\cos\phi$$

which, with Equation (4.27), gives

$$2v = 3w\,\cos\phi$$

and

$$2u\cos\theta = w\,\cos\phi$$

so that

$$\begin{aligned}
w^2 &= (w\cos\phi)^2 + (w\sin\phi)^2 \\
&= (\tfrac{2}{3}v)^2 + (u\sin\theta)^2 \\
&= \tfrac{4}{9}v^2 + u^2 - u^2\cos^2\theta
\end{aligned}$$

With $v = 3u\cos\theta$ (adding Equations (4.27) and (4.29) with $e = \tfrac{1}{2}$) we have

$$w^2 - u^2 = \tfrac{1}{3}v^2$$

as required $(\tfrac{1}{2}mw^2 - \tfrac{1}{2}mu^2 = \tfrac{1}{3}(\tfrac{1}{2}mv^2))$.

Topic Guide

Accretion Problems
Rocket Problems
Connected Masses

5 Variable Mass

5.1 Fact Sheet

Use

$$\text{Impulse} = \text{change of momentum}$$

which was introduced in Chapter 4.

Draw the problem in the general position (see Fig. 5.1), and write down the forces on each particle separately. Work out the total momentum of each particle at time $t + \delta t$, including that of material shed in the last (δt) instant of time. Subtract from this the momentum of each particle at time t. Since force $\times$ δt is impulse, we can now use

$$\text{force} \times \delta t = (\text{momentum at time } t + \delta t) - (\text{momentum at time } t)$$

for each particle. (Most often there is just one; a rocket for example.)

For accretion problems, where a particle is gathering material which is stationary (for example a rolling snowball or a falling raindrop) we can safely use

$$F = \frac{\mathrm{d}}{\mathrm{d}t}(mv)$$

All problems in this chapter are one-dimensional. The use of vectors is unnecessary and hence avoided.

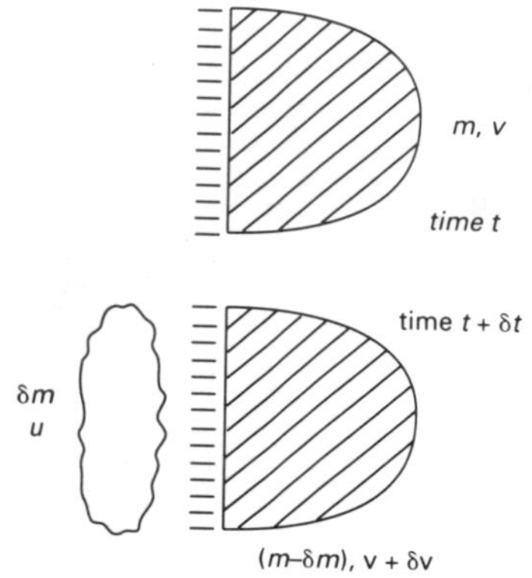

Figure 5.1

5.2 Worked Examples

5.1 A raindrop falls under the influence of gravity through a stationary cloud, and its mass increases at a constant time rate. The raindrop starts from rest and its initial mass is zero. Find the value of its constant acceleration through the cloud.

Solution Let the raindrop start at level $x = 0$ with the x-axis pointing downwards, as in Fig. 5.2. To derive an equation, we use the conservation of momentum. At time t the momentum of the raindrop is mv. At time $t + \delta t$, its momentum is $(m + \delta m)(v + \delta v)$. It has also acquired a mass δm from its surroundings. However, since these surroundings are at rest, they contribute nothing to the momentum. The change in momentum over the time interval δt is thus

$$(m + \delta m)(v + \delta v) - mv = mg\delta t \tag{5.1}$$

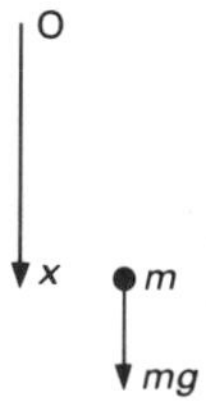

Figure 5.2

The right-hand side really should be the integral of mg over the time interval, but δt is infinitesimal; hence we can assume this to be $mg\delta t$, especially in the limit as $\delta t \to 0$. Equation (5.1) gives, on dividing by δt and taking the limit as $\delta t \to 0$,

$$v\frac{\mathrm{d}m}{\mathrm{d}t} + m\frac{\mathrm{d}v}{\mathrm{d}t} = mg$$

or

$$\frac{\mathrm{d}}{\mathrm{d}t}(mv) = mg$$

We are given that m increases at a constant rate and that $m = 0$ when $t = 0$. Hence let $m = \alpha t$, where α is a constant. This gives that

$$\frac{\mathrm{d}}{\mathrm{d}t}(mv) = g\alpha t$$

(This is indeed Newton's second law, and could have been written down at once, since the gathered material had no momentum.) Integrating gives

$$mv = \tfrac{1}{2}g\alpha t^2 + A$$

but $A = 0$, since $v = 0$ when $t = 0$.
Thus

$$mv = \tfrac{1}{2}g\alpha t^2$$

$$= \tfrac{1}{2}mgt$$

substituting $\alpha t = m$. Hence $v = \tfrac{1}{2}gt$ and the acceleration $\mathrm{d}v/\mathrm{d}t$ is thus $g/2$, which is the required value.

5.2 A scale model of a rocket sits on a launch pad. The total mass of rocket and fuel is 1 kg. The mass of the rocket M satisfies the equation.

$$\frac{\mathrm{d}M}{\mathrm{d}t} = -\frac{t}{33}$$

If the exhaust gas is ejected at a constant rate of 95 m s^{-1} relative to the rocket, determine the reaction force on the ground and how long before the rocket takes off. Take $g = 10$ m s^{-2}.

Solution In this problem, we are only concerned with the period of time when the rocket is stationary. We can still use the rocket equation with $v = 0$. The external upwards thrust is $R - Mg$, where R is the reaction of the ground on the rocket. The equation of 'motion' is thus

$$R - Mg = 0 + 95\frac{\mathrm{d}M}{\mathrm{d}t}$$

Hence

$$R = Mg - \frac{95t}{33}$$

(substituting for $\mathrm{d}M/\mathrm{d}t$ from the equation).
Also, since

$$\frac{\mathrm{d}M}{\mathrm{d}t} = -\frac{t}{33}$$

integrating gives

$$M = -\frac{t^2}{66} + M_0$$

and the arbitrary constant $M_0 = 1$, since the initial mass of the rocket and fuel is 1 kg. The equation for the reaction R is thus

$$R = 10\left(1 - \frac{t^2}{66}\right) - \frac{95t}{33}$$

$$= \frac{10}{66}(3 - t)(22 + t)$$

on factorising. Obviously when $t > 3$, R is zero and the rocket will take off. After this time, $v \neq 0$ and the above equation for R is invalid.

5.3   A sledge is propelled by a rocket engine along a smooth horizontal track. At $t = 0$ its mass is M_0 and it is at rest. All the products of combustion are ejected from the engine at a constant speed c relative to the sledge. Show that the kinetic energy of the sledge when all the fuel is used is

$$\tfrac{1}{2}M_B c^2 \left[\ln (M_0/M_B)\right]^2$$

where M_B is the mass of the sledge with no fuel. What proportion of the initial mass M_0 should the initial mass of the fuel be so that the kinetic energy of the sledge at the moment the fuel is used up is maximised?

Solution   To solve this problem, consider the sledge at time t, when it has mass m and velocity v, and δt seconds later, when it has ejected mass $(-\delta m)$, has mass $(m + \delta m)$ and velocity $(v + \delta v)$. Figure 5.3 summarises the situation.

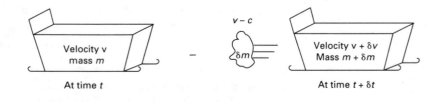

Figure 5.3   At time t At time $t + \delta t$

Momentum at time $t = mv$ and momentum at time $t + \delta t = (m + \delta m)(v + \delta v) - \delta m(v - c)$. The momentum, in total, must be conserved; thus

$$(m + \delta m)(v + \delta v) - \delta m(v - c) = mv$$

$$\therefore \qquad mv + v\delta m + m\delta v - \delta mv - c\delta m = mv$$

$$m\delta v + c\delta m = 0.$$

Dividing by δt and taking the limit, which finally justifies the neglect of products such as $\delta m\delta v$, gives

$$m\frac{dv}{dt} + c\frac{dm}{dt} = 0$$

Hence

$$\frac{dv}{dt} = -c\frac{1}{m}\frac{dm}{dt}$$

Integrating with respect to t gives

$$v = -c\ln m + A$$

At time $t = 0$, $m = M_0$ and $v = 0$; hence $A = c\ln M_0$. Thus

$$v = c\ln(M_0/m)$$

When the fuel has all gone, $m = M_B$; hence

$$v = c\ln(M_0/M_B)$$

and the kinetic energy $= \frac{1}{2}M_B v^2 = \frac{1}{2}M_B c^2 [\ln(M_0/M_B)]^2$, as required

If α denotes the proportion of the initial mass that is fuel, we have that $M_B = M_0 (1 - \alpha)$. If E denotes the kinetic energy, then

$$E = \frac{1}{2}M_0 c^2 (1 - \alpha) \left[\ln \left(\frac{1}{1 - \alpha} \right) \right]^2$$

$$= \frac{1}{2}M_0 c^2 (1 - \alpha)[\ln (1 - \alpha)]^2$$

since

$$\ln \left(\frac{1}{1 - \alpha} \right) = -\ln (1 - \alpha)$$

For an extremum, $dE/d\alpha = 0$, which gives

$$\frac{dE}{d\alpha} = -\frac{1}{2}M_0 c^2 [\ln(1 - \alpha)]^2 + \frac{1}{2}M_0 c^2 (1 - \alpha) 2\ln (1 - \alpha) \frac{1}{1 - \alpha} (-1)$$

on repeated use of the chain rule.

$$\therefore \quad \frac{dE}{d\alpha} = -\frac{1}{2}M_0 c^2 [\ln(1 - \alpha)]^2 + \frac{1}{2}M_0 c^2 \ln (1 - \alpha) = 0$$

Thus

$$[\ln(1 - \alpha)]^2 + 2\ln(1 - \alpha) = 0$$

so either

$$\ln(1 - \alpha) = 0$$

whence $\alpha = 0$, or

$$\ln(1 - \alpha) = -2$$

whence $\alpha = 1 - e^{-2}$. $\alpha = 0$ means there is no fuel, obviously a minimum, and $\alpha = 1 - e^{-2} = 0.865$ is the required maximum.

5.4 Two bags containing sand are attached by an inextensible string which hangs over a smooth peg held in a fixed horizontal position. Initially, the mass of each bag of sand is M_0 and the system is at rest. One bag develops a small hole, out of which sand runs, the mass of the bag decreasing with time at a constant rate β. If it is assumed that all the weight of this bag is sand, calculate the speed of the system when the sand runs out.

Solution The system at time t is displayed in Fig. 5.4. Newton's second law for bag B (the one with no hole) gives

$$M_0 g - T = M_0 \frac{dv}{dt}$$

The momentum of bag A at time t is mv. The momentum of bag A at time $t + \delta t$, when sand of mass δm has leaked out of the hole, is

$$(m - \delta m)(v + \delta v) + \delta m v$$

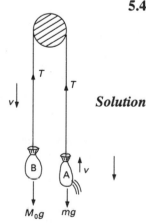

Figure 5.4

61

where we assume that the speed of the sand is v. Hence the change in momentum in time δt is

$$(m - \delta m)(v + \delta v) - mv + \delta mv = m\delta v - v\delta m$$

The impulse is force $\times \delta t = (T - mg)\delta t$. Using *impulse = change in momentum*, we obtain

$$(T - mg)\delta t = m\delta v$$

or, dividing by δt and taking the limit as the infinitesimal quantities tend to zero, gives

$$T - mg = m\frac{dv}{dt}$$

Adding this to

$$M_0 g - T = M_0 \frac{dv}{dt}$$

to eliminate T gives

$$(M_0 - m)g = (M_0 + m)\frac{dv}{dt} \tag{5.2}$$

Now, $dm/dt = -\beta$, where β is constant; hence

$$m = -\beta t + \text{constant}$$

Using $m = M_0$ when $t = 0$ gives $m = M_0 - \beta t$. Therefore, Equation (5.2) becomes

$$g\beta t = (2M_0 - \beta t)\frac{dv}{dt}$$

This equation is solved by separation of variables as follows:

$$\int \frac{dv}{g} = \int \frac{\beta t \, dt}{2M_0 - \beta t}$$

so that

$$v = -gt - \frac{2M_0 g}{\beta} \ln (2M_0 - \beta t) + C$$

$v = 0$ when $t = 0$; hence

$$C = \frac{2M_0 g}{\beta} \ln (2M_0)$$

Thus

$$v = -gt - \frac{2M_0 g}{\beta} \ln \left(1 - \frac{\beta t}{2M_0} \right) \tag{5.3}$$

Since $m = M_0 - \beta t$, the sand runs out when $t = M_0/\beta$. Inserting this value in Equation (5.5) gives the speed as v_0, where

$$v_0 = \frac{M_0 g}{\beta} (2\ln 2 - 1)$$

5.5 A rocket is moving in a straight line in outer space, where there are no forces acting. An alien observes that its displacement from a fixed point, $x(t)$, obeys the law

$$x(t) = \tfrac{1}{3}ut^3$$

where u is the constant speed of the ejected fuel relative to the rocket. Find how the mass of the rocket must vary with time if its mass is 10^4 kg initially. When will it have a mass of 10^2 kg?

Solution Since $x(t) = \tfrac{1}{3}ut^3$, we have, by direct differentiation,

$$v = \dot{x}(t) = ut^2$$

and

$$\frac{dv}{dt} = 2ut$$

o
(fixed point)

$v+u$ v

Figure 5.5

We need to be careful about relative velocity in this problem. The velocity of ejected matter *relative to the rocket* is u; hence its velocity relative to the fixed point is $v + u$, where v is the velocity of the rocket (see Fig. 5.5).

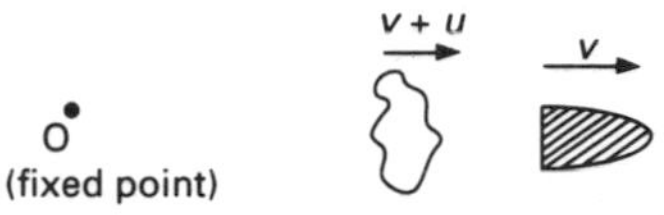

Once again, it is better to construct the equation of motion from first principles, using conservation of momentum. At time $(t + \delta t)$, the mass of the rocket is $(m - \delta m)$ and its velocity is $(v + \delta v)$. In addition, the mass ejected, δm, has velocity $v + u$ and momentum $\delta m(v + u)$. The conservation of momentum requires that, in the absence of forces, these two momenta are the same. Thus

$$mv = (m - \delta m)(v + \delta v) + \delta m(v + u)$$

so that

$$mv = mv - v\delta m + m\delta v + v\delta m + u\delta m$$

ignoring products of infinitesimals. Cancelling and rearranging gives

$$m\delta v = -u\delta m$$

Dividing by δt and taking the limit as $\delta t \to 0$,

$$m\frac{dv}{dt} = -u\frac{dm}{dt}$$

Using $dv/dt = 2ut$ gives

$$2utm = -u\frac{dm}{dt}$$

so that

$$\frac{1}{m}\frac{dm}{dt} = -2t$$

which integrates to

$$m = m_0 e^{-t^2}$$

When $t = 0$, $m_0 = 10^4$; hence

$$m = 10^4 e^{-t^2}$$

If $m_0 = 10^2$, then $e^{-t^2} = 10^{-2}$ so that $t^2 = \ln 100$ or $t = 2.15$ s.

5.6 A chain lies on the deck of a ship. One end is drawn up over a light smooth pulley, with the chain hanging freely over the end of the ship, as shown in Fig. 5.6, where the x-axis is also defined. If, initially, a length $2l$ is hanging free, and the pulley is at a height l above the deck,

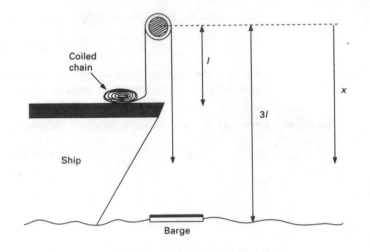

Figure 5.6

(a) Show that the velocity v satisfies the equation

$$3v^2 = 2g(x - 2l)$$

and that the acceleration of the chain is $g/3$.

(b) If a barge is distance $3l$ below the pulley, and the chain coils up on hitting it, show that

$$3v^2 = g(3x - 7l)$$

and that the acceleration of the chain instantaneously increases to $g/2$.

Solution This problem, which involves the motion of a heavy chain, is best tackled using momentum. Let the chain have density ρ per unit length. The mass of the hanging portion is thus ρx, for example. The total momentum of the chain at time t is

$$\rho(x + l)v \tag{5.4}$$

remembering that the total length moving is $x + l$, l on the left of the pulley and x on the right. Also, all the uncoiled chain has the same speed, namely v. By the same token, the momentum of the chain at time $t + \delta t$ is

$$\rho(x + l + \delta x)(v + \delta v) \tag{5.5}$$

Note that the portion of length δx which is in the coil at time t, but in the air δt seconds later, contributes nothing to the momentum at time t because it is not moving then. This is similar to accretion problems.

The change in momentum in time δt is thus the difference between expressions (5.4) and (5.5), and is

$$\rho(x + l)\delta v + \rho v \delta x$$

ignoring products of infinitesimal quantities.

To deduce the net force on the chain, which is entirely due to gravity, note that the gravitational pull on the left of the pulley is $\rho l g$, whereas the pull on the right is $\rho x g$. The net force in the x-direction is thus $\rho(x - l)g$ and the impulse is this times δt. *Impulse = change of momentum* gives the relation

$$\rho g(x - l)\delta t = \rho(x + l)\delta v + \rho v \delta x$$

which we turn into a differential equation by dividing by δt and taking the limit as δt, δv and $\delta x \to 0$, as follows:

$$\rho g(x - l) = \rho(x + l)\frac{dv}{dt} + \rho v\frac{dx}{dt}$$

We cannot solve this without eliminating t; hence we write

$$\frac{dx}{dt} = v \quad \text{and} \quad \frac{dv}{dt} = v\frac{dv}{dx}$$

to obtain

$$\rho g(x - l) = \rho(x + l)v\frac{dv}{dx} + \rho v^2$$

Cancelling ρ, this is written as a first-order ordinary differential equation for v^2 in terms of x:

$$\tfrac{1}{2}(x + l)\frac{d(v^2)}{dx} + v^2 = g(x - l) \tag{5.6}$$

This equation can be solved using integrating factor methods, which are equivalent to multiplying Equation (5.6) by $2(x + l)$ and grouping the left-hand side to give

$$\frac{d}{dx}[v^2(x + l)^2] = 2g(x^2 - l^2)$$

Integrating this with respect to x yields

$$v^2(x + l)^2 = 2g(\tfrac{1}{3}x^3 - l^2x) + A$$

where A is a constant of integration. Initially, $x = 2l$ and $v = 0$; hence

$$A = -\tfrac{4}{3}gl^3$$

which gives

$$v^2 (x + l)^2 = 2g(\tfrac{1}{3}x^3 - l^2x - \tfrac{2}{3}l^3)$$

$$= \tfrac{2}{3}g(x + l)^2 (x - 2l)$$

upon factorising. Note that $(x - 2l)$ must be a factor of the right-hand side, as a consequence of the boundary condition. Cancelling the $(x + l)^2$ term gives

$$v^2 = \tfrac{2}{3}g(x - 2l)$$

or

$$3v^2 = 2g(x - 2l) \tag{5.7}$$

as required.

We can either substitute for v^2 in the equation

$$(x + l)\frac{dv}{dt} + v^2 = g(x - l)$$

or we can differentiate Equation (5.7) with respect to x and note that

$$v\frac{dv}{dx} = \frac{dv}{dt}$$

Either way, we obtain

$$\frac{dv}{dt} = \tfrac{1}{3}g$$

This completes part (a).

For part (b) the chain is now coiling on the deck. Hence at all times, the length of chain now no longer depends on x. In particular, l is on the left and $3l$ is on the right. The net force is thus $2\rho g l$ pulling the chain off the deck. The momentum of the length of chain in the air is $4l\rho v$, which changes to $4l\rho(v + \delta v)$ in time $(t + \delta t)$. *Impulse* = *change of momentum* thus gives

$$4l\rho\delta v = 2\rho g l\delta t$$

or, taking limits,

$$4l\rho\frac{dv}{dt} = 2\rho g l$$

so that

$$\frac{dv}{dt} = \tfrac{1}{2}g$$

Writing

$$v\frac{dv}{dx} = \frac{dv}{dt}$$

and integrating gives

$$v^2 = gx + B$$

where B is the constant of integration. When $x = 3l$, Equation (5.7) implies $v^2 = \tfrac{2}{3}gl$. Hence

$$\tfrac{2}{3}gl = 3gl + B$$

so

$$B = -\tfrac{7}{3}gl$$

and

$$3v^2 = g(3x - 7l)$$

as required. Note that this last part of the problem can be solved directly by applying Newton's second law. It is not a 'variable mass' problem, but a 'distributed mass' problem.

5.3 Exercises

5.1 A rocket of mass M is travelling vertically upwards with speed v m s^{-1} and is burning fuel at a rate of r kg s^{-1} and ejecting mass at a constant speed of u m s^{-1} relative to the rocket. If $M = M_0$ at time $t = 0$, find an expression for v in terms of time. If the rocket runs out of fuel after a time $M_0/2r$, find the maximum height reached by the rocket, given that it started from the ground.

$$V \ln = \left(\frac{M}{M'}\right) - g\left(1 - \frac{M'}{M}\right)$$

Show also that the greatest height reached is

$$\frac{V^2}{2g}\left(\ln\frac{M}{M'}\right)^2 + \frac{V}{e}\left(1 - \frac{M'}{M} - \ln\frac{M}{M'}\right)$$

5.2 A rocket of total mass M originally, including the mass of the cone M', throws off a mass eM s^{-1} with relative velocity V, where e is a constant. Show that it cannot rise at once unless $eV > g$, nor at all unless $eMV > M'g$. If it rises vertically at once, show that its greatest velocity is

5.3 A snowball is rolling down a slope which makes an angle of $30°$ with the horizontal. It starts with zero speed, travels in a straight line with negligible resistance, and gathers snow at a constant rate k. Determine k, in terms of the snowball's mass m_0 at time $t = 0$, if its mass doubles after 10 s. Find a general expression for the speed of the snowball and show that, after 10 s, its speed is three quarters of the value it would have had if it were moving freely down the slope not gathering any mass ($k = 0$). (You may ignore all inertial effects of rotation – rolling and sliding may be treated synonymously here.)

5.4 A spherical raindrop is falling in a constant gravitational field through a stationary cloud. Its volume increases at a rate which is proportional to its instantaneous surface area. The raindrop starts from rest with a small radius r_0. Show that, initially, the acceleration of the raindrop is g. Show also that the velocity at time t is given by

$$\frac{g}{4k}(r_0 + kt) - \frac{gr_0^4}{4k}(r_0 + kt)^{-3}$$

where k is a constant. Hence deduce that the eventual acceleration of the raindrop is $g/4$.

5.5 A particle falls from rest under gravity through a stationary cloud. The mass of the particle increases by accretion from the cloud; the value of this accretion rate at any time is mkv, where m is the mass, v is the speed of particle at that instant, and k is a constant. Show that after the particle has fallen a distance x,

$$kv^2 = g(1 - e^{-2kx})$$

and find the distance the particle has fallen after a time t.

5.6 A heavy chain, length a, hangs over a frictionless pulley. Initially, a length ka hangs over one side ($k < 1$). Calculate the speed of the chain when one end reaches the pulley.

5.7 A rocket of initial mass M_0 of which αM_0, where $0 < \alpha < 1$, consists of rocket fuel, is fired vertically upward. Rocket fuel is shot downward by the rocket motor at a steady rate of βM_0, where β is a positive constant, with a constant velocity relative to the rocket. Neglecting any heating-up period, the exhaust velocity is assumed to be the minimum required to effect the take-off instantaneously upon starting the motor. By ignoring the rotation of the Earth, the resistance of the air and variations in the acceleration g due to gravity, show that by the time the rocket has exhausted its fuel it has acquired an upward velocity

$$-\frac{g}{\beta}[\ln(1 - \alpha) + \alpha]$$

relative to the Earth. Find also the maximum height attained by the rocket. (L.U.)

5.8 Two buckets of water each of total mass M are attached to the ends of a light cord which passes over a smooth pulley of negligible mass. The buckets are at rest. Water starts to leak from one bucket at a constant rate k. Find the equations of motion of each bucket. If v and m are the velocity and mass of the leaky bucket deduce that

$$\frac{dv}{dm} = \frac{g(m - M)}{k(m + M)}$$

If εM ($0 < \varepsilon < 1$) is the mass of water in this bucket initially, determine its speed the instant the bucket becomes empty.

5.4 Outline Solutions to Exercises

5.1 Using

$$F = M\frac{dv}{dt} + (u - v)\frac{dM}{dt}$$

with

$$\frac{dM}{dt} = -r$$

(which integrates to $M = M_0 - rt$) and $F = -Mg$, we obtain

$$\frac{dv}{dt} = -g + \frac{ru}{M_0 - rt}$$

Whence, with $v = 0$ at $t = 0$

$$v = u\ln\left(\frac{M_0}{M_0 - rt}\right) - gt \qquad \textbf{(5.8)}$$

Putting $t = M_0/2r$ gives

$$v = v_1 = u\ln 2 - \frac{gM_0}{2r}$$

Writing $v = dx/dt$ in Equation (5.8) we can integrate to obtain

$$x = -\frac{u}{r}(M_0 - rt)\ln\left(\frac{M_0}{M_0 - rt}\right) + ut - \tfrac{1}{2}gt^2$$

which at $t = M_0/2r$ is

$$x = x_1 = \frac{uM_0}{2r}(1 - \ln 2) - \frac{gM_0^2}{8r^2}$$

A particle projected vertically upward with speed v_1 attains a height $v_1^2/2g$; hence the total height is $x_1 + v_1^2/2g$ or

$$\frac{u^2(\ln 2)^2}{2g} - \frac{uM_0}{r}\ln 2 + \frac{uM_0}{2r}$$

5.2 By considering the change in momentum of the rocket while still on the launch pad, we can obtain the equation

$$R - mg = m\frac{dv}{dt} - V\frac{dm}{dt} \qquad \textbf{(5.9)}$$

where $m = M - eMt$ is the mass of the rocket at time t. Thus, when $t = 0$ and the rocket does not move,

$$R - Mg = -eMV \qquad \textbf{(5.10)}$$

So $R = M(g - eV)$ and $R < 0$ if $eV > g$. The rocket thus rises if $eV > g$. Suppose all the fuel is used up, and the rocket has still not moved. This means $M = M'$ in the LHS of Equation (5.10), so $R < 0$ if $eMV > M'g$. Equation (5.9) in flight means $R = 0$. With $m = M(1 - et)$ this integrates to

$$v = -gt - V\ln(1 - et)$$

When all the fuel is used up,

$$t = t_m = \frac{1}{e}\left(1 - \frac{M'}{M}\right)$$

This gives the required value of v $(= v_m$ say). The rocket has risen a distance x_m, where

$$x_m = \frac{V}{e}(1 - et_m)\ln(1 - et_m) + Vt_m - \tfrac{1}{2}gt_m^2$$

Additionally, the rocket rises a further distance $(1/2g)V_m^2$. The total distance is $x_m + (1/2g)V_m^2$, which gives the required result (after some algebra).

5.3 The component of the force acting on the snowball in the direction of the slope is half its weight. The mass of the snowball is $m_0(1 + \tfrac{1}{10}t)$; hence

$$\frac{d}{dt}[m_0(1 + \tfrac{1}{10}t)v] = \tfrac{1}{2}m_0(1 + \tfrac{1}{10}t)g.$$

Integrating gives

$$v = \frac{t^2 + 20t}{4t + 40}g$$

After 10 s,

$$v = \frac{15}{4}g$$

Without accretion, $v = gt/2 = 5g$ after 10 s. Since $\frac{15}{4}g = \frac{3}{4}(5g)$ we have proved the result.

5.4 Since the volume increases at a rate proportional to its instantaneous surface area, and volume time density is mass,

$$\frac{dm}{dt} \propto r^2 \quad \text{and} \quad m = \frac{4\pi}{3}\rho r^3$$

Hence

$$\frac{4\pi}{3}\rho\, 3r^2\frac{dr}{dt} \propto r^2, \quad \text{or} \quad \frac{dr}{dt} = k$$

so that $r = r_0 + kt$.

$$\frac{d}{dt}(mv) = mg$$

thus gives

$$\frac{d}{dt}[(r_0 + kt)^3 v] = (r_0 + kt)^3 g$$

which gives

$$v = \frac{g}{4k}(r_0 + kt) - \frac{gr_0^4}{4k(r_0 + kt)^3}$$

Thus

$$\frac{dv}{dt} = \frac{g}{4} + \frac{gr_0^4}{4(r_0 + kt)^4} \rightarrow \frac{g}{4}\text{ as } t \rightarrow \infty$$

5.5 For accretion problems,

$$\frac{d}{dt}(mv) = mg \quad \text{with} \quad \frac{dm}{dt} = mkv$$

Thus

$$\frac{dv}{dt} = g - kv^2 = v\frac{dv}{dx}$$

Hence

$$-\frac{1}{2k}\ln(g - kv^2) = x + A$$

$v = 0$ when $x = 0$ implies

$$A = -\frac{1}{2k}\ln g$$

which gives

$$kv^2 = g(1 - e^{-2kx})$$

as required. Thus

$$\frac{dx}{dt} = \left(\frac{g}{k}\right)^{1/2}e^{-kx}(e^{2kx} - 1)^{1/2}$$

which integrates to

$$\frac{1}{k}\cosh^{-1}(e^{kx}) = t\left(\frac{g}{k}\right)^{1/2}$$

from which

$$x = \frac{1}{k}\ln\cosh t(gk)^{1/2}$$

5.6 Consider the chain as in Fig. 5.7. This will have force ρx on one side and $\rho(a - x)$ on the other. Using

$$\text{Force} = \rho a v\frac{dv}{dx}$$

leads to

$$av\frac{dv}{dx} = g(2x - a)$$

(provided $k \neq \tfrac{1}{2}$, when the chain does not move). Hence

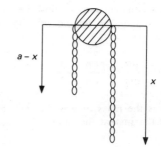

Figure 5.7

$$\tfrac{1}{2}av^2 = g(x^2 - ax + A), \qquad A = \text{constant}$$

With $v = 0$ when $x = ak$, this leads to $A = -g(a^2k^2 - a^2k)$, so that, when $x = a$, $v^2 = 2agk(1 - k)$.

5.7 The mass at any time is $M_0(1 - \beta t)$. If the velocity is v, *impulse = change of momentum* leads to

$$\frac{dv}{dt} = -g + \frac{\beta U}{1 - \beta t}$$

where U is the velocity of the exhaust relative to the rocket. Integrating this gives

$$v = -gt - U \ln (1 - \beta t)$$

The initial mass is M_0, and $M_0\beta$ is ejected in the instant δt. This gives an impulse $M_0\beta U \delta t$ to counter the impulse $M_0 g \delta t$. Thus $U = g/\beta$.

When the rocket has exhausted its fuel, $M = M_0(1 - \alpha)$, so that $t = \alpha/\beta$, whence

$$v = -\frac{g}{\beta}[\ln(1 - \alpha) + \alpha]$$

Integrating with respect to t, using $x = 0$ when $t = 0$ and inserting $t = \alpha/\beta$ gives the distance

$$-\frac{g\alpha^2}{2\beta^2} - \frac{g\alpha}{\beta^2}\ln(1 - \alpha) + \frac{g\alpha}{\beta^2} + \frac{g}{\beta^2}\ln(1 - \alpha)$$

The rocket travels an additional height $v_1^2/2g$, where $v_1 = -(g/\beta)$ $[\ln (1 - \alpha) + \alpha]$. Adding $v_1^2/2g$ to the above expression, with some algebraic simplification, gives

$$\frac{g}{2\beta^2}[1 + \ln(1 - \alpha)]^2 + \frac{g}{2\beta^2}(2\alpha - 1)$$

5.8 This resembles Example 5.4. Try that first. Using the notation of Fig. 5.8, for bucket A:

$$Mg - T = M\frac{dv}{dt} \qquad\qquad (5.11)$$

Impulse = change in momentum for bucket B gives

$$(T - mg)\delta t = \underset{\substack{\text{momentum of bucket and} \\ \text{remaining water at} \\ t + \delta t}}{(m - \delta m)(v + \delta v)} + \underset{\substack{\text{momentum of} \\ \text{shed water at} \\ t}}{v\delta m} - \underset{\substack{\text{momentum} \\ \text{at } t}}{mv}$$

whence

$$T - mg = m\frac{dv}{dt} \qquad\qquad (5.12)$$

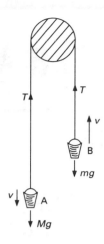

Figure 5.8

Equations (5.11) and (5.12) are the required equations. Adding gives

$$(M - m)g = (M + m)\frac{dv}{dt}$$

and since

$$\frac{dm}{dt} = k$$

so that

$$k\frac{dv}{dm} = \frac{dv}{dt}$$

we obtain

$$\frac{dv}{dm} = \frac{M - m}{M + m}\frac{g}{k}$$

as required, from which

$$v = \frac{g}{k}\left[m - M - 2M \ln\left(\frac{m + M}{2m}\right)\right]$$

When $m = M(1 - \varepsilon)$, therefore,

$$v = \frac{Mg}{k}[-\varepsilon - 2\ln(1 - \tfrac{1}{2}\varepsilon)]$$

which, incidentally, is always positive, despite appearances to the contrary.

Topic Guide

Undamped Springs
Damping
Resonance
Forced Oscillations
Normal Modes

6 Vibrations

6.1 Fact Sheet

In one dimension,

$$F = m\frac{d^2x}{dt^2}$$

If this force also equals $-kx$, then, in general, x takes the form

$$x = A_1\cos\omega t + B_1\sin\omega t$$

where $\omega^2 = k/m$. ω is called the **frequency** of the oscillation, k is called the **stiffness**, and of course m is the **mass**. The *period* of the oscillation is $2\pi/\omega$.

Sometimes it is more convenient to write

$$x = A\cos(\omega t - \phi)$$

so that $A\cos\phi = A_1$ and $A\sin\phi = B_1$, in which case A is the **amplitude** of the oscillation and ϕ is the **phase**. This kind of behaviour of a mechanical system is called simple harmonic motion (or SHM) and arises from springs or elastic strings which obey Hooke's law in the form

$$F = \text{force exerted by string (or spring) in the } x\text{-direction}$$

$$= -k \times \text{extension of string (or spring)}$$

See Fig. 6.1. In this figure, $l = $ natural length, so that

$$F = -k(x - l)$$

Analysis is simplified if the origin is at the equilibrium point of a mass (especially in problems involving gravity; see Examples 6.1 and 6.2).

A perfect dashpot has resistance R, where

$$R = r\left|\frac{dx}{dt}\right|$$

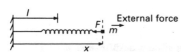

Figure 6.1

so that R always opposes motion (it is a form of friction). The equation of motion becomes

$$F = m\frac{d^2x}{dt^2} + r\left|\frac{dx}{dt}\right| = -kx.$$

A non-dimensional form of this equation is obtained by dividing through by m to give

$$\frac{d^2x}{dt^2} + 2\alpha\omega\frac{dx}{dt} + \omega^2x = 0$$

where $\alpha = r/2(mk)^{1/2}$ is called the **damping factor**.

The solution to this equation is

$$x = Ae^{-\alpha\omega t}\cos[(1 - \alpha^2)^{1/2}\omega t - \phi]$$

provided $\alpha < 1$. If $\alpha > 1$ the solution is of the form

$$x = e^{-\alpha\omega t} (A_2 e^{-\omega t(\alpha^2 - 1)^{1/2}} + B_2 e^{\omega t(\alpha^2 - 1)^{1/2}})$$

(Note that the B_2 term is always decaying since $\alpha > (\alpha^2 - 1)^{1/2}$, but for very large α it is this term that will always dominate.)

If $\alpha = 1$,

$$x = e^{-\omega t}(A_3 + B_3 t)$$

which is **critical damping**.

Forced oscillations give rise to the equation

$$\frac{d^2x}{dt^2} + 2\alpha\omega \frac{dx}{dt} + \omega^2 x = f(t)$$

where $f(t)$ represents the forcing. If we take $f(t)$ to be $\omega^2 A_0 \cos\sigma t$, i.e. a sinusoid of frequency σ and amplitude $\omega^2 A_0$, then the solution, x, called the **response**, can be written

$$x = \frac{A_0[1 - (\sigma^2/\omega^2)]\cos\sigma t + 2A_0(\alpha\sigma/\omega)\sin\sigma t}{\{[1 - (\sigma^2/\omega^2)]^2 + 4\alpha^2(\sigma^2/\omega^2)\}} + Ae^{-\alpha\omega t}\cos((1 - \alpha^2)^{1/2}\omega t - \phi))$$

in general.

The first part of this general solution is termed the **steady state response**, and the second is called the **transient**. This terminology is obvious once it is realised that this second term (the complementary function for the differential equation) always decays, whereas the first (the particular solution of the differential equation) does not and dominates after only a little time. If $\sigma = \omega$, x is large, and as $\alpha \to 0$ increases without limit, this is called **resonance**.

If there is more than one degree of freedom, then the equation of motion (no forcing, no damping) can be written

$$\frac{d^2\mathbf{x}}{dt^2} = \mathbf{Ax}$$

where $\mathbf{x} = (x_1, x_2, \ldots, x_n)^T$ is an n-vector whose components are the coordinates (n is usually 2 or 3) and $\mathbf{A}$ is an $n \times n$ matrix. The matrix $\mathbf{A}$ will have eigenvalues $-\omega_1^2$, $-\omega_2^2, \ldots, -\omega_n^2$, where $\omega_1, \omega_2, \ldots, \omega_n$ are the **natural frequencies** of the n degrees of freedom system (see Example 6.6). These frequencies $\{\omega_1, \omega_2, \ldots, \omega_n\}$ are called the **normal modes** of the system.

The normal modes of a system are excited by particular initial conditions. The **displacement ratios** $\mathbf{x}_i$ are the eigenvectors associated with each eigenvalue $-\omega_i^2$, and setting $\mathbf{x} = \mathbf{x}_i$ at time $t = 0$ excites the normal mode ω_i.

6.2 Worked Examples

6.1 A particle of mass m is attached to a fixed point by a spring of stiffness $4(mg/a)$ and natural length a. The particle moves in a vertical straight line under gravity. If x is the length of the spring at any time, obtain the equation of motion of the particle. Hence find the particular solution corresponding to initial conditions.

$$x(0) = \frac{5a}{4}, \qquad \dot{x}(0) = 2(ag)^{1/2}$$

Solution Figure 6.2 shows the forces acting, and the x-axis. Hooke's law gives

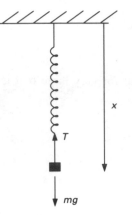

Figure 6.2

$$T = 4\,\frac{mg}{a}\,(x - a)$$

Newton's second law gives

$$mg - T = m\ddot{x}$$

Hence

$$\ddot{x} = g - 4\,\frac{g}{a}\,(x - a) = -4g\frac{x}{a} + 5g$$

The particular solution to this equation is $x = \frac{5}{4}a$. (Note that this corresponds to the equilibrium position of m.) The general solution is thus

$$x = A\,\cos\,\omega t + B\,\sin\,\omega t + \frac{5a}{4}$$

where $\omega^2 = 4g/a$ and A and B are arbitrary constants. However,

$$x(0) = A + \frac{5a}{4}$$

and

$$\dot{x}(0) = \omega B$$

Hence, using the conditions given in the question we obtain

$$\frac{5a}{2} = A + \frac{5a}{4} \text{ or } A = \frac{5a}{4}$$

and

$$2(ag)^{1/2} = \omega B \text{ or } B = \frac{2(ag)^{1/2}}{\omega}\left(\frac{a}{4g}\right)^{1/2} = a$$

whence

$$x = \frac{5a}{4}\,\cos\,\omega t + a\,\sin\,\omega t + \frac{5a}{4}$$

is the particular solution for x required.

6.2 A particle of mass m is attached to the ceiling by a vertical spring of natural length l_0, stiffness k, which has damping $r|dx/dt|$. It is also attached to the floor by a spring of stiffness k and natural length l_0. The distance between floor and ceiling is $3l_0$. Determine the equation of motion of the system referred to the equilibrium position as the origin, and hence find the stiffness and damping factor.

Solution Figure 6.3 shows the system in arbitrary position, referred to the (temporary) coordinate X. Note the diagrammatic representation of damping as a piston plus cylinder (dashpot). Newton's second

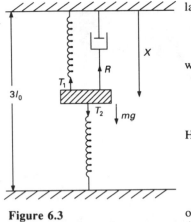

Figure 6.3

law applied to the mass gives

$$m\ddot{X} = mg + T_2 - T_1 - R$$

where $R = r\,dX/dt$ if X is increasing ($-r\,dX/dt$ if X is decreasing).

Using Hooke's law, tension = stiffness × extension:

$$T_1 = k(X - l_0), \quad T_2 = k(3l_0 - X)$$

Hence

$$m\frac{d^2X}{dt^2} = mg + k(3l_0 - X) - k(X - l_0) - r\frac{dX}{dt}$$

or

$$m\frac{d^2X}{dt^2} + r\frac{dX}{dt} + 2kX = mg + 4kl_0$$

Note that the *total* stiffness of the system is the sum of the stiffnesses of the (two) springs. We now transfer the origin to the equilibrium position. At equilibrium ($d^2X/dt^2 = dX/dt = 0$) we have

$$2kX = mg + 4kl_0$$

so that

$$X = \frac{mg}{2k} + 2l_0$$

Writing

$$x = X - \frac{mg}{2k} - 2l_0$$

means that $x = 0$ corresponds to equilibrium.

Of course,

$$\frac{dx}{dt} = \frac{dX}{dt}$$

and

$$\frac{d^2x}{dt^2} = \frac{d^2X}{dt^2}$$

Thus the equation of motion is as written previously, but with zero on the right-hand side:

$$m\frac{d^2x}{dt^2} + r\frac{dx}{dt} + 2kx = 0$$

This is *always* the case – we could miss out the details with confidence. Dividing by m, we obtain

$$\frac{d^2x}{dt^2} + \frac{r}{m}\frac{dx}{dt} + \frac{2k}{m}x = 0$$

which must be

$$\frac{d^2x}{dt^2} + 2\omega\alpha\frac{dx}{dt} + \omega^2x = 0$$

73

where $\alpha = r/[2(2mk)^{1/2}]$ is the damping factor and $\omega = (2k/m)^{1/2}$ is the natural frequency.

6.3 Show that a forced mass spring damping system

$$\ddot{x} + 2\alpha\omega\dot{x} + \omega^2 x = \omega^2 A_0 \cos \sigma t$$

has solution

$$x = \frac{A_0 [1 - (\sigma^2/\omega^2) \cos \sigma t + 2A_0 (\alpha\sigma/\omega) \sin \sigma t}{(1 - \sigma^2/\omega^2)^2 + 4\alpha^2 (\sigma^2/\omega^2)} + Ae^{-\alpha\omega t} \cos [(1 - \alpha^2)^{1/2}\omega t - \phi]$$

where A and ϕ are arbitrary constant.

Solution In order to determine the solution, we use the method of phasors. Write x as the real part of a complex quantity $ze^{i\sigma t}$ so that

$$\dot{x} = \mathrm{Re}(i\sigma z e^{i\sigma t})$$

and

$$\ddot{x} = \mathrm{Re}(-\sigma^2 z e^{i\sigma t})$$

Once we write $\omega^2 A_0 \cos\sigma t$ as $\mathrm{Re}(\omega^2 A_0 e^{i\sigma t})$ we can drop the Re, so that $\ddot{x} + 2\alpha\omega\dot{x} + \omega^2 x = \omega^2 A_0 \cos\sigma t$ implies $-\sigma^2 z e^{i\sigma t} + 2i\sigma\omega\alpha z e^{i\sigma t} + \omega^2 z e^{i\sigma t} = \omega^2 A_0 e^{i\sigma t}$. Cancelling $e^{i\sigma t}$ and rearranging gives

$$z = \frac{\omega^2 A_0}{\omega^2 - \sigma^2 + 2i\sigma\omega\alpha}$$

or, rationalising,

$$z = \frac{A_0[1 - (\sigma^2/\omega^2) - 2i\alpha(\sigma/\omega)]}{[1 - (\sigma^2/\omega^2)]^2 + 4\alpha^2\sigma^2/\omega^2}$$

Hence $x = \mathrm{Re}(ze^{i\sigma t})$ is given by

$$x = \frac{A_0[1 - (\sigma^2/\omega^2)]\cos \sigma t + 2A_0\alpha(\sigma/\omega)\sin \sigma t}{[1 - (\sigma^2/\omega^2)]^2 + 4\alpha^2\sigma^2/\omega^2} \tag{6.1}$$

This is the particular solution. The complementary function is the solution of the homogeneous equation

$$\ddot{x} + 2\alpha\omega\dot{x} + \omega^2 x = 0$$

The auxiliary equation is

$$\lambda^2 + 2\alpha\omega\lambda + \omega^2 = 0$$

$$\lambda = -\alpha\omega \pm i\omega (1 - \alpha^2)^{1/2}$$

so that

$$x = Ae^{-\alpha\omega t}\cos[\omega t(1 - \alpha^2)^{1/2} - \phi]^{1/2}. \tag{6.2}$$

The general solution is the sum of Equations (6.1) and (6.2), as required.

6.4 Determine the maximum values of the amplitude of the steady state response to a general sinusoidal forcing of a linear mass–spring damping system.

Solution   Using the notation of the previous example, the steady state response to a sinusoidal forcing $\omega^2 A_0 \cos\sigma t$ is

$$x = \frac{A_0[1 - (\sigma^2/\omega^2)]\cos\sigma t + 2A_0\alpha\,(\sigma/\omega)\sin\sigma t}{[1 - (\sigma^2/\omega^2)]^2 + 4\alpha^2\sigma^2/\omega^2}$$

Writing this as

$$x = a\cos\sigma t + b\sin\sigma t$$
$$= (a^2 + b^2)^{1/2}\cos(\sigma t + \varepsilon)$$

where

$$a = \frac{A_0[1 - (\sigma^2/\omega^2)]}{[1 - (\sigma^2/\omega^2)]^2 + 4\alpha^2\sigma^2/\omega^2}$$

and

$$b = \frac{2A_0\alpha\,\sigma/\omega}{[1 - (\sigma^2/\omega^2)]^2 + 4\alpha^2\sigma^2/\omega^2}$$

gives the amplitude $(a^2 + b^2)^{1/2}$ as

$$A = \frac{A_0}{\{[1 - (\sigma^2/\omega^2)]^2 + 4\alpha^2\sigma^2/\omega^2\}^{1/2}}$$

In order to find maximum (or minimum) values of this amplitude, we use calculus. We could find $\mathrm{d}A/\mathrm{d}\sigma$, but it is far more convenient to define $A = 1/p^{1/2}$, where

$$p = \left(1 - \frac{\sigma^2}{\omega^2}\right)^2 + \frac{4\alpha^2\sigma^2}{\omega^2}$$

and investigate the zeros of $\mathrm{d}p/\mathrm{d}\sigma$. Differentiating p gives

$$\frac{\mathrm{d}p}{\mathrm{d}\sigma} = -\frac{4\sigma}{\omega^2}\left(1 - \frac{\sigma^2}{\omega^2}\right) + \frac{8\alpha^2\sigma}{\omega^2}$$

and this is zero at $\sigma = 0$ and where $\sigma^2/\omega^2 = 1 - 2\alpha^2$.
    Further,

$$\frac{\mathrm{d}^2p}{\mathrm{d}\sigma^2} = -\frac{4}{\omega^2} + \frac{12\sigma^2}{\omega^4} + \frac{8\alpha^2}{\omega^2}$$

When $\sigma = 0$,

$$\frac{\mathrm{d}^2p}{\mathrm{d}\sigma^2} = \frac{4}{\omega^2}(2\alpha^2 - 1)$$

When $\sigma^2/\omega^2 = 1 - 2\alpha^2$,

$$\frac{\mathrm{d}^2p}{\mathrm{d}\sigma^2} = \frac{8}{\omega^2}(1 - 2\alpha^2)$$

    If $\alpha < 1/\sqrt{2}$, $\sigma = 0$ is a maximum and $\sigma^2/\omega^2 = 1 - 2\alpha^2$ is a minimum.
    If $\alpha > 1/\sqrt{2}$, $\sigma = 0$ is a minimum, but $\sigma^2/\omega^2 = 1 - 2\alpha^2$ is not possible, as the right-hand side is negative. Therefore, $A\,(= A_0/p^{1/2})$ behaves as follows. If $\alpha < 1/\sqrt{2}$, $\sigma = 0$ is minimum and $\sigma^2/\omega^2 = 1 - 2\alpha^2$ is a maximum. If $\alpha > 1/\sqrt{2}$, $\sigma = 0$ is a maximum.

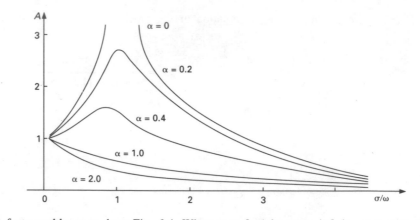

Figure 6.4

These facts enable us to draw Fig. 6.4. When $\alpha = 0$, A becomes infinite at $\sigma = \omega$. Otherwise, A has a maximum which can be very large if α is small (less than 0.2). This exaggerated maximum is called resonance, and is the cause of many engineering disasters (e.g. the vibration to destruction of some cooling towers and the Tacoma Narrows bridge). It is also utilised in amplifier circuits.

6.5 Figure 6.5 shows a two-particle model of the tone arm and stylus of a record player.

(a) Indicate all the forces acting on the system.
(b) Write down the two equations of motion using the coordinates shown if there is also a contact force between record and stylus (m_2).
(c) Now assume that there is an external force acting on m_2 such that

$$x_2 = a + A_0 \cos \omega t$$

Find a condition on ω that will predict whether the stylus will jump on the record (assume $m_2 \ll m_1$).

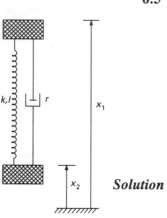

Figure 6.5

Solution Figure 6.6 shows the forces that are acting on masses m_1 and m_2. The tension in the spring and the force in the dashpot are drawn assuming that the spring is in tension, and so the masses want to move together. Therefore, T, the tension in the spring, acts to bring the masses together. The dashpot force, R, depends in sign on whether the masses are actually moving or not. It does not matter whether we take T and R in these directions, or whether we assume another direction for either T or R (or both). The crucial thing to remember is to be consistent: if it turned out that T is in compression all the time, it will be negative. Similarly, R may be negative. Pick on a convention and remain with it. F_c is the contact force between record and stylus.

The equations of motion for the two particles, using Newton's second law, are:

$$m_2 \frac{\mathrm{d}^2 x_2}{\mathrm{d}t^2} = T - R - m_2 g + F_c \quad \text{(for } m_2\text{)} \tag{6.3}$$

and

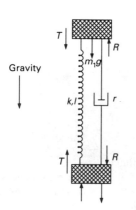

Figure 6.6

$$m_1 \frac{\mathrm{d}^2 x_1}{\mathrm{d}t^2} = R - T - m_1 g \quad \text{(for } m_1\text{)} \tag{6.4}$$

Adding these two equations of motion gives:

$$m_2 \frac{\mathrm{d}^2 x_2}{\mathrm{d}t^2} + m_1 \frac{\mathrm{d}^2 x_1}{\mathrm{d}t^2} = -(m_1 + m_2)g + F_c$$

or, rearranging:

$$F_c = m_2 \frac{\mathrm{d}^2 x_2}{\mathrm{d}t^2} + g + m_1 \frac{\mathrm{d}^2 x_1}{\mathrm{d}t^2} + g$$

$$\approx m_1 \frac{d^2x_1}{dt^2} + g$$

since m_2 is much less than m_1. To find x_1, we need to solve Equation (6.4). To do this, we note that:

$$T = k \times \text{extension}$$
$$= k(x_1 - x_2 - l)$$

and

$$R = -r(\dot{x}_1 - \dot{x}_2)$$

(the negative sign being present only because we assume that the parenthesis is positive). Equation (6.4) is thus:

$$m_1\ddot{x}_1 + r\dot{x}_1 + kx_1 = r\dot{x}_2 + kx_2 + kl - m_1g$$

We follow the fact sheet and introduce the frequency ω_0 and the damping factor α, whence this equation may be rewritten:

$$\ddot{x}_1 + 2\alpha\omega_0\dot{x}_1 + \omega_0^2x_1 = 2\alpha\omega_0\dot{x}_2 + \omega_0^2(x_2 + l) - g \qquad (6.5)$$

(In both these equations, we have used the dot to denote differentiation with respect to t.) Now we insert

$$x_2 = a + A\cos\omega t$$

This means that a is the mean distance of the stylus above the record, so we look for a solution that is sinusoidal. However, in this case the mean is not zero, but has value $a + l - m_1g/k$, arising from a plus the natural length of the spring minus the compression due to the weight of the tone arm. Hence, x_1 will be of the form:

$$x_1 = a + l - \frac{m_1g}{k} + B\cos\omega t + C\sin\omega t$$

Substituting for x_1 and x_2 into Equation (6.5) yields:

$$-\omega^2(B\cos\omega t + C\sin\omega t) + 2\alpha\omega_0\omega(-B\sin\omega t + C\cos\omega t) + \omega_0^2(B\cos\omega t + C\sin\omega t)$$
$$= -2\alpha\omega_0 A\sin\omega t + \omega_0^2A\cos\omega t$$

Equating coefficients of $\cos\omega t$ and $\sin\omega t$ gives the following two equations for B and C:

$$\left(1 - \frac{\omega_0^2}{\omega^2}\right)B + \frac{2\alpha\omega_0 C}{\omega} = A$$

and

$$\frac{-2\alpha\omega_0 B}{\omega} + \left(1 - \frac{\omega_0^2}{\omega^2}\right)C = \frac{-2\alpha\omega_0 A}{\omega}$$

Solving these by determinant methods or otherwise gives:

$$B = \left(\frac{(1 - \omega_0^2/\omega^2) - (2\alpha\omega_0/\omega)^2}{(1 - \omega_0^2/\omega^2)^2 + (2\alpha\omega_0/\omega)^2}\right)A$$

and

$$C = \left(\frac{-2\alpha\omega_0^3/\omega^3}{(1 - \omega_0^2/\omega^2)^2 + (2\alpha\omega_0/\omega)^2} \right) A$$

The amplitude ratio is $(B^2 + C^2)^{1/2}/A$. The algebra looks worse than it actually is. Writing $p = 1 - \omega_0^2/\omega^2$ and $q = 2\alpha\omega_0/\omega$ means that $B^2 + C^2$ is given by

$$B^2 + C^2 = \frac{A^2}{(p^2 + q^2)^2} [(p + q^2)^2 + q^2 (1 - p)^2]$$

$$= \frac{A^2}{(p^2 + q^2)^2} (p^2 + 2pq^2 + q^4 + q^2 - 2pq^2 + q^2p^2)$$

$$= \frac{A^2}{(p^2 + q^2)^2} (p^2 + q^2 + q^4 + q^2p^2)$$

$$= \frac{A^2}{(p^2 + q^2)^2} (p^2 + q^2)(1 + q^2)$$

$$= \frac{A^2(1 + q^2)}{(p^2 + q^2)}$$

Hence, the amplitude ratio is

$$\frac{(B^2 + C^2)^{1/2}}{A} = \left(\frac{1 + q^2}{p^2 + q^2} \right)^{1/2}$$

$$= \left(\frac{1 + (2\alpha\omega_0/\omega)^2}{(1 - \omega_0^2/\omega^2)^2 + (2\alpha\omega_0/\omega)^2} \right)^{1/2}$$

The denominator should look familiar: it tends to be the same in all these mass–spring damping problems.

Now, we derived earlier that:

$$F_c \approx m_1 \frac{d^2x_1}{dt^2} + g$$

Using the fact that

$$x_1 = a + l - \frac{m_1 g}{k} + B\cos\omega t + C\sin \omega t$$

and differentiating twice gives

$$\frac{d^2x_1}{dt^2} = -\omega^2(B\cos\omega t + C\sin \omega t)$$

$$= -\omega^2(B^2 + C^2)^{1/2} \cos(\omega t - \Phi)$$

where $\cos\Phi = B/(B^2 + C^2)^{1/2}$ and $\sin \Phi = C/(B^2 + C^2)^{1/2}$. Substituting for this acceleration into our expression for F_c yields

$$F_c \approx m_1[-\omega^2(B^2 + C^2)^{1/2} \cos(\omega t - \Phi) + g]$$

Now $\cos(\omega t - \Phi)$ always has values between -1 and $+1$. This means that F_c is at its smallest when $\cos(\omega t - \Phi) = 1$, at which time

$$F_c \approx m_1[-\omega^2(B^2 + C^2)^{1/2} + g]$$

Hence, F_c is positive if

$$-\omega^2(B^2 + C^2)^{1/2} + g > 0 \text{ or } \omega^2(B^2 + C^2)^{1/2} < g = 9.81$$

Using our expression for $(B^2 + C^2)$, this inequality can be put in terms of the amplitude and frequency of the system, thus:

$$\omega^2 A \left(\frac{1 + (2\alpha\omega_0/\omega)^2}{(1 - \omega_0^2/\omega^2)^2 + (2\alpha\omega_0/\omega)^2} \right)^{1/2} < 9.81$$

This inequality must hold if the stylus is not to jump (and ruin your listening pleasure).

6.6 A taut string of length $4l$ has its ends fixed and is under a constant tension T. It carries three equal particles, each of mass m, which divide the string into four equal lengths. Show that the modes of small planar vibrations normal to the string are represented by the column eigenvectors of the 3×3 matrix

$$\begin{bmatrix} 2 & -1 & 0 \\ -1 & 2 & -1 \\ 0 & -1 & 2 \end{bmatrix}$$

Find these eigenvectors and the frequencies of the vibrations that they represent.

Solution This problem is interesting in that it does not demand any assumptions about the elasticity (or otherwise) of the string. Instead, as you will see, the dynamics of the vibration of these three particles is wholly dependent on the geometry of the situation. Figure 6.7 shows the three particles having each undergone one small but arbitrary displacement. The angles that the string makes with the original equilibrium position of the string are also defined in this figure.

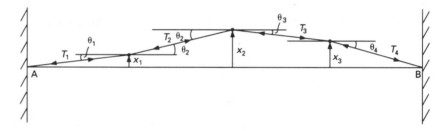

Figure 6.7

Labelled from the left, the displacements of the particles are x_1, x_2 and x_3, and the angles that the four strings make with the original, undisplaced, line of the string are θ_1, θ_2, θ_3 and θ_4 as shown. Now, since all the angles are small, the horizontal equilibrium of each particle implies that all tensions are equal. For example, $T_1\cos\theta_1 = T_2\cos\theta_2$; hence $T_1 = T_2$ to first order in powers of θ_1 and θ_2, and similarly $T_1 = T_2 = T_3 = T_4 = T$ (say).

Newton's law for each particle, in a direction perpendicular to the line AB, gives the three equations

$$m\ddot{x}_1 = T(\sin\theta_2 - \sin\theta_1) \approx T(\theta_2 - \theta_1) \tag{6.6}$$

$$m\ddot{x}_2 = -T(\sin\theta_2 + \sin\theta_3) \approx T(-\theta_2 - \theta_3) \tag{6.7}$$

and

$$m\ddot{x}_3 = T(\sin\theta_3 - \sin\theta_4) \approx T(\theta_3 - \theta_4) \tag{6.8}$$

where, once more, expansions of trigonometric functions have been made to leading order in small angles. The geometry of Fig. 6.7 implies that

$$\sin\theta_1 = \frac{x_1}{l}, \quad \sin\theta_2 = \frac{x_2 - x_1}{l}, \quad \sin\theta_3 = \frac{x_2 - x_3}{l}, \quad \sin\theta_4 = \frac{x_3}{l}$$

Hence

$$\theta_1 \approx \frac{x_1}{l}, \quad \theta_2 \approx \frac{x_2 - x_1}{l}, \quad \theta_3 \approx \frac{x_2 - x_3}{l}, \quad \theta_4 \approx \frac{x_3}{l}$$

where $4l$ is the length of the string as defined in the question. Substituting for θ_1, θ_2, θ_3 and θ_4 into Equations (6.6), (6.7) and (6.8) gives

$$\ddot{x}_1 + \frac{T}{ml}(2x_1 - x_2) = 0$$

$$\ddot{x}_2 + \frac{T}{ml}(-x_1 + 2x_2 - x_3) = 0$$

and

$$\ddot{x}_3 + \frac{T}{ml}(-x_2 + 2x_3) = 0$$

or

$$\ddot{x} + \frac{T}{ml}\mathbf{A}\mathbf{x} = \mathbf{0}$$

where

$$\mathbf{A} = \begin{bmatrix} 2 & -1 & 0 \\ -1 & 2 & -1 \\ 0 & -1 & 2 \end{bmatrix}$$

In order to determine the eigenvalues of $\mathbf{A}$ we solve the determinant equation

$$\begin{vmatrix} 2-\lambda & -1 & 0 \\ -1 & 2-\lambda & -1 \\ 0 & -1 & 2-\lambda \end{vmatrix} = 0$$

which is

$$(2 - \lambda)[(2 - \lambda)^2 - 1] - (2 - \lambda) = 0$$

$$(\lambda - 2)[(\lambda - 2)^2 - 2] = 0$$

or

$$(\lambda - 2)(\lambda - 2 + \sqrt{2})(\lambda - 2 - \sqrt{2}) = 0$$

so that $\lambda = 2, 2 \pm \sqrt{2}$.

$\lambda = \omega^2$ where ω are the possible frequencies of the system. These frequencies are thus $(2 - \sqrt{2})^{1/2}$ $\sqrt{2}$, $(2 + \sqrt{2})^{1/2}$ or, in decimals, 0.765, 1.414, 1.848.

We now find the associated eigenvectors. For $\lambda = 2 - \sqrt{2}$, the eigenvector

$$\begin{pmatrix} x_1 \\ x_2 \\ x_3 \end{pmatrix}$$

satisfies the equations

$$x_1\sqrt{2} - x_2 = 0$$

$$-x_1 + x_2\sqrt{2} - x_3 = 0$$

and

$$-x_2 + x_3\sqrt{2} = 0$$

whence

$$x_2 = x_1\sqrt{2}$$

and

$$x_2 = x_3\sqrt{2}$$

Hence $x_1 = x_3$ and the second equation holds (it is a good idea to check that there is the correct level of redundancy in these eigenvector equations). A suitable eigenvector is thus

$$\begin{pmatrix} 1 \\ \sqrt{2} \\ 1 \end{pmatrix}$$

For $\lambda = 2$, this time the eigenvector

$$\begin{pmatrix} x_1 \\ x_2 \\ x_3 \end{pmatrix}$$

satisfies the equations

$$- x_2 = 0$$
$$-x_1 - x_3 = 0$$

and

$$- x_2 = 0$$

from which the obvious eigenvector

$$\begin{pmatrix} 1 \\ 0 \\ -1 \end{pmatrix}$$

emerges.

For $\lambda = 2 + \sqrt{2}$, the arithmetic here is similar to case 1, $\lambda = 2 - \sqrt{2}$, with a change of sign in front of all $\sqrt{2}$s. Hence the eigenvector is

$$\begin{pmatrix} 1 \\ -\sqrt{2} \\ 1 \end{pmatrix}$$

Figures 6.8 (a), (b) and (c) display these normal modes. (The displacements have been exaggerated of course.)

6.7 Two masses, connected in series by two springs, hang from the ceiling. The spring nearest the ceiling has stiffness $2k$ and the second spring has stiffness k. The top mass is $2m$, the lower mass

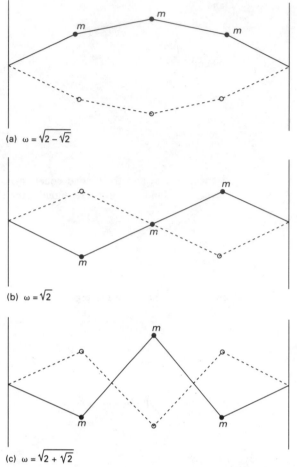

(a) $\omega = \sqrt{2 - \sqrt{2}}$

(b) $\omega = \sqrt{2}$

Figure 6.8

(c) $\omega = \sqrt{2 + \sqrt{2}}$

is m, and both springs have natural length l_0. Find the equations for each mass referred to their equilibrium positions, and hence calculate the frequencies of the normal modes of vibration. Determine also the initial displacements of each mass required to excite each normal mode.

Solution   Figure 6.9 shows the setup together with (temporary) coordinates X and Y. The equations of motion are thus

$$2m\ddot{X} = 2mg + T_2 - T_1$$

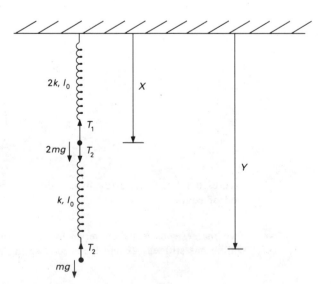

Figure 6.9

and

$$m\ddot{Y} = mg - T_2$$

where, using Hooke's law,

$$T_1 = 2k(X - l_0)$$

and

$$T_2 = k(Y - X - l_0)$$

Hence

$$2m\ddot{X} = 2mg + k(Y - X - l_0) - 2k(X - l_0)$$

and

$$m\ddot{Y} = mg - k(Y - X - l_0)$$

At equilibrium, $\ddot{X} = \ddot{Y} = 0$; hence

$$0 = 2mg + kY - 3kX + kl_0$$

$$0 = mg - kY + kX + kl_0$$

Adding gives $0 = 3mg - 2kX + 2kl_0$, or

$$X = l_0 + \frac{3mg}{2k}$$

and

$$Y = X + \frac{mg}{k} + l_0$$

so

$$Y = 2l_0 + \frac{5mg}{2k}$$

Writing

$$x = X - l_0 - \frac{3mg}{2k}$$

and

$$y = Y - 2l_0 - \frac{5mg}{2k}$$

yields the equations

$$2m\ddot{x} = ky - 3kx = k(-3x + y)$$

and

$$m\ddot{y} = -ky + kx = k(x - y)$$

83

where $x = y = 0$ at equilibrium.

In matrix notation this is

$$\frac{m}{k}\begin{bmatrix} \ddot{x} \\ \ddot{y} \end{bmatrix} = \begin{bmatrix} -\frac{3}{2} & \frac{1}{2} \\ 1 & -1 \end{bmatrix}\begin{bmatrix} x \\ y \end{bmatrix}$$

The normal mode frequencies are given by finding the eigenvalues of the matrix

$$\begin{bmatrix} -\frac{3}{2} & \frac{1}{2} \\ 1 & -1 \end{bmatrix}$$

namely λ, where

$$\begin{vmatrix} -\frac{3}{2}-\lambda & \frac{1}{2} \\ 1 & -1-\lambda \end{vmatrix} = 0$$

i.e.

$$(-\tfrac{3}{2} - \lambda)(-1-\lambda) - \tfrac{1}{2} = 0$$

so that

$$\lambda^2 + \tfrac{5}{2}\lambda + \tfrac{3}{2} - \tfrac{1}{2} = 0$$

or

$$2\lambda^2 + 5\lambda + 2 = 0$$
$$(2\lambda + 1)(\lambda + 2) = 0$$
$$\lambda = -\tfrac{1}{2}, \ -2$$

The eigenvalue itself is $-(k/m)\omega^2$ (recall that $(m/k)\ddot{\mathbf{x}} = -\omega^2\mathbf{x}$); hence

$$\omega = \left(\frac{k}{2m}\right)^{1/2} \text{ or } \left(\frac{2k}{m}\right)^{1/2}$$

are the natural frequencies (normal modes). Write

$$\omega_1 = \left(\frac{k}{2m}\right)^{1/2} \text{ and } \omega_2 = \left(\frac{2k}{m}\right)^{1/2}$$

To find the initial displacements required to excite these modes, we find the corresponding eigenvectors. For $\lambda = -1/2$ we have

$$\begin{bmatrix} -1 & \frac{1}{2} \\ 1 & -\frac{1}{2} \end{bmatrix}\begin{bmatrix} x \\ y \end{bmatrix} = \begin{bmatrix} 0 \\ 0 \end{bmatrix}$$

so that $x = y/2$, giving a displacement $x = 1$, $y = 2$. For $\lambda = -2$ we have

$$\begin{bmatrix} \frac{1}{2} & \frac{1}{2} \\ 1 & 1 \end{bmatrix}\begin{bmatrix} x \\ y \end{bmatrix} = \begin{bmatrix} 0 \\ 0 \end{bmatrix}$$

so that $x = -y$, giving a displacement $x = 1$, $y = -1$.

It is instructive to check that these initial values (both with $\dot{x} = \dot{y} = 0$ at $t = 0$) do indeed excite the normal modes. The general solution for

$$\begin{pmatrix} x \\ y \end{pmatrix} = \mathbf{x}$$

can be written

$$\mathbf{x} = \mathbf{a}\cos\omega_1 t + \mathbf{b}\cos\omega_2 t$$

where **a** and **b** are arbitrary vectors given by the initial conditions, and we have chosen **x** to be in terms of $\cos\omega t$, because this means that $\dot{\mathbf{x}}$ is solely in terms of $\sin\omega t$, which, as required, is zero when $t = 0$. Now, differentiating **x** twice gives

$$\ddot{\mathbf{x}} = -\omega_1^2\mathbf{a}\cos\omega_1 t - \omega_2^2\mathbf{b}\cos\omega_2 t$$

Now, we require $\ddot{\mathbf{x}} = A\mathbf{x}$, where

$$A = \begin{bmatrix} -\frac{3}{2} & \frac{1}{2} \\ 1 & -1 \end{bmatrix}\frac{k}{m}$$

Hence

$$-\omega_1^2\mathbf{a}\cos\omega_1 t - \omega_2^2\mathbf{b}\cos\omega_2 t = A(\mathbf{a}\cos\omega_1 t + \mathbf{b}\cos\omega_2 t)$$

which implies

$$-\omega_1^2\mathbf{a} = A\mathbf{a}$$

and

$$-\omega_2^2\mathbf{b} = A\mathbf{b}$$

Thus **a** is the eigenvector associated with eigenvalue $-\omega_1^2$ and **b** is the eigenvector associated with eigenvalue $-\omega_2^2$. The most general solution is therefore conveniently written:

$$\mathbf{x} = C_1\begin{pmatrix} 1 \\ 2 \end{pmatrix}\cos\left[t\left(\frac{k}{2m}\right)^{1/2}\right] + C_2\begin{pmatrix} 1 \\ -1 \end{pmatrix}\cos\left[t\left(\frac{2k}{m}\right)^{1/2}\right]$$

If

$$\mathbf{x} = \begin{pmatrix} 1 \\ 2 \end{pmatrix}$$

i.e. $x = 1$, $y = 2$ (for example, any multiple in the ratio $x{:}y = 1{:}2$ will do), at $t = 0$, $C_1 = 1$ and $C_2 = 0$ and the normal mode $\omega_1 = (k/2m)^{1/2}$ is excited.
  If

$$\mathbf{x} = \begin{pmatrix} 1 \\ -1 \end{pmatrix}$$

i.e. $x = 1$, $y = -1$ (for example, any multiple in the ratio $x{:}y = 1{:}-1$ will do), at $t = 0$, $C_1 = 0$ and $C_2 = 1$ and the normal mode $\omega_2 = (2k/m)^{1/2}$ is excited.

6.8 A particle of mass m is suspended from a fixed point by a light elastic string of unstretched length l and modulus of elasticity $3\lambda^2 l m$. Another particle of the same mass is suspended from the first by a light elastic string of unstretched length l and modulus of elasticity $2\lambda^2 l m$. Initially the positions of the particles coincide with their equilibrium positions. The higher particle has velocity $7v$ downwards and the lower particle has velocity v upwards. Determine the displacements of the particles from their equilibrium positions as functions of time under the assumption that v is sufficiently small to ensure that neither string ever becomes slack. Show that this latter assumption is justified if

$$v < (3\sqrt{6} - 2)g/50\lambda \qquad \text{(L.U.)}$$

Solution With this kind of problem, it is always a good idea to take the *equilibrium positions* of each particle as the origin of displacements. However, we have to determine these first.

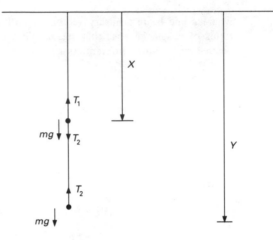

Figure 6.10

Let us, temporarily, use X and Y as coordinates of each particle, mass m (see Fig. 6.10). At equilibrium, for particle A:

$$mg + T_2 = T_1$$

and for particle B:

$$mg = T_2$$

Now

$$T_1 = 3\lambda^2 \frac{lm(X - l)}{l} = 3\lambda^2 m(X - l)$$

and

$$T_2 = 2\lambda^2 \frac{lm(Y - X - l)}{l} = 2\lambda^2 m(Y - X - l)$$

Hence

$$mg + 2\lambda^2 m(Y - X - l) = 3\lambda^2 m(X - l)$$

and

$$mg = 2\lambda^2 m(Y - X - l)$$

at equilibrium, from which

$$2mg = 3\lambda^2 m(X - l)$$

or

$$X = l + \frac{2g}{3\lambda^2}$$

and

$$Y = X + l + \frac{g}{2\lambda^2}$$

so that

$$Y = \frac{7g}{6\lambda^2} + l$$

We now define

$$y = Y - \left(\frac{7g}{6\lambda^2} + l\right)$$

and

$$x = X - \left(\frac{2g}{3\lambda^2} + l\right)$$

and proceed to use Newton's second law with both masses in general positions. These are

$$m\ddot{x} = mg + T_2 - T_1$$

and

$$m\ddot{y} = mg - T_2$$

which, upon insertion of the expressions for T_1 and T_2 become

$$\ddot{x} = 2\lambda^2 y - 5\lambda^2 x = 2\lambda^2(y - x) - 3\lambda^2 x$$

and

$$\ddot{y} = -2\lambda^2 y + 2\lambda^2 x$$

By selecting the equilibrium position as origin, there *cannot* be constant terms.

If we assign a frequency ω to the system, then $\ddot{x} = -\lambda^2\omega^2 x$ and $\ddot{y} = -\lambda^2\omega^2 y$, and we are finding the normal modes.

The λ^2 term is there merely for convenience – it makes λ^2s all cancel. The equations (eigenvalue equations) are

$$2y - 5x = -\omega^2 x$$

and

$$-2y + 2x = -\omega^2 y$$

or, in matrix form,

$$\begin{bmatrix} -5 + \omega^2 & 2 \\ 2 & -2 + \omega^2 \end{bmatrix} \begin{bmatrix} x \\ y \end{bmatrix} = \begin{bmatrix} 0 \\ 0 \end{bmatrix}$$

so that

$$\begin{vmatrix} -5 + \omega^2 & 2 \\ 2 & -2 + \omega^2 \end{vmatrix} = 0$$

$$(-5 + \omega^2)(-2 + \omega^2) - 4 = 0$$
$$\omega^4 - 7\omega^2 + 6 = 0$$
$$\omega^2 = 1, 6$$
$$\omega = 1, \sqrt{6}$$

Now, since motion starts with $x = y = 0$ (from the equilibrium position), we can write x (and y) in terms of sines alone. Let

$$x = A\sin \lambda t + b\sin(\lambda t\sqrt{6}) \qquad (6.9)$$

where A and B are arbitrary constant. In order to find y, we substitute back into the equation

$$\ddot{x} = 2\lambda^2 y - 5\lambda^2 x$$

Now

$$\ddot{x} = -\lambda^2 A\sin \lambda t - 6\lambda^2 B\sin(\lambda t\sqrt{6})$$

on differentiating twice. Hence

$$-\lambda^2 A\sin \lambda t - 6\lambda^2 B\sin(\lambda t\sqrt{6}) = 2\lambda^2 y - 5\lambda^2[A\sin \lambda t + B\sin(\lambda t\sqrt{6})]$$

giving

$$y = 2A\sin \lambda t - \tfrac{1}{2}B\sin(\lambda t\sqrt{6}) \qquad (6.10)$$

(The equation $\ddot{y} = -2\lambda^2 y + 2\lambda^2 x$ can be used as a check.) In order to find the constant A and B, we impose the conditions that $\dot{x} = 7v$ at $t = 0$ and $\dot{y} = -v$ at $t = 0$, giving

$$7v = \lambda A + \lambda B\sqrt{6}$$

and

$$-v = 2\lambda A - \frac{\lambda\sqrt{6}}{2} B$$

Solving gives $A = v/\lambda$ and $B = (v/\lambda)\sqrt{6}$. The solutions for x and y are thus

$$x = \frac{v}{\lambda}\left[\sin \lambda t + \sqrt{6} \sin(\lambda t\sqrt{6})\right]$$

and

$$y = \frac{v}{\lambda}\left[2\sin \lambda t - \tfrac{1}{2} \sin(\lambda t\sqrt{6})\right]$$

Now, the extension of the elastic string connecting A to B must always be positive (it must not go slack), i.e. $X - Y > 0$ (reverting to old coordinates) or

$$y = x + \frac{g}{2\lambda^2} > 0$$

so that

$$\frac{v}{\lambda}\left[\sin\lambda t - \tfrac{3}{2} \sqrt{6} \sin(\lambda t\sqrt{6})\right] + \frac{g}{2\lambda^2} > 0$$

i.e.

$$\frac{v}{\lambda}\left[-\sin\lambda t + \tfrac{3}{2}\sqrt{6}\,\sin(\lambda t\sqrt{6})\right] < \frac{g}{2\lambda^2}$$

Now the greatest value that the left-hand side cannot exceed is

$$\frac{v}{\lambda}\left(1 + \tfrac{3}{2}\sqrt{6}\right)$$

(when $\sin\lambda t = -1$ and $\sin(\lambda t\sqrt{6}) = 1$). Actually, this value can never be *attained* let alone exceeded, since each equation demands a different t: $t = 3\pi/2\lambda$ for the first, $t = \pi/2\lambda\sqrt{6}$ for the second. However, numerical methods are required to find a better upper bound.
Hence

$$\frac{v}{\lambda}\left(1 + \tfrac{3}{2}\sqrt{6}\right) < \frac{g}{2\lambda^2}$$

or

$$v < \frac{g}{\lambda(2 + 3\sqrt{6})} = \frac{g}{50\lambda}(3\sqrt{6} - 2)$$

as required.

6.3 Exercises

6.1 A particle of mass m hangs from a fixed point by a light elastic string. The tension in the string is proportional to its extension, which in the equilibrium position is a. If the particle performs free oscillations in a vertical plane, find its greatest speed if the string is not to become slack.

6.2 A light elastic string has one end attached to a fixed point and a mass m suspended from the end. The equilibrium extension of the string is c. The mass is pulled down a further distance $2c$ and them released. Show that the period of the subsequent motion is

$$2\left(\frac{c}{g}\right)^{1/2}\left(\frac{2\pi}{3} + \sqrt{3}\right)$$

6.3 A particle of mass m is attached to two fixed points by springs of stiffness $k_1 = k$, $k_2 = 2k$. They have the same natural length l. If the fixed points are a distance $3l$ apart, determine the equilibrium position of the particle and its period of small oscillations.

6.4 A particle of mass m is attached to two fixed points A and B (B is vertically below A) by springs. The upper spring has stiffness k and the lower spring a stiffness $3k$, but their natural lengths are equal at l. AB is $3l$. Determine the equilibrium position and the maximum speed of m.

6.5 An inextensible string hangs over two small smooth pegs at the same level a distance $2a$ apart. The string carries equal masses M at its ends and a third mass m ($<2M$) at its midpoint. It hangs symmetrically in equilibrium with the strings at an angle α to the vertical. Determine the period of oscillation if m is displaced by a small amount, and show that the length of an equivalent simple pendulum is $a\cot\alpha/(1 - \cos\alpha)$.

6.6 Figure 6.11 is a model of a seismograph, where $y(t)$ de-

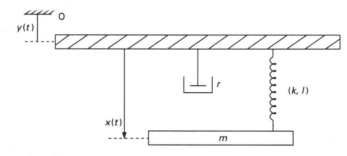

Figure 6.11

notes the forcing and $x(t)$ the response of the seismograph. Show that

$$m\ddot{x} + r\dot{x} + kx = mg + kl - m\ddot{y}$$

Hence determine the resonant frequency if the parameters have the following values:

$$m = 1, \quad r = 4, \quad y = \frac{2\cos\omega t}{\omega^2}$$

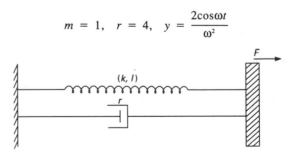

Figure 6.12

6.7 The suspension system in a car is modelled using a simple mass–spring–damping system, shown in Fig. 6.12. For this system, the natural frequency is 10 Hz and the damping factor 0.5. At what frequency is the steady state response if the forcing frequency is 5 Hz? Calculate the ratio of the input amplitude to the output amplitude, and find the maximum value of this ratio.

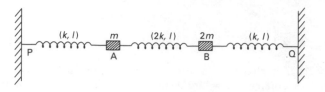

Figure 6.13

6.8 Three springs of stiffness, k, $2k$, k and natural lengths, l, l, l and two masses m, $2m$ are arranged on a horizontal table as shown in Fig. 6.13, where the supports P and Q are $4l$ apart. At equilibrium, what are the lengths of PA and BQ? The whole is now turned through a right angle, and Q is directly below P. What are the new equilibrium lengths of PA and BQ? Find the limiting value of m that will ensure that the springs remain in tension.

6.9 Calculate the normal modes of vibration for the system of the last question.

6.10 A light string of length $3a$ is suspended from one end and has particles of masses $6m$, $2m$ and m attached to it at distances a, $2a$, $3a$ from this end. Find the normal modes of vibration for small oscillations as a triple pendulum.

6.4 Outline Solutions to Exercises

6.1 a is the *extension* in this problem, so at equilibrium $T = mg$ and $T = a\lambda$, where λ is the stiffness, so $\lambda = mg/a$. If x is the departure from equilibrium, then

$$m\ddot{x} = mg - T$$

so that

$$\ddot{x} + \frac{gx}{a} = 0$$

This gives the maximum speed $(ag)^{1/2}$ (which occurs at $x = 0$ and is such that x varies between $-a$ and $+a$ so that the string has zero extension at the topmost position of m).

6.2 For the first part of the motion, the string is taut and the motion is SHM (see Section 6.1), given by $x = 2c \cos nt$ ($n^2 c = g$) measured from the equilibrium position. At $x = -c$, the string goes slack. This happens when $\cos nt = -\frac{1}{2}$ or $nt = 2\pi/3$. At this stage, $\dot{x} = -2cn \sin nt = -(3gc)^{1/2}$. The mass m rises as a particle under gravity for a time

$$t = \frac{v}{g} = \left(\frac{3c}{g}\right)^{1/2}$$

The time from release to highest position is thus

$$\frac{2\pi}{3n} + \left(\frac{3c}{g}\right)^{1/2} = \left(\frac{c}{g}\right)^{1/2}\left(\frac{2\pi}{3} + \sqrt{3}\right)$$

and the period is twice this. This motion is *not* simple harmonic, but it is periodic.

6.3 Figure 6.14 shows the setup. Choose x from the right-hand support.

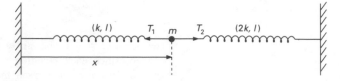

Figure 6.14

$$m\ddot{x} = T_2 - T_1$$
$$T_2 = 2k(3l - x - l)$$

and

$$T_1 = k(x - l)$$

so that $m\ddot{x} + 3kx = 5kl$.
The equilibrium position is thus at $x = 5l/3$, and the period $= 2\pi(m/3k)^{1/2}$.

6.4 Figure 6.15 shows the mass and the coordinate x, taken from A.

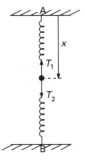

Figure 6.15

$$T_1 = k(x - l)$$
$$T_2 = k(3l - x - l).$$

At equilibrium,

$$T_1 = mg + T_2$$

so

$$x = \frac{7l}{4} + \frac{mg}{4k}$$

The equation of motion is $m\ddot{x} + 4kx = mg + 7kl$. Thus

$$x = A\cos\left[t\left(\frac{4k}{m}\right)^{1/2} + \varepsilon\right] + \frac{mg}{4k} + \frac{7l}{4}$$

The critical value of x is when it is closest to B. This must not exceed $2l$, so that

$$A + \frac{mg}{4k} + \frac{7l}{4} = 2l$$

is the extreme case, giving

$$A = \tfrac{1}{4}\left(l - \frac{mg}{k}\right)$$

The maximum value of $\dot{x}$ is thus

$$\left(\frac{k}{2m}\right)^{1/2}\left(l - \frac{mg}{k}\right)$$

6.5 Figure 6.16 gives the notation. At equilibrium, $m = M\cos\alpha$ ($\theta = \alpha$).

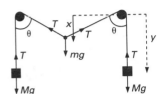

Figure 6.16

Otherwise

$$Mg - T = M\ddot{y} \tag{6.11}$$

and

$$mg - 2T\cos\theta = m\ddot{x} \tag{6.12}$$

Also

$$x = a\cot\theta$$

so that

$$\dot{x} = -a\mathrm{cosec}^2\theta\dot\theta$$

and hence

$$\ddot{x} = 2a\mathrm{cosec}\theta\,\cot\theta\dot\theta^2 - a\mathrm{cosec}^2\theta\ddot\theta$$

Put $\theta = \alpha + \varepsilon$, where $\varepsilon \ll 1$ (so that $\dot\theta = \dot\varepsilon$, $\ddot\theta = \ddot\varepsilon$). Finally $y = l - a\mathrm{cosec}\theta$ (l = length of string), so that

$$\dot{y} = a\mathrm{cosec}\theta\cot\theta\dot\theta$$

and

$$\ddot{y} = a\mathrm{cosec}\theta\cot\theta\ddot\theta - a(\mathrm{cosec}^3\theta + \mathrm{cosec}\theta\,\cot^3\theta)\dot\theta^2$$

Now we eliminate T, $\ddot{x}$ and $\ddot{y}$, ignoring squares and higher powers. This gives

$$g\cos\alpha - g\cos\theta = \ddot{x}\cos\alpha - \ddot{y}\cos\theta$$

Using

$$\ddot{x} = -\frac{a\ddot\theta}{\sin^2\theta}, \quad \ddot{y} = \frac{a\cos^2\theta}{\sin^2\theta}\ddot\theta \text{ (to order } \varepsilon)$$

we obtain

$$\ddot\theta \approx \ddot\varepsilon \approx -\frac{g}{a}\frac{\sin^3\alpha}{(\cos\alpha + \cos^2\alpha)}\varepsilon - -\frac{g}{a}\varepsilon\tan\alpha(1 - \cos\alpha)$$

The period is

$$2\pi\left(\frac{a\cot\alpha}{g(1 - \cos\alpha)}\right)^{1/2}$$

and the length of the equivalent simple pendulum follows (l in $2\pi(l/g)^{1/2}$).

6.6 Take a *fixed* origin, and m has displacement $x + y$ so that

$$m(\ddot{x} + \ddot{y}) = T - r\dot{x} + mg$$

with $T = k(x - l)$. Hence the result.
  With the values given,

$$\ddot{x} + 4\dot{x} + 16x = \text{constant} + 2\cos\omega t$$

This has a steady state response

$$x = A\cos(\omega t + \phi) + \frac{\text{constant}}{16}$$

where

$$A^2 = \frac{4}{(16 - \omega^2)^2 + 16\omega^2}$$

Setting

$$\frac{\mathrm{d}}{\mathrm{d}\omega}A^2 = 0$$

for a maximum gives $\omega = 2\sqrt{2}$ as the resonant frequency.

6.7 The equation of motion is

$$\frac{\mathrm{d}^2x}{\mathrm{d}t^2} + 2 \times 0.5 \times 10\frac{\mathrm{d}x}{\mathrm{d}t} + (10)^2x = \text{forcing}$$

The response frequency is $\omega_r = \omega(1 - \alpha^2)^{1/2}$. The amplitude ratio is

$$A_r = \left[\left(1 - \frac{\sigma^2}{\omega^2}\right)^2 + \frac{4\alpha^2\sigma^2}{\omega^2}\right]^{1/2}$$

$\omega = 10$, $\alpha = 0.5$, $\sigma = 5$ gives $\omega_r = 8.66$ Hz and $A_r = 1.109$.
  A_r is a maximum at $\sigma = \omega(1 - 2\alpha^2)^{1/2} = 7.1$ Hz, at which value $A_r = 1.155$ (not very large because α is large).

6.8 In the horizontal, all tensions are equal. Labelling PA = x, PB = y:

$$T = k(x - l), \quad T = 2k(y - x - l), \quad T = k(4l - y - l)$$

solving these gives $x = \tfrac{7}{5}l$, $y = \tfrac{13}{5}l$.
  When suspended, if PA now has tension T_1, AB tension T_2 and BQ tension T_3, then in vertical equilibrium

$$T_2 = T_1 + mg = 0, \quad T_3 - T_2 + 2mg = 0$$

together with $T_1 = k(x - l)$, $T_2 = 2k(y - x - l)$, $T_3 = k(4l - y - l)$. Solving for x and y gives

$$x = \tfrac{7}{5}\left(l + \frac{mg}{k}\right)$$

$$y = \tfrac{1}{5}\left(13l + \frac{8mg}{k}\right)$$

In order for $T_3 > 0$, $3l > y$, which gives $mg < kl/4$. Demanding $T_2 > 0$ leads to $mg < kl$, obviously a milder condition on m.

6.9 Using coordinates referred to the equilibrium position (whether horizontal or vertical they are the same equations, but the former is easier to work with), and assuming that the springs are always in tension,

$$m\ddot{x}_1 = -3kx_1 + 2kx_2 \qquad \left(x = x_1 + \frac{7l}{5}\ ,\ y = x_2 + \frac{13l}{5}\right)$$

$$2m\ddot{x}_2 = 2kx_1 - 3kx_2$$

From this,

$$\left(\omega^2 - \frac{3k}{m}\right)^2 = \left(\frac{2k}{m}\right)^2$$

giving the normal mode frequencies

$$\left(\frac{k}{m}\right)^{1/2},\quad \left(\frac{5k}{m}\right)^{1/2}$$

6.10 Adopting the notation of Fig. 6.17, the equations are ($\cos\theta \approx 1$, $\sin\theta \approx \theta$) as follows. Vertically:

$$T_2 + 6mg = T_1$$

$$T_3 + 2mg = T_2$$

and

$$mg = T_3$$

Horizontally:

$$-T_1\theta_1 + T_2\theta_2 = 6ma\ddot{\theta}_1$$

$$-T_2\theta_2 + T_3\theta_3 = 2ma\ddot{\theta}_2$$

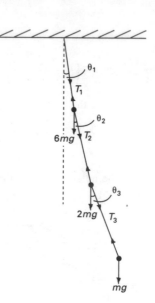

Figure 6.17

and

$$-T_3\theta_3 = ma\ddot{\theta}_3$$

Hence $T_1 = 9mg$, $T_2 = 3mg$, $T_3 = mg$. Writing $\ddot{\theta}_1 = -\omega^2\theta_1$, $\ddot{\theta}_2 = -\omega^2\theta_2$, $\ddot{\theta}_3 = -\omega^2\theta_3$ leads to

$$\begin{vmatrix} 6\omega^2 a - 9g & 3g & 0 \\ 0 & 2\omega^2 a - 3g & g \\ 0 & 0 & \omega^2 a - g \end{vmatrix} = 0$$

whence the normal modes are

$$\left(\frac{3g}{a}\right)^{1/2},\ \left(\frac{3g}{2a}\right)^{1/2},\ \left(\frac{g}{a}\right)^{1/2}$$

Topic Guide

Angular Velocity
Velocity and Acceleration
Rotating Axes
Coriolis Acceleration
Constrained Motion

7 Circular Motion and Rotating Axes

7.1 Fact Sheet

Polar Coordinates In two dimensions, these are related to Cartesian coordinates (x, y) via the relations

$$x = r\cos\theta, \; y = r\sin\theta$$

$$\mathbf{r} = r\hat{\mathbf{r}} = x\hat{\mathbf{i}} + y\hat{\mathbf{j}}$$

Velocity:

$$\dot{\mathbf{r}} = \dot{r}\hat{\mathbf{r}} + r\dot{\theta}\hat{\boldsymbol{\theta}}$$

Acceleration:

$$\ddot{\mathbf{r}} = (\ddot{r} - r\dot{\theta}^2)\hat{\mathbf{r}} + \frac{1}{r}\frac{d}{dt}(r^2\dot{\theta})\hat{\boldsymbol{\theta}}$$

In three dimensions, there are two commonly used polar coordinate systems: one associated with the geometry of the cylinder, the other associated with the geometry of the sphere. In cylindrical polar coordinates (R, ϕ, z)

$$x = R\cos\phi, \; y = R\sin\phi, \; z = z$$

so that

$$\hat{\mathbf{r}} = \hat{\mathbf{i}}R\cos\phi + \hat{\mathbf{j}}R\sin\phi + \hat{\mathbf{k}}z$$

In spherical polar coordinates (r, θ, λ)

$$x = r\cos\theta\sin\lambda, \; y = r\sin\theta\sin\lambda, \; z = r\cos\lambda$$

so that

$$\mathbf{r} = \hat{\mathbf{i}}r\cos\theta\sin\lambda + \hat{\mathbf{j}}r\sin\theta\sin\lambda + \hat{\mathbf{k}}r\cos\lambda$$

Angular velocity is the rate of change of angle, commonly denoted by $\omega = d\theta/dt = \dot{\theta}$. It has dimensions of s^{-1}. Angular acceleration $= \dot{\omega} = d^2\theta/dt^2 = \ddot{\theta}$.

Motion in a circle is described by a velocity

$$\mathbf{v} = \dot{\mathbf{r}} = r\dot{\theta}\hat{\boldsymbol{\theta}} \qquad (r = \text{constant})$$

Vector angular velocity $\boldsymbol{\omega} = \omega\hat{\mathbf{n}}$ where $\hat{\mathbf{n}}$ is in the direction of a right-handed corkscrew (which rotates such that θ increases with time). In the case of circular motion.

$$\mathbf{v} = \boldsymbol{\omega} \times \mathbf{r}$$

The vectors $\hat{\mathbf{r}}$, $\hat{\boldsymbol{\theta}}$, $\hat{\boldsymbol{\omega}}$ form a right-handed system.

Rotating Axes   If it is not possible to use a fixed frame of reference, but it is possible to use axes which rotate with angular velocity $\boldsymbol{\omega}$, then the velocity and acceleration relative to the rotating coordinate system (or frame of reference) are given by the expressions:

$$\text{velocity} \quad = \dot{\mathbf{r}} + \boldsymbol{\omega} \times \mathbf{r}$$

$$\text{acceleration} = \ddot{\mathbf{r}} + \dot{\boldsymbol{\omega}} \times \mathbf{r} + 2\boldsymbol{\omega} \times \mathbf{r} + \boldsymbol{\omega} \times (\boldsymbol{\omega} \times \mathbf{r})$$

$2\boldsymbol{\omega} \times \mathbf{r}$ is called the Coriolis acceleration and $\boldsymbol{\omega} \times (\boldsymbol{\omega} \times \mathbf{r})$ is called the centripetal acceleration ($\dot{\boldsymbol{\omega}} \times \mathbf{r}$ is often zero). These accelerations are measured relative to the frame of reference which rotates with angular velocity $\boldsymbol{\omega}$.

7.2 Worked Examples

7.1   A two-dimensional frame $\mathbf{e}_1$, $\mathbf{e}_2$, where $\mathbf{e}_1 \cdot \mathbf{e}_2 = 0$, rotates with constant angular velocity $\boldsymbol{\omega}$ in the plane of $\mathbf{e}_1$ and $\mathbf{e}_2$. Show that $\dot{\mathbf{e}}_1 = \boldsymbol{\omega} \times \mathbf{e}_1$ and $\dot{\mathbf{e}}_2 = \boldsymbol{\omega} \times \mathbf{e}_2$.

Solution   Let $\mathbf{e}_1 = \cos\theta\,\hat{\mathbf{i}} + \sin\theta\,\hat{\mathbf{j}}$, so that $\mathbf{e}_2 = -\sin\theta\,\hat{\mathbf{i}} + \cos\theta\,\hat{\mathbf{j}}$ (obtained by resolving $\mathbf{e}_1$ and $\mathbf{e}_2$ into components – see Fig. 7.1). Now, θ is increasing uniformly with time so that $d\theta/dt = \omega$. Moreover, $\dot{\boldsymbol{\theta}} = \omega\hat{\mathbf{k}} = \boldsymbol{\omega}$. Differentiating $\mathbf{e}_1$ and $\mathbf{e}_2$ with respect to t gives

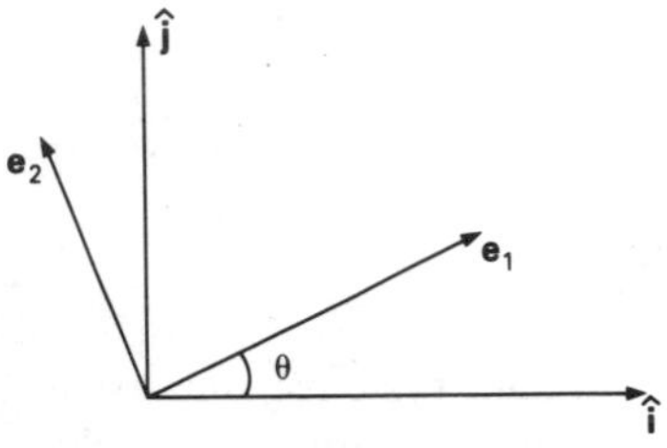

$$\dot{\mathbf{e}}_1 = -\dot{\theta}\sin\theta\,\hat{\mathbf{i}} + \dot{\theta}\cos\theta\,\hat{\mathbf{j}}$$

and

$$\dot{\mathbf{e}}_2 = -\dot{\theta}\cos\theta\,\hat{\mathbf{i}} + \dot{\theta}\sin\theta\,\hat{\mathbf{j}}$$

Now, $\hat{\mathbf{i}} = -\hat{\mathbf{k}} \times \hat{\mathbf{j}}$ and $\hat{\mathbf{j}} = \hat{\mathbf{k}} \times \hat{\mathbf{i}}$. Therefore

$$\dot{\mathbf{e}}_1 = \dot{\theta}\sin\theta\hat{\mathbf{k}} \times \hat{\mathbf{j}} + \dot{\theta}\cos\theta\hat{\mathbf{k}} \times \hat{\mathbf{i}}$$

$$= \dot{\theta}\hat{\mathbf{k}} \times (\hat{\mathbf{j}}\sin\theta + \hat{\mathbf{i}}\cos\theta)$$

$$= \boldsymbol{\omega} \times \mathbf{e}_1$$

Figure 7.1

Similarly, $\dot{\mathbf{e}}_2 = \boldsymbol{\omega} \times \mathbf{e}_2$.

7.2   Establish that, in plane polar coordinates, $\dot{\mathbf{r}} = \dot{r}\hat{\mathbf{r}} + r\dot{\theta}\hat{\boldsymbol{\theta}}$ and that

$$\ddot{\mathbf{r}} = (\ddot{r} - r\dot{\theta}^2)\hat{\mathbf{r}} + \frac{1}{r}\frac{d}{dt}(r^2\dot{\theta})\hat{\boldsymbol{\theta}}$$

Solution   From Example 7.1 we have that $\dot{\mathbf{e}}_1 = \boldsymbol{\omega} \times \mathbf{e}_1$ and $\dot{\mathbf{e}}_2 = \boldsymbol{\omega} \times \mathbf{e}_2$. Now, we can write $\hat{\mathbf{e}}_1 = \hat{\mathbf{r}}$ and $\hat{\mathbf{e}}_2 = \hat{\boldsymbol{\theta}}$, so that $\dot{\hat{\mathbf{r}}} = \boldsymbol{\omega} \times \mathbf{r}$ and $\dot{\hat{\boldsymbol{\theta}}} = \boldsymbol{\omega} \times \hat{\boldsymbol{\theta}}$. Also $\mathbf{r} = r\hat{\mathbf{r}}$, which, on differentiating with respect to t, gives

$$\frac{d\mathbf{r}}{dt} = \dot{\mathbf{r}} = \dot{r}\hat{\mathbf{r}} + r\frac{d\hat{\mathbf{r}}}{dt}$$

$$= \dot{r}\hat{\mathbf{r}} + r\boldsymbol{\omega} \times \hat{\mathbf{r}}$$

$$= \dot{r}\hat{\mathbf{r}} + r\dot{\theta}\hat{\mathbf{k}} \times \hat{\mathbf{r}}$$

Therefore $\dot{\mathbf{r}} = \dot{r}\hat{\mathbf{r}} + r\dot{\theta}\hat{\boldsymbol{\theta}}$, since $\hat{\mathbf{r}}$, $\hat{\boldsymbol{\theta}}$, $\hat{\mathbf{k}}$ form a mutually orthogonal right-handed system. Differentiating again with respect to t gives

$$\ddot{\mathbf{r}} = \frac{d}{dt}(\dot{r}\hat{\mathbf{r}}) + \frac{d}{dt}(r\dot{\theta}\boldsymbol{\theta})$$

$$= \ddot{r}\hat{\mathbf{r}} + \dot{r}\,\frac{d\hat{\mathbf{r}}}{dt} + \hat{\boldsymbol{\theta}}\,\frac{d}{dt}(r\dot{\theta}) + r\dot{\theta}\,\frac{d\hat{\boldsymbol{\theta}}}{dt}$$

so that

$$\ddot{\mathbf{r}} = \ddot{r}\hat{\mathbf{r}} + \dot{r}\boldsymbol{\omega} \times \hat{\mathbf{r}} + \hat{\boldsymbol{\theta}}\,\frac{d}{dt}(r\dot{\theta}) + r\dot{\theta}\boldsymbol{\omega} \times \hat{\boldsymbol{\theta}}$$

$$= \ddot{r}\hat{\mathbf{r}} + \dot{r}\dot{\theta}\hat{\boldsymbol{\theta}} + \hat{\boldsymbol{\theta}}\,(\dot{r}\dot{\theta} + r\ddot{\theta}) + r\dot{\theta}^2\hat{\mathbf{k}} \times \hat{\boldsymbol{\theta}}$$

$$= \ddot{r}\hat{\mathbf{r}} + 2\dot{r}\dot{\theta}\hat{\boldsymbol{\theta}} + r\ddot{\theta}\hat{\boldsymbol{\theta}} - r\dot{\theta}^2\hat{\mathbf{r}}$$

Hence

$$\ddot{\mathbf{r}} = (\ddot{r} - r\dot{\theta}^2)\hat{\mathbf{r}} + (2\dot{r}\dot{\theta} + r\ddot{\theta})\hat{\boldsymbol{\theta}}$$

$$= (\ddot{r} - r\dot{\theta}^2)\hat{\mathbf{r}} + \frac{1}{r}\,(2r\dot{r}\dot{\theta} + r^2\ddot{\theta})\hat{\boldsymbol{\theta}}$$

$$= (\ddot{r} - r\dot{\theta}^2)\hat{\mathbf{r}} + \frac{1}{r}\,\frac{d}{dt}\,(r^2\dot{\theta})\hat{\boldsymbol{\theta}}$$

as required.

7.3 If $\mathbf{V}'$ denotes the velocity of a particle referred to fixed axes, and $\mathbf{V}$ denotes the velocity of the same particle referred to axes that rotate with angular velocity $\boldsymbol{\omega}$, show that

$$\mathbf{V}' = \mathbf{V} + \boldsymbol{\omega} \times \mathbf{r}$$

Solution Without loss of generality, we can align the axis of rotation to coincide with $\hat{\mathbf{k}}$. Hence $\boldsymbol{\omega} = \omega\hat{\mathbf{k}}$. From now, there are two approaches. We could use Example 7.1 and identify $\mathbf{e}_1$ and $\mathbf{e}_2$ as (rotating) $\hat{\mathbf{i}}$ and $\hat{\mathbf{j}}$. However, it is also instructive to work from first principles. In Fig. 7.2 axes $\hat{\mathbf{i}}$ and $\hat{\mathbf{j}}$ rotate with constant angular velocity ω and their positions are shown at time t and at time $t + \delta t$. From this figure, we see that, in the limit as $\delta t \to 0$,

$$\frac{d\hat{\mathbf{j}}}{dt} = -\omega\hat{\mathbf{i}} \quad \text{and} \quad \frac{d\hat{\mathbf{i}}}{dt} = \omega\hat{\mathbf{j}}$$

Figure 7.2

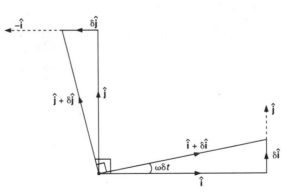

The velocity vector $\mathbf{V}'$ referred to fixed axes $\hat{\mathbf{i}}$ and $\hat{\mathbf{j}}$ can be expressed as

$$\mathbf{V} = \frac{d\mathbf{r}}{dt} = \frac{d}{dt}\,(x\hat{\mathbf{i}} + y\hat{\mathbf{j}})$$

$$= \frac{dx}{dt}\,\hat{\mathbf{i}} + \frac{dy}{dt}\,\hat{\mathbf{j}} + x\frac{d\hat{\mathbf{i}}}{dt} + y\frac{d\hat{\mathbf{j}}}{dt}$$

$$- \frac{dx}{dt}\,\hat{\mathbf{i}} + \frac{dy}{dt}\,\hat{\mathbf{j}} + \omega x\hat{\mathbf{j}} - \omega y\hat{\mathbf{i}}$$

using the equations for $\mathrm{d}\hat{\mathbf{i}}/\mathrm{d}t$ and $\mathrm{d}\hat{\mathbf{j}}/\mathrm{d}t$. The first two terms are the velocity, $\mathbf{V}$, referred to $\hat{\mathbf{i}}$ and $\hat{\mathbf{j}}$ as if they were fixed in space. The second two terms can be rewritten as follows:

$$\omega x\hat{\mathbf{j}} - \omega y\hat{\mathbf{i}} = \omega\hat{\mathbf{k}} \times x\hat{\mathbf{i}} + \omega\hat{\mathbf{k}} \times y\hat{\mathbf{j}}$$

$$= \omega\hat{\mathbf{k}} \times (x\hat{\mathbf{i}} + y\hat{\mathbf{j}})$$

$$= \boldsymbol{\omega} \times \mathbf{r}$$

Thus we have derived the expression

$$\mathbf{V} = \mathbf{V}' + \boldsymbol{\omega} \times \mathbf{r}$$

In fact, we have derived the general relationship

$$\left.\frac{\mathrm{d}}{\mathrm{d}t}\right|_{\text{fixed}} \equiv \left.\frac{\mathrm{d}}{\mathrm{d}t}\right|_{\text{rotating}} + \boldsymbol{\omega} \times$$

where the three lines denote operator identity.

7.4 Using the previous example, derive an expression for the acceleration of a particle referred to axes that rotate with angular velocity $\boldsymbol{\omega}$.

Solution Since $\mathrm{d}/\mathrm{d}t$ must be replaced by $\mathrm{d}/\mathrm{d}t + \boldsymbol{\omega} \times$ we have that

$$\mathbf{V} = \frac{\mathrm{d}\mathbf{r}}{\mathrm{d}t} + \boldsymbol{\omega} \times \mathbf{r}$$

and

$$\frac{\mathrm{d}\mathbf{V}}{\mathrm{d}t} = \left(\frac{\mathrm{d}}{\mathrm{d}t} + \boldsymbol{\omega} \times\right)\left(\frac{\mathrm{d}\mathbf{r}}{\mathrm{d}t} + \boldsymbol{\omega} \times \mathbf{r}\right)$$

$$= \frac{\mathrm{d}^2\mathbf{r}}{\mathrm{d}t^2} + \boldsymbol{\omega} \times \frac{\mathrm{d}\mathbf{r}}{\mathrm{d}t} + \frac{\mathrm{d}}{\mathrm{d}t}(\boldsymbol{\omega} \times \mathbf{r}) + \boldsymbol{\omega} \times (\boldsymbol{\omega} \times \mathbf{r})$$

$$= \ddot{\mathbf{r}} + 2\boldsymbol{\omega} \times \dot{\mathbf{r}} + \dot{\boldsymbol{\omega}} \times \mathbf{r} + \boldsymbol{\omega} \times (\boldsymbol{\omega} \times \mathbf{r})$$

The term $\dot{\boldsymbol{\omega}} \times \mathbf{r}$ is usually zero, since $\boldsymbol{\omega}$ is normally constant. $2\boldsymbol{\omega} \times \dot{\mathbf{r}}$ is the Coriolis acceleration and $\boldsymbol{\omega} \times (\boldsymbol{\omega} \times \mathbf{r})$ is the centripetal acceleration.

7.5 On the Earth, x points east, y points north and z is up. The Earth rotates with an angular speed of magnitude $\Omega = 7.29 \times 10^{-5}$ s^{-1}. Show that, to a good approximation, the equations obeyed by a very large iceberg are

$$\ddot{x} - f\dot{y} = 0$$

and

$$\ddot{y} + f\dot{x} = 0$$

where $f = 2\Omega\sin\lambda$, λ = latitude of the origin. Further, the iceberg floats freely, far away from any obstacle on a quiescent sea and at time $t = 0$ is given a velocity $U\hat{\mathbf{i}} + V\hat{\mathbf{j}}$. Find its subsequent path.

Solution The equation of motion is

$$m[\ddot{\mathbf{r}} + 2\boldsymbol{\Omega} \times \dot{\mathbf{r}} + \boldsymbol{\Omega} \times (\boldsymbol{\Omega} \times \mathbf{r})] = -m\mathbf{g} = -mg\hat{\mathbf{k}}$$

where $|\boldsymbol{\Omega}| = 7.29 \times 10^{-5}$ s^{-1}, g = acceleration due to gravity, and $\mathbf{r}$ is referred to an origin on the Earth (see Fig. 7.3).

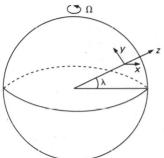

Figure 7.3

Now the angular velocity vector $\mathbf{\Omega}$ is in the direction indicated on Fig. 7.3, that is pointing out of the North Pole. In terms of our axes, $(x = $ east, $y = $ north, $z = $ up) at latitude λ (say) this gives

$$\mathbf{\Omega} = 0\hat{\mathbf{i}} + \Omega \cos\lambda\hat{\mathbf{j}} + \Omega\sin\lambda\hat{\mathbf{k}}$$

so that

$$2\mathbf{\Omega} \times \dot{\mathbf{r}} = \begin{vmatrix} \hat{\mathbf{i}} & \hat{\mathbf{j}} & \hat{\mathbf{k}} \\ 0 & 2\Omega\cos\lambda & 2\Omega\sin\lambda \\ \dot{x} & \dot{y} & \dot{z} \end{vmatrix}$$

$$= \hat{\mathbf{i}}(2\dot{z}\Omega\cos\lambda - 2\dot{y}\Omega\sin\lambda) + \hat{\mathbf{j}}2\dot{x}\Omega\sin\lambda - \hat{\mathbf{k}}2\dot{x}\Omega\cos\lambda$$

We ignore the $\hat{\mathbf{k}}$ term, since we assume that the neutral buoyancy of the iceberg indicates vertical equilibrium, and hence no motion in the $\hat{\mathbf{k}}$ direction. Further, $\dot{z}$ is also zero; hence

$$2\mathbf{\Omega} \times \dot{\mathbf{r}} = \hat{\mathbf{i}}(-2\dot{y}\Omega\sin\lambda) + \hat{\mathbf{j}}(2\dot{x}\Omega\cos\lambda)$$

$$= -f\dot{y}\hat{\mathbf{i}} + f\dot{x}\hat{\mathbf{j}}$$

(writing $f = 2\Omega\sin\lambda$). Now, the quantity $\mathbf{g}' = \mathbf{g} - \mathbf{\Omega} \times (\mathbf{\Omega} \times \mathbf{r})$ is called apparent gravity ($\mathbf{g}$ is true gravity) and is the quantity that is actually measured (one cannot stop the Earth to measure g). Thus the equation of motion is, in component form,

$$\ddot{x} - f\dot{y} = 0$$

$$\ddot{y} + f\dot{x} = 0$$

where $\mathbf{g}'$ is assumed to act in the $-\hat{\mathbf{k}}$ direction. (This is justified $|\mathbf{g}| \approx 10$ m s^{-2} and $|\mathbf{\Omega} \times (\mathbf{\Omega} \times \mathbf{r})| = \Omega^2 r \approx 10^{-2}$ and so does not alter the direction of true gravity unduly.) Writing $\dot{x} = u$ and $\dot{y} = v$ gives

$$\dot{u} - fv = 0$$

and

$$\dot{v} + fu = 0$$

Eliminating $\dot{u}$ by differentiating the second equation with respect to t gives

$$\ddot{v} + f^2 v = 0$$

whence $v = A\sin ft + B\cos ft$, where A and B are arbitrary constants. Differentiating gives

$$\dot{v} = fA\cos ft - fB\sin ft$$

Hence

$$u = -\frac{\dot{v}}{f} = B\sin ft - A\cos ft$$

We are given that, at time $t = 0$, $u = U$ and $v = V$. Hence $B = V$ and $A = -U$, giving

$$v = -U \sin ft + V \cos ft$$

and

$$u = U \cos ft + V \sin ft$$

Setting $v = \dot{y}$ and $u = \dot{x}$ and integrating gives

$$y = \frac{U}{f} \cos ft + \frac{V}{f} \sin ft + Y_0$$

and

$$x = \frac{U}{f} \sin ft + \frac{V}{f} \cos ft + X_0$$

We can rewrite these expressions as

$$f(x - X_0) = (U^2 + V^2)^{1/2} \sin(ft + \phi)$$

and

$$f(y - Y_0) = (U^2 + V^2)^{1/2} \cos(ft + \phi)$$

Here, X_0, Y_0 are constants, $\cos\phi = U/(U^2 + V^2)^{1/2}$ and $\sin \phi = -V/(U^2 + V^2)^{1/2}$. Squaring and adding, then dividing by f^2, yields

$$(x - X_0)^2 + (y - Y_0)^2 = \frac{(U^2 + V^2)}{f^2}$$

which is a circle, radius $(U^2 + V^2)^{1/2}/f$. This circle is called an **inertial circle** by oceanographers, and the length scale $(U^2 + V^2)^{1/2}/f$ is called the Rossby radius of deformation.

7.6 A bomb of mass m is dropped from a stationary helicopter which is at a height that is small compared with the radius of the Earth. Find an expression for the easterly deflection of the bomb by Coriolis acceleration. What is the value of this deflection for a bomb that takes 30 s to reach the Earth at latitude 60° N? (Assume that squares of the Earth's rotation can be ignored.)

Solution Since we can ignore squares of the Earth's rotation, the vector equation of motion is

$$\ddot{\mathbf{r}} + 2\boldsymbol{\omega} \times \dot{\mathbf{r}} = -g\mathbf{k} \tag{7.1}$$

where $\boldsymbol{\omega} = (0, \Omega\cos\lambda, \Omega\sin\lambda)$ and $\mathbf{r} = (x,y,z)$. (Note: x points east, y points north and z points up.) Hence

$$\boldsymbol{\omega} \times \dot{\mathbf{r}} = \begin{vmatrix} \hat{\mathbf{i}} & \hat{\mathbf{j}} & \hat{\mathbf{k}} \\ 0 & \Omega\cos\lambda & \Omega\sin\lambda \\ \dot{x} & \dot{y} & \dot{z} \end{vmatrix}$$

$$= (\dot{z}\Omega\cos\lambda - \dot{y}\Omega\sin\lambda)\,\hat{\mathbf{i}} + (\dot{x}\Omega\sin\lambda)\hat{\mathbf{j}} + (-\dot{x}\Omega\cos\lambda)\hat{\mathbf{k}}$$

Equation (7.1) leads thus to the three scalar equations

$$\ddot{x} = \dot{y}2\Omega\sin\lambda - \dot{z}2\Omega\cos\lambda \tag{7.2}$$

$$\ddot{y} = -\dot{x}2\Omega\sin\lambda \tag{7.3}$$

and

$$\ddot{z} = -g + \dot{x}2\Omega\cos\lambda \tag{7.4}$$

To solve these exactly is very unwieldy. However, with a systematic neglect of Ω^2 (and higher powers) it is quite easy. First of all, we integrate all three of these equations with respect to time to give

$$\dot{x} = y2\Omega\sin\lambda - z2\Omega\cos\lambda + A \tag{7.5}$$

$$\dot{y} = -x2\Omega\sin\lambda + B \qquad\qquad (7.6)$$

$$\dot{z} = -gt + x2\Omega\cos\lambda + C \qquad\qquad (7.7)$$

where A, B and C are the constants of integration.

With $\dot{x} = 0$, $\dot{y} = 0$, $\dot{z} = 0$, $x = 0$, $y = 0$, $z = h$ (the height of the bomb), the boundary conditions give

$$A = 2\Omega\cos\lambda, \; B - 0, \; C - 0$$

Inserting the expression for $\dot{x}$ from Equation (7.5) into Equation (7.4) gives

$$\ddot{z} = -g + (y2\Omega\sin\lambda - z2\Omega\cos\lambda + 2\Omega h\cos\lambda)2\Omega\cos\lambda$$

and we see that the complicated expression involving parentheses is of order Ω^2 and so may be ignored.

Hence $\ddot{z} \approx -g$, and integrating gives

$$\dot{z} = -gt + D$$

where D is another constant of integration. $D = 0$ since $\dot{z} = 0$ when $t = 0$. Hence, $\dot{z} = -gt$. This equation for $\dot{z}$, together with Equation (7.6) for y, inserted into the equation for $\ddot{x}$, Equation (7.2), will give the differential equation for x, the easterly deflection that the problem requires us to find. This is

$$\ddot{x} = 2\Omega\sin\lambda(-x2\Omega\sin\lambda) - 2\Omega\cos\lambda \, (-gt)$$

or, ignoring the first term, which is of order Ω^2,

$$\ddot{x} = 2\Omega gt\cos\lambda$$

Integrating once with respect to time:

$$\dot{x} = \Omega gt^2\cos\lambda + E$$

where E is our fifth constant of integration. However, $E = 0$, since $\dot{x} = 0$ when $t = 0$. Integrating again with respect to time gives

$$x = \tfrac{1}{3}\Omega gt^3 \cos\lambda + F$$

where F is the sixth (and final) constant of integration. Again $F = 0$, since $x = 0$ when $t = 0$ Hence the final expression for the easterly deflection of the bomb is

$$x = \tfrac{1}{3}\Omega gt^3 \cos\lambda$$

If $t = 30$ s, and with $g = 10 \, \text{m s}^{-2}$, $\Omega = 7.29 \times 10^{-5} \, \text{rad s}^{-1}$ and $\lambda = 60°$, we obtain

$$x = \tfrac{1}{3} \times 10 \times (7.29 \times 10^{-5}) \times (30)^3 \times \cos 60°$$

$$= 3.28 \, \text{m}$$

(Note that the initial height of the bomb must be $gt^2/2$, which with $t = 30$ and $g = 10 \, \text{m s}^{-2}$ is 4500 m, which might be thought of as quite high.)

7.7   A point P moves in a plane and has polar coordinates (r, θ). Find the rate of change of acceleration in polar coordinates $\dddot{r}$ if $\dot{\theta} = \omega = $ constant and $\ddot{r}$ is only in the **r** direction. Find the curve that P describes, given that initially $r = a$, $\theta = 0$ and $\dot{r} = 0$.

Solution   This problem is pure vector calculus, but it serves to familiarise the reader with the kind of manipulation involved in using particle dynamics in polar coordinates. We have already derived an expression for $\ddot{\mathbf{r}}$ from Example 7.2:

$$\ddot{\mathbf{r}} = (\ddot{r} - r\dot{\theta}^2)\hat{\mathbf{r}} + \frac{1}{r}\frac{d}{dt}(r^2\dot{\theta})\hat{\boldsymbol{\theta}}$$

We are given that $\dot{\theta} = \omega$; hence we may write

$$\ddot{\mathbf{r}} = (\ddot{r} - r\omega^2)\hat{\mathbf{r}} + 2\dot{r}\omega\hat{\boldsymbol{\theta}}$$

From the equations $\hat{\mathbf{r}} = \hat{\mathbf{i}}\cos\theta + \hat{\mathbf{j}}\sin\theta$ and $\hat{\boldsymbol{\theta}} = -\hat{\mathbf{i}}\sin\theta + \hat{\mathbf{j}}\cos\theta$ (see Fig. 7.1, Example 7.1) we easily derive

$$\frac{d\hat{\mathbf{r}}}{dt} = \dot{\theta}\hat{\boldsymbol{\theta}}, \qquad \frac{d\hat{\boldsymbol{\theta}}}{dt} = -\dot{\theta}\hat{\mathbf{r}}$$

Thus

$$\dddot{\mathbf{r}} = \frac{d}{dt}[(\ddot{r} - r\omega^2)\hat{\mathbf{r}} + 2\dot{r}\omega\hat{\boldsymbol{\theta}})]$$

$$= (\dddot{r} - \dot{r}\omega^2)\hat{\mathbf{r}} + (\ddot{r} - r\omega^2)\hat{\boldsymbol{\theta}}\omega + 2\ddot{r}\omega\hat{\boldsymbol{\theta}} - 2\dot{r}\omega\hat{\mathbf{r}}\omega$$

on using the expressions for differentiating a product. Simplifying gives

$$\dddot{\mathbf{r}} = (\dddot{r} - 3\dot{r}\omega^2)\hat{\mathbf{r}} + (3\ddot{r}\omega - r\omega^3)\hat{\boldsymbol{\theta}}$$

Now $\dddot{\mathbf{r}}$ is in the $\hat{\mathbf{r}}$ direction; thus the $\hat{\boldsymbol{\theta}}$ component must vanish so that

$$3\ddot{r}\omega - r\omega^3 = 0$$

or

$$\ddot{r} - \frac{\omega^2}{3}r = 0$$

This has the solution

$$r = A\cosh\frac{\omega t}{\sqrt{3}} + B\sinh\frac{\omega t}{\sqrt{3}}$$

where A and B are arbitrary. $\dot{r} = 0$ at $t = 0$ implies $B = 0$; $r = a$ at $t = 0$ implies $A = a$; whence

$$r = a\cosh\frac{\omega t}{\sqrt{3}}$$

Also, $\dot{\theta} = \omega$ implies $\theta = \omega t$, giving the path as

$$r = a\cosh\frac{\theta}{\sqrt{3}}$$

which resembles a spiral, moving out from $r = a$.

7.8 A smooth hollow tube is made to rotate in a horizontal plane with constant angular velocity Ω about an end O which is fixed. A particle of mass m inside the tube is connected to O by a light elastic string of natural length a and modulus mgk.

Prove that if $a\Omega^2 < kg$ then the particle can remain at rest relative to the tube. If in these circumstances the particle is displaced slightly from the position P of relative rest, prove that it executes simple harmonic oscillations relative to the tube, of the same period as small oscillations of a simple pendulum of length OP/k.

Solution Figure 7.4 shows the particle in the general position in the tube. T is the tension in the string and N is the normal reaction of the tube to the particle. Using Hooke's law,

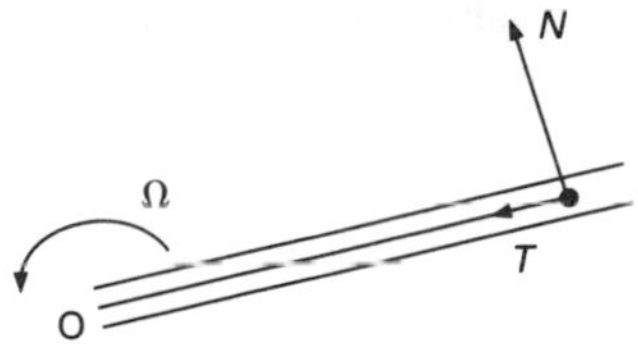

$$T = \frac{mgk}{a}\,(r - a)$$

whence

$$m(\ddot{r} - r\Omega^2) = -\,\frac{mgk}{a}\,(r - a)$$

so that

$$\ddot{r} + \left(\frac{kg}{a} - \Omega^2\right)r = kg \tag{7.8}$$

For relative rest $\ddot{r} = 0$, so that

$$r = r_0 = \frac{kga}{kg - a\Omega^2} \tag{7.9}$$

where we have written OP $= r_0$. Obviously $r > 0$, so we require $kg/a > \Omega^2$ or $a\Omega^2 < kg$. If r is displaced from the value given by Equation (7.9), we substitute

$$\frac{kg}{a} - \Omega^2 = \frac{kg}{r_0}$$

into Equation (7.8) to give

$$\ddot{r} + r\,\frac{kg}{r_0} = kg$$

This is simple harmonic motion of frequency $(kg/r_0)^{1/2}$. A simple pendulum of length l has frequency $(g/l)^{1/2}$; thus we can identify $l = r_0/k = \text{OP}/k$ as the length of the equivalent simple pendulum.

7.9 A small bead can move on a smooth circular wire, and is initially at rest at a point A. The wire is made to rotate uniformly in its own plane with a unit angular velocity about the other end of the diameter through A. Show that the reaction between the bead and the wire vanishes at a time $\ln\left[\frac{1}{2}(3 + \sqrt{5})\right]$ after the start.

Solution In order to solve this problem, we need to use intrinsic coordinates. This coordinate system gives us equations in the directions tangential and normal to the wire. These are, for this problem, rotating coordinates, since the wire itself rotates (with unit angular velocity, but let us retain the symbol ω for its magnitude for clarity, and put $\omega = 1$ when calculations are performed). The coordinates used and the forces are displayed in Fig. 7.5.

The acceleration in intrinsic coordinates (s,ϕ) is given by

$$\ddot{\mathbf{r}} = \ddot{s}\hat{\mathbf{T}} + \frac{\dot{s}^2}{\rho}\hat{\mathbf{N}}$$

(see Example 3.7), where ρ is the radius of curvature. Of course, this equation assumes that the curve upon which the bead slides is fixed. In order to be correct for the rotating wire, Coriolis and centripetal accelerations need to be added. Thus, the equation in the $\hat{\mathbf{T}}$ direction is

$$m(\ddot{s} - r\omega^2\sin\theta) = 0 \tag{7.10}$$

and in the $\hat{\mathbf{N}}$ direction is

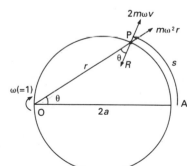

Figure 7.4

Figure 7.5

$$m\left(\frac{\dot{s}^2}{\rho} + 2\omega\dot{s} + r\omega^2\cos\theta\right) = R \tag{7.11}$$

In these equations, the Coriolis term is $2\omega\dot{s}$ and acts to the right of the motion, as shown in Fig. 7.5. The $r\omega^2$ (centripetal acceleration) acts along OP; hence the two components in the $\hat{\mathbf{T}}$ and $\hat{\mathbf{N}}$ directions are as in Equations (7.10) and (7.11). From the geometry of the circle

$$r = 2a\cos\theta \tag{7.12}$$

As the bead moves a small distance dr, $d\theta$ and ds are related as shown in Fig. 7.6. From this infinitesimal triangle we can write down the following expressions for $\sin\theta$ and $\cos\theta$:

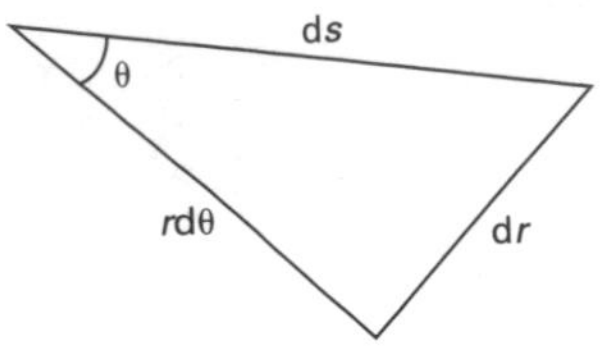

$$\sin\theta = \frac{dr}{ds}$$

$$\cos\theta = r\frac{d\theta}{ds}$$

Figure 7.6

If you have trouble seeing this, look at Fig. 7.5 and notice that, when $\theta = 0$, $rd\theta$ and ds must be parallel.

We now have enough information to solve the problem. From these last two equations, by squaring and adding, we obtain

$$\left(\frac{dr}{ds}\right)^2 + r^2\left(\frac{d\theta}{ds}\right)^2 = 1$$

or

$$\left(\frac{dr}{d\theta}\right)^2 + r^2 = \left(\frac{ds}{d\theta}\right)^2$$

But

$$\frac{dr}{d\theta} = \frac{d}{d\theta}(2a\cos\theta) = -2a\sin\theta$$

Hence

$$\left(\frac{ds}{d\theta}\right)^2 = r^2 + 4a^2\sin^2\theta$$

$$= 4a^2 \qquad (r = 2a\cos\theta)$$

so that $ds/d\theta = \pm 2a$. Equation (7.10) is rewritten as

$$v\frac{dv}{ds} = r\omega^2\frac{dr}{ds}$$

using $\ddot{s} = dv/dt = v\,dv/ds$ and $\sin\theta = dr/ds$. We can integrate this to obtain

$$\tfrac{1}{2}v^2 = \tfrac{1}{2}r^2\omega^2 + C$$

where C is an arbitrary constant. Since $v = -2a\omega$, when $r = 2a$, $C = 0$, so that

$$v^2 = r^2\omega^2$$

As $v = ds/dt$, we thus have

$$\frac{ds}{dt} = \pm r\omega$$

Now

$$\frac{d\theta}{dt} = \frac{ds}{dt}\frac{d\theta}{ds}$$

$$= \pm r\omega/\pm 2a = \omega\cos\theta$$

from Equation (7.12). Therefore

$$\int \frac{d\theta}{\cos\theta} = \int \omega dt$$

or

$$\ln(\sec\theta + \tan\theta) = \omega t + A$$

where A is an arbitrary constant. But $\theta = 0$ when $t = 0$, giving $A - 0$. Hence $\omega t = \ln(\sec\theta + \tan\theta)$.

We now use Equation (7.11) to find information about the normal reaction of the bead, R. For a circle, $\rho = a$; therefore Equation (7.11) is

$$m\left(\frac{r^2\omega^2}{a} \mp 2\omega^2 r + \omega^2 r^2 \frac{d\theta}{ds}\right) = R$$

Using $d\theta/ds = 1/2a$ and rearranging gives

$$R = \frac{3mr^2\omega^2}{2a} \pm 2m\omega^2 r$$

so that $R = 0$ if $r = 0$ or $4a/3$. At this point we can put $\omega = 1$, as justified by the question. $r = 0$ can be excluded since at this location $\theta = \pi/2$ and $t = \ln(\sec\theta + \tan\theta) \to \infty$ (The bead never reaches $r = 0$; no real surprise there.) $r = 4a/3$ implies

$$\cos\theta = \frac{r}{2a} = \tfrac{2}{3}$$

i.e. $\sec\theta = 3/2$, which gives

$$\tan^2\theta = \sec^2\theta - 1 = \tfrac{9}{4} - 1 = \tfrac{5}{4}$$

Thus

$$\sec\theta + \tan\theta = \tfrac{3}{2} + \frac{\sqrt{5}}{2}$$

whence

$$t = \ln\left[\tfrac{1}{2}(3 + \sqrt{5})\right]$$

as required.

7.10 A particle is at rest on a smooth wire in the shape of the curve $r^n = a^n\cos n\theta$, at the point $\theta = 0$. The wire begins to rotate with constant angular velocity ω about the origin O in its own plane. Prove that the reaction on the wire vanishes when the bead is at a distance $a[2/(n + 2)]^{1/n}$ from the origin, and that the time taken to reach this point is $(2/n\omega)\sinh^{-1}(\sqrt{n/2})$.

Solution This is similar to Example 7.9 in that we adopt intrinsic coordinates (s, ϕ) (see Fig. 7.7), where $s = 0$ when $\theta = 0$. This time, however, $\phi = \pi/2 - \theta$. The equations of motion in the $\hat{\mathbf{T}}$ and $\hat{\mathbf{N}}$ directions are

$$m(\ddot{s} - r\omega^2\cos\phi) = 0$$

and

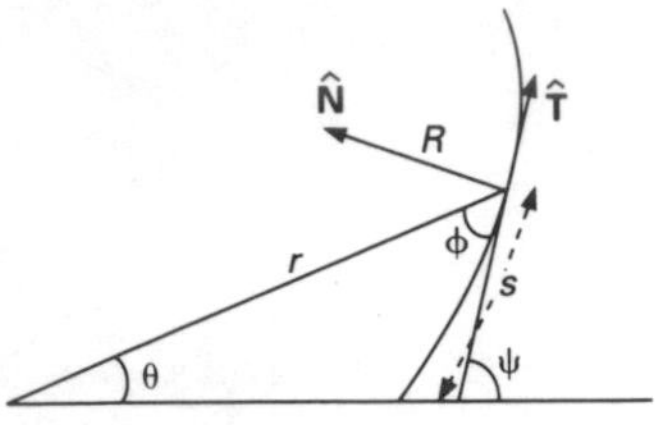

$$m\left(\frac{\dot{s}^2}{\rho} + 2\omega\dot{s} + r\omega^2\sin\phi\right) = R$$

respectively. Also $r^n = a^n\cos n\theta$ (given). Using the infinitesimal triangle (Fig. 7.6), with ϕ replacing $(\pi/2) - \theta$, we obtain

$$\cos\phi = \frac{dr}{ds}, \qquad \sin\phi = r\frac{d\theta}{ds}$$

whence

$$\left(\frac{dr}{d\theta}\right)^2 + r^2 = \left(\frac{ds}{d\theta}\right)^2$$

all as before (see Example 7.9). The angle ψ, as defined in Fig. 7.7, is given by $\psi = \phi + \theta$. Also, the curvature of the wire, $1/\rho$, is the rate that this angle changes with s. That is

$$\frac{1}{\rho} = \frac{d\psi}{ds} = \frac{d\phi}{ds} + \frac{d\theta}{ds}$$

so that

$$\frac{1}{\rho} = \frac{1}{r}\sin\phi + \cos\phi\,\frac{d\phi}{dr}$$

using

$$\frac{d\phi}{ds} = \frac{\sin\theta}{r}$$

and

$$\frac{d\phi}{ds} = \frac{d\phi}{dr}\frac{dr}{ds} = \cos\phi\,\frac{d\phi}{dr}$$

Hence

$$\frac{1}{\rho} = \frac{1}{r}\frac{d}{dr}\,(r\sin\phi)$$

$$= \frac{1}{r}\frac{d}{dr}\left(r^2\frac{d\theta}{ds}\right)$$

Now $r^n = a^n\cos n\theta$ (the equation of the wire). Differentiating with respect to θ:

$$nr^{n-1}\frac{dr}{d\theta} = -na^n\sin n\theta$$

so

$$\frac{dr}{d\theta} = -a^n\frac{\sin n\theta}{r^{n-1}}$$

This enables us to find $d\theta/ds$, and hence ρ, as follows:

$$\left(\frac{ds}{d\theta}\right)^2 = r^2 + \left(\frac{dr}{d\theta}\right)^2$$

$$= r^2 + \frac{a^{2n}\sin^2 n\theta}{r^{2n-2}}$$

Figure 7.7

$$= \frac{1}{r^{2n-2}} \; (r^{2n} + a^{2n}\sin^2 n\theta)$$

$$= \frac{1}{r^{2n-2}} \; (a^{2n}\cos^2 n\theta + a^{2n}\sin^2 n\theta)$$

$$= \frac{a^{2n}}{r^{2n-2}}$$

so that

$$\frac{d\theta}{ds} = \frac{r^{n-1}}{a^n}$$

Hence

$$\frac{1}{\rho} = \frac{1}{r} \frac{d}{dr} \left(\frac{r^{n+1}}{a^n} \right) = \frac{(n+1)r^{n-1}}{a^n}$$

The second equation of motion gives the normal reaction R:

$$R = m\left(\frac{(n+1)r^{n-1}}{a^n} \; \dot{s}^2 + 2\omega\dot{s} + r\omega^2\sin\phi \right)$$

Now, $\dot{s}^2 = \omega^2 r^2$ (as in Example 7.9), so $\dot{s} = \pm\omega r$, whence

$$R = m\left(\frac{(n+1)r^{n-1}}{a^n} \; \omega^2 r^2 \pm 2\omega^2 r + r\omega^2 \; \frac{r^n}{a^n} \right)$$

(using $\sin \phi = r \, d\theta/ds = r^n/a^n$) or

$$R = m\left[(n+2)r^{n+1} \; \frac{\omega^2}{a^n} \pm 2\omega^2 r \right]$$

This equals zero when

$$\frac{(n+2)r^{n+1}}{a^n} = 2r$$

(taking the negative sign), so $r = 0$ or $r^n = 2a^n/(n+2)$, i.e.

$$r = a[2/(n+2)]^{1/n}$$

as required.
  Now,

$$\dot{s} = \frac{ds}{dt} = -\omega r$$

(from above), so that

$$\frac{d\theta}{dt} = \frac{d\theta}{ds} \frac{ds}{dt} = -\omega r \; \frac{r^{n-1}}{a^n} = -\omega\cos n\theta$$

Hence

$$-\int \frac{d\theta}{\cos n\theta} = \omega t + C$$

where C is the constant of integration, or

$$-\frac{1}{n} \ln(\tan n\theta + \sec n\theta) = \omega t$$

($C = 0$ since $t = 0$ when $\theta = 0$). Now, $\ln[x + (1 + x^2)^{1/2}] = \sinh^{-1} x$ (an identity); hence

$$\ln(\tan n\theta + \sec n\theta) = \sinh^{-1}(\tan n\theta)$$

Therefore

$$\sinh^{-1}(\tan n\theta) = -\omega nt$$
$$\tan n\theta = \sinh(-\omega nt)$$
$$\tan n\theta = -\sinh(\omega nt)$$

Since $1 + \tan^2 n\theta = \sec^2 n\theta$ and $1 + \sinh^2 \omega nt = \cosh^2 \omega nt$ we also have $\sec n\theta = \cosh \omega nt$ (both sec and cosh must be positive). At the point where the reaction R vanishes,

$$r^n = 2a^n/(n + 2)$$

Hence

$$\cos n\theta = \frac{r^n}{a^n} = \frac{2}{n + 2}$$

or

$$\sec n\theta = \frac{n + 2}{2} = 1 + \frac{n}{2}$$

Thus

$$\cosh n\omega t = 1 + \frac{n}{2}$$

at the point where $R = 0$. Using $\cosh^2 n\omega t = 1 + 2 \sinh^2 \frac{1}{2} n\omega t$, we obtain

$$\sinh^2 \tfrac{1}{2} n\omega t = \frac{n}{4}$$

whence

$$t = \frac{2}{n\omega} \sinh^{-1}(\sqrt{n}/2)$$

as required.

7.3 Exercises

7.1 A body of mass 20 kg is made to move outwards along a radius of a circular platform at a constant speed of $1\,\mathrm{m\,s^{-1}}$ relative to the platform. If the platform rotates at a constant rate of 1 revolution per minute, calculate the applied force acting on the body when it is 3 m from the centre of the platform.

7.2 A particle of mass m moves under the action of a force P towards the origin O and a force Q in the direction of the line $\theta = 0$ so that it describes the curve $r = a + b\cos\theta$, and the angular velocity ω of the radius vector is constant. Find the magnitude of P and Q in terms of ω and show that

$$aP + \left(b + \frac{a^2}{2b}\right)\Omega = 2mV^2$$

where V is the speed of the particle.

7.3 A particle on a rotating Earth is projected with a velocity $\mathbf{u}$ relative to the Earth from a point taken as the origin. Show that its position vector $\mathbf{r}$ is given by

$$\mathbf{r} = \mathbf{u}t + (\tfrac{1}{2}\mathbf{g} + \mathbf{u} \times \mathbf{\Omega})t^2 + \tfrac{1}{3}\mathbf{g} \times \mathbf{\Omega}t^3$$

where terms of order Ω^2, air resistance and variations in $\mathbf{g}$ (apparent gravity) are ignored.

Show also that, to this order of approximation, the rotation of the Earth diminishes the time of flight on the horizontal plane in the ratio

$$1{:}1 + \frac{2}{g^2}\,\dot{\mathbf{g}}(\mathbf{u} \times \boldsymbol{\omega}) \qquad \text{(L.U)}$$

7.4 A particle falls from a height h above the Earth's surface. Show that it experiences a horizontal deviation of

$$\tfrac{1}{3}\left(\frac{8h^3}{g}\right)^{1/2}\Omega\cos\lambda$$

where λ is the latitude.

7.5 In plane polar coordinates (r,θ), a line of clouds lies along the line $\theta = \theta_0$ at time $t = 0$. These clouds are subject to a frictional force $c\mathbf{v}$ per unit mass (where $\mathbf{v}$ is the velocity and c is a constant). If $mp\hat{\mathbf{r}}$ is the pressure force, show that, approximately,

$$f\mathbf{k}\times\mathbf{v} = -mp\hat{\mathbf{r}} - c\mathbf{v}$$

where $f = 2\Omega\sin$ (latitude). Hence calculate what happens to the line of clouds.

7.6 A thin hollow tube rotates in a vertical plane with constant angular velocity ω about a horizontal axis through the centre O of the tube. A particle of mass m fits inside the tube. Neglecting friction, determine the motion of the particle.

If initially the particle is a distance x_0 from O and has speed v_0 away from O, show that the particle will oscillate with simple harmonic motion along the tube if and only if its initial motion is horizontal and $x_0 = 0$, $v_0 = g/2\omega$. What happens if these conditions are not satisfied?

7.7 A small bead moves freely on a smooth wire, in the shape of cardioid $r = a(1 + \cos\theta)$ in a horizontal plane. The wire is set rotating with constant angular velocity ω about an axis through the cusp, perpendicular to the plane. If the bead starts from the apse, show that the bead moves towards the cusp but never reaches it. Show also that the reaction on the curve vanishes when $\cos\tfrac{1}{2}\theta = \tfrac{4}{5}$. (The radius of curvature of the cardioid is $\tfrac{4}{3}a\cos\tfrac{1}{2}\theta$.)

7.8 A toy consists of a light hollow loop of radius a and a plug of mass m which slides along it without friction. Show that, if the hoop is spun about a vertical diameter with constant angular velocity ω, then $a\omega^2\cos\theta = g$ is an equilibrium position where θ is the angle the radius vector through the plug makes with the vertical. Investigate the stability of this equilibrium position, and discuss the case $\omega = (g/a)^{1/2}$.

7.4 Outline Solutions to Exercises

7.1 Using $m[\ddot{\mathbf{r}} + 2\boldsymbol{\omega}\times\mathbf{r} + \boldsymbol{\omega}\times(\boldsymbol{\omega}\times\mathbf{r})] = $ force, with the mass m moving in the direction $\hat{\mathbf{i}}$ fixed on the rotating turntable. We have $\ddot{\mathbf{r}} = 0$, $\boldsymbol{\omega} = (\pi/30)\hat{\mathbf{k}}$, $\dot{\mathbf{r}} = \hat{\mathbf{i}}$, $\mathbf{r} = 3\hat{\mathbf{i}}$ and $m = 20$ giving a force $= (\pi^2/15, 8\pi/3, 0)$.

7.2 We have

$$m(\ddot{r} - r\dot{\theta}^2) = -P + Q\cos\theta$$

and

$$\frac{m}{r}\frac{\mathrm{d}}{\mathrm{d}t}(r^2\dot{\theta}) = -Q\sin\theta$$

$\dot{\theta} = \omega = $ constant, and $r = a + b\cos\theta$, $\dot{r} = -b\sin\theta\dot{\theta}$; hence

$$Q\sin\theta = 2m\omega^2 b\sin\theta$$

so

$$Q = 2m\omega^2 b$$

Also,

$$-2mb\omega^2\cos\theta - ma\omega^2 = -P + Q\cos\theta$$

which gives

$$P = ma\omega^2 + 4m\omega^2 b\cos\theta$$

and

$$V = [\dot{r}^2 + (r\dot{\theta})^2]^{1/2} = [b^2\omega^2\sin^2\theta + \omega^2(a + b\cos\theta)^2]^{1/2}$$
$$= (b^2\omega^2 + a^2\omega^2 + 2\omega^2 ab\cos\theta)^{1/2}$$

Hence

$$aP + \left(b + \frac{a^2}{2b}\right)Q = 2m(b^2\omega^2 + a^2\omega^2 + 2\omega^2 ab\cos\theta) = 2mV^2$$

as required.

7.3 We have that

$$\ddot{\mathbf{r}} = \mathbf{g} - 2\boldsymbol{\Omega}\times\dot{\mathbf{r}} \qquad (7.13)$$

(centripetal acceleration is included in $\mathbf{g}$). Integrating:

$$\dot{\mathbf{r}} = \mathbf{g}t - 2\boldsymbol{\Omega}\times\mathbf{r} + \mathbf{A}$$

$t = 0$, $\mathbf{r} = 0$, $\dot{\mathbf{r}} = \mathbf{u}$; hence $\mathbf{u} = \mathbf{A}$. Substitute for $\dot{\mathbf{r}}$ into Equation (7.13) and neglect Ω^2 to give

$$\ddot{\mathbf{r}} = \mathbf{g} - 2\boldsymbol{\Omega}\times\mathbf{u} - 2\boldsymbol{\Omega}\times\mathbf{g}t$$

Integrating:

$$\dot{\mathbf{r}} = \mathbf{g}t - 2\boldsymbol{\Omega}\times\mathbf{u}t - \boldsymbol{\Omega}\times\mathbf{g}t^2 + \mathbf{B}$$

Initial conditions give $\mathbf{u} = \mathbf{B}$. Integrating again

$$\mathbf{r} = \mathbf{u}t + (\tfrac{1}{2}\mathbf{g} + \mathbf{u}\times\boldsymbol{\Omega})t^2 + \tfrac{1}{3}\mathbf{g}\times\boldsymbol{\Omega})t^3$$

as required.

On the surface of the Earth, $\mathbf{r}\cdot\mathbf{g} = 0$. Dotting the expression for $\mathbf{r}$ with $\mathbf{g}$ gives either $t = 0$ (start) or

$$t = -\frac{\mathbf{u}\cdot\mathbf{g}}{\tfrac{1}{2}\mathbf{g}^2 + \mathbf{g}\cdot(\mathbf{u}\times\boldsymbol{\omega})}$$

Neglecting rotation,

$$t = -\frac{\mathbf{u}\cdot\mathbf{g}}{\tfrac{1}{2}\mathbf{g}^2}$$

The ratio of these two times is

$$1:1 + \frac{2}{\mathbf{g}^2}\mathbf{g}\cdot(\mathbf{u}\times\boldsymbol{\omega})$$

as required.

7.4 The expressions for x and z are

$$z = h - \tfrac{1}{2}gt^2$$

and

$$x = \tfrac{1}{3}\Omega gt^3 \cos\lambda$$

so when $z = 0$, $t^2 = 2h/g$ which gives the required value of x.

7.5 Since

$$\begin{aligned}
2\boldsymbol{\Omega} \times \dot{\mathbf{r}} &= 2(-\dot{y}\Omega\sin\lambda\hat{\mathbf{i}} + \dot{x}\Omega\sin\lambda\hat{\mathbf{j}}) \\
&= f(-\dot{y}\hat{\mathbf{i}} + \dot{x}\hat{\mathbf{j}}) \\
&= f\hat{\mathbf{k}} \times \dot{\mathbf{r}}
\end{aligned}$$

$m2\boldsymbol{\Omega} \times \dot{\mathbf{r}} = $ pressure $+$ friction gives

$$f\hat{\mathbf{k}} \times \mathbf{v} = -p\hat{\mathbf{r}} - c\mathbf{v}$$

whence

$$f\dot{r} = -cr\dot{\theta}$$

and

$$-fr\dot{\theta} = -p - c\dot{r}$$

Solving gives

$$r = r_0 - \frac{cpt}{c^2 + f^{2'}} \qquad r = r_0 e^{c(\theta_0 - \theta)/f}$$

an inward spiralling motion.

7.6 The particle in the general position is shown in Fig. 7.8, which defines the notation. Hence

$$\ddot{r} - r\dot{\theta}^2 = -g\sin\theta$$

and

$$\frac{1}{r}\frac{d}{dt}(r^2\dot{\theta}) = R - g\cos\theta$$

$\dot{\theta} = \omega = $ constant, $\ddot{r} - r\omega^2 = -g\sin\omega t$. The general solution is

$$r = A\cosh\omega t + B\sinh\omega t + \frac{g}{2\omega^2}\sin\omega t$$

which means that usually the mass flies away from O unless conditions are such that $A = B = 0$.

If $x_0 = 0$ then $A = 0$. Hence $\dot{r} = \omega B + (g/2\omega)$ when $\theta(= \omega t) = 0$. Only if this is $g/2\omega$ is $B = 0$ and we have SHM. Otherwise the mass will fly away from O exponentially.

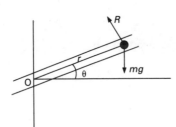

Figure 7.8

7.7 Following Examples 7.9 and 7.10, we use intrinsic coordinates

$$\ddot{s} = r\omega^2 \cos\phi$$

and

$$\frac{mv^2}{\rho} = N - 2m\omega v - mr\omega^2 \sin\phi \qquad \textbf{(7.14)}$$

and

$$r = a(1 + \cos\theta) = 2a\cos^2\tfrac{1}{2}\theta$$

We obtain

$$\left(\frac{ds}{d\theta}\right)^2 = 4a^2\cos^2\frac{\theta}{2}, \qquad \frac{ds}{dt} = \pm\omega r$$

and hence

$$\dot{\theta} = \omega\cos\tfrac{1}{2}\theta$$

so that

$$t = \frac{2}{\omega}\ln(\tan\tfrac{1}{2}\theta + \sec\tfrac{1}{2}\theta)$$

With $\rho = \tfrac{4}{3}a\cos\tfrac{1}{2}\theta$ and $v^2 = \omega^2 r^2$, Equation (7.14) gives

$$\frac{3}{4}\frac{mr^2\omega^2}{a\cos\tfrac{1}{2}\theta} = N \pm 2m\omega^2 r - \frac{mr^2\omega^2}{2a\cos\tfrac{1}{2}\theta}$$

with $N = 0$ and $r = a\cos^2\tfrac{1}{2}\theta \Rightarrow \cos\tfrac{1}{2}\theta = \tfrac{4}{3}$, as required.
At the cusp, $r = 0$, $\cos\theta = -1$ $(\theta = \pi)$ implies

$$t = \frac{2}{\omega}\ln\left(\tan\frac{\pi}{2} + \sec\frac{\pi}{2}\right)$$

which is infinite. Hence $r = 0$ is never reached.

7.8 Adopting the notation of Fig. 7.9, the equation of motion is

$$m[\ddot{\mathbf{r}} + 2\boldsymbol{\omega} \times \dot{\mathbf{r}} + \boldsymbol{\omega}(\boldsymbol{\omega} \times \mathbf{r})] = -mg\mathbf{k} + \mathbf{R}$$

Since $\mathbf{r} = a\hat{\mathbf{r}} = (-a\cos\theta\hat{\mathbf{k}} + a\sin\theta\hat{\mathbf{j}})$, $\boldsymbol{\omega} = \omega\mathbf{k}$ and so $\boldsymbol{\omega} \times \mathbf{r} = -a\omega\sin\theta\hat{\mathbf{i}}$. Thus $\boldsymbol{\omega} \times (\boldsymbol{\omega} \times \mathbf{r}) = -a\omega^2\sin\theta\hat{\mathbf{j}}$. Also, $\dot{\mathbf{r}} = a\dot{\theta}\hat{\boldsymbol{\theta}}$, $\ddot{\mathbf{r}} = a\ddot{\theta}\hat{\boldsymbol{\theta}} - a\dot{\theta}^2\hat{\mathbf{r}}$ and so $\boldsymbol{\omega} \times \dot{\mathbf{r}} = -\omega a\dot{\theta}\cos\theta\hat{\mathbf{i}}$. Thus

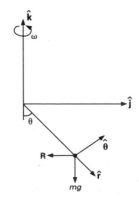

Figure 7.9

$$a\ddot{\theta} = \sin\theta(a\omega^2 \cos\theta - g) \qquad (7.15)$$

is the $\overset{\wedge}{\theta}$ equation.

When $a\omega^2 \cos\theta = g$, $\ddot{\theta} = 0$, giving an equilibrium position. Put $\theta = \theta_0 + \varepsilon$, where $a\omega^2 \cos\theta_0 = g$ into Equation (7.15), using $\cos\theta = (g/a\omega^2)\, \varepsilon\sin\theta_0$ and $\sin\theta = \sin\theta_0 + (\varepsilon g/a\omega^2)$, to give

$$\ddot{\varepsilon} = -\frac{\varepsilon}{a^2\omega^2}\, (a^2\omega^4 - g^2)$$

We have stability if $a\omega^2 > g$ and instability if $a\omega^2 < g$.

If $a\omega^2 = g$ we need a more accurate analysis to derive

$$\ddot{\theta} = -\tfrac{1}{2}g\theta^3 \quad \text{or} \quad \dot{\theta}^2 = (\theta_0^4 - \theta^4)\omega^2/4$$

which is a stable non-linear oscillation with exact solution given in terms of elliptic functions.

8 Orbits

8.1 Fact Sheet

Central Forces A central force is the name given to a force which is of the form $-F(r)\hat{\mathbf{r}}$. That is, it is **attractive** and directed towards the origin. Under this kind of force, the equations of motion for a particle become

$$m(\ddot{r} - r\dot{\theta}^2) = -F(r)$$

and

$$\frac{d}{dt}(r^2\dot{\theta}) = 0$$

This last equation expresses the fact that

$$r^2\dot{\theta} = \text{constant}$$

$r^2\dot{\theta}$ (which is the magnitude of the angular momentum of a particle of unit mass) is usually given the letter h.

Angular momentum:

$$\mathbf{L} = \mathbf{r} \times m\dot{\mathbf{r}}$$

The path of m lies in a plane, $\mathbf{L}$ is perpendicular to this plane, and $r^2\dot{\theta} = h$ generalises to $\mathbf{L} = \text{constant}$.

Gravitational attraction according to Newton's gravitational law implies

$$F(r) = \frac{Gm_1 m_2}{r^2}$$

where m_1 is the mass of one particle (say the one at the origin) and m_2 the mass of the second. G is the universal gravitational constant $(= 6.7 \times 10^{-11}\,\text{m}^3\text{kg}^{-1}\text{s}^2)$. Under this force, the mass moves according to the polar equation

$$\frac{l}{r} = e\cos(\theta - \theta_0) + 1$$

where l, e and θ_0 are constants. The equation is a conic and e is positive (or zero). If $e = 0$, the orbit (path) is circular; if $0 < e < 1$, the orbit is elliptical; if $e = 1$, the orbit is parabolic; and if $e > 1$, the orbit is hyperbolic. In the latter two cases, the value of r increases without limit and we say that the mass m_2 **escapes**. The escape velocity of a mass (for example a rocket) is that velocity a mass must be given in order that it just fails to be retained in a closed orbit, that is $e = 1$.

Kepler's Laws   Kepler's Laws of planetary motion are:

1. Planets move in elliptical paths about the Sun.
2. The position vector of a planet sweeps out equal areas in equal times.
3. The ratio of the square of the orbital period to the cube of the semi-major axis is the same constant for all planets.

Energy   The energy equation for an orbit of magnitude of angular momentum per unit mass h is

$$\tfrac{1}{2}mr^2 + \frac{mh^2}{2r^2} = -\int F(r)dr + \text{constant}$$

Problems involving energy are postponed until Chapter 10; however, see Example 8.4 (Equation 8.3).

8.2 Worked Examples

8.1   Show that, for motion under a central force, the angular momentum is a constant. Deduce that planetary motion is planar.

Solution   The angular momentum of a mass m is defined as $m\dot{\mathbf{r}} \times \mathbf{r}$ (the cross product of linear momentum and position vector).

Newton's second law for a central force is

$$m\ddot{\mathbf{r}} = \mathbf{F} = -F(r)\mathbf{r}$$

The rate of change of angular momentum is

$$\frac{d}{dt}(\mathbf{r} \times m\dot{\mathbf{r}}) = \dot{\mathbf{r}} \times m\dot{\mathbf{r}} + \mathbf{r} \times m\ddot{\mathbf{r}}$$
$$= \dot{\mathbf{r}} \times m\dot{\mathbf{r}} + \mathbf{r} \times [-F(r)\mathbf{r}]$$
$$= \mathbf{0}$$

(since the cross product of a vector with itself is zero). Hence $\mathbf{r} \times m\dot{\mathbf{r}} = \mathbf{L}$ = constant vector. This means that $\mathbf{r} \times \dot{\mathbf{r}}$ is not only constant in magnitude, but constant in direction. Both $\dot{\mathbf{r}}$ and $\mathbf{r}$ must therefore lie in the plane perpendicular to $\mathbf{r} \times \dot{\mathbf{r}}$ (which is constant). This plane is thus the plane that contains the path of m (the planet). Planetary motion is thus planar.

8.2   Show that, under Newton's gravitational law, the equation of motion of a planet possessing (constant) angular momentum h about a sun of mass M is

$$\frac{d^2u}{d\theta^2} + u = \frac{\gamma}{h^2}$$

where $u = 1/r$ and $\gamma = GM$.

Solution   This question may seem somewhat contrived, but it leads to the derivation of the *general* equation of an orbit. Newton's law in the $\hat{\mathbf{r}}$ direction is

$$m(\ddot{r} - r\dot{\theta}^2) = -\frac{GMm}{r^2}$$

and

$$r^2\dot{\theta} = h$$

giving

$$\dot{\theta}^2 = h^2/r^4$$

Hence

$$\ddot{r} - \frac{h^2}{r^3} = -\frac{GM}{r^2}$$

We now convert to u $(= 1/r)$:

$$\dot{r} = \frac{dr}{dt} = \frac{d}{dt}\left(\frac{1}{u}\right) = -\frac{1}{u^2}\frac{du}{dt} = -\frac{\dot{\theta}}{u^2}\frac{du}{d\theta}$$

But

$$\dot{\theta} = h/r^2 = hu^2$$

giving

$$\dot{r} = -h\frac{du}{d\theta}$$

Differentiating again with respect to t gives

$$\ddot{r} = \frac{d}{dt}\left(-h\frac{du}{d\theta}\right)$$

$$= -h\dot{\theta}\frac{d^2u}{d\theta^2} = -h^2u^2\frac{d^2u}{d\theta^2}$$

Hence

$$\ddot{r} - \frac{h^2}{r^3} = -\frac{GM}{r^2}$$

is

$$-h^2u^2\frac{d^2u}{d\theta^2} - h^2u^3 = -GMu^2$$

or

$$\frac{d^2u}{d\theta^2} + u = \frac{GM}{h^2} = \frac{\gamma}{h^2}$$

as required.

8.3 By solving the equation derived in the previous problem, show that

$$\frac{l}{r} = e\cos(\theta - \theta_0) + 1$$

(where θ_0 is a constant). Hence deduce the path of the planet.

Solution The equation of motion in u $(= 1/r)$ and θ coordinates (sometimes called reciprocal polar coordinates) was derived (see Example 8.2) as

$$\frac{d^2u}{d\theta^2} + u = \frac{\gamma}{h^2}$$

The solution to this second-order ordinary differential equation is

$$u = \frac{\gamma}{h^2} + A' \cos(\theta - \theta_0)$$

where θ_0, A' are arbitrary constants. Hence

$$\frac{1}{r} = \frac{\gamma}{h^2} + A'\cos(\theta - \theta_0) \qquad (8.1)$$

or

$$\frac{l}{r} = e\cos(\theta - \theta_0) + 1 \qquad (8.2)$$

as required ($l = h^2/\gamma$). The constants ε, θ_0 depend on initial conditions; $r = l$ when $\theta - \theta_0 = \pi/2$ and l is called the semi-latus rectum (the vertical line through the focus will cut the conic at two points, the distance between these points being called the latus rectum). This is the polar equation of a conic with eccentricity e. (We shall demonstrate the truth of this at the end.)

Equations (8.1) and (8.2) are, of course, the same. We immediately deduce that the point where $\theta - \theta_0 = \pi/2$ corresponds to $r = l$ (from either equation). Also, where $\theta = \theta_0$,

$$r = \frac{l}{1 + e}$$

and where $\theta = \theta_0 + \pi$,

$$r = \frac{l}{|1 - e|}$$

Half the distance between these two extremes is a, the semi-major axis. Thus

$$a = \tfrac{1}{2}\left(\frac{l}{1 + e} + \frac{l}{|1 - e|}\right) = \frac{l}{|1 - e^2|} \qquad (e \neq 1)$$

so that

$$l = a|1 - e^2|$$

i.e.

$$l = a(1 - e^2) \quad \text{for an ellipse}$$
$$l = a(e^2 - 1) \quad \text{for a hyperbola}$$

To see that $l/r = e\cos(\theta - \theta_0) + 1$ is a conic, write $r \cos(\theta - \theta_0) = x$, $r \sin(\theta - \theta_0) = y$; then

$$l = r + xe$$

or

$$r^2 = (l - xe)^2 = l^2 - 2lxe + x^2e^2$$

so that

$$x^2(1 - e^2) + y^2 = l^2 - 2lxe$$

which is a conic of eccentricity e. The case $e = 1$ gives the parabola

$$y^2 = l^2 - 2lx$$

for which $l = 2a$.

The geometry of the three conics is displayed in Fig. 8.1.

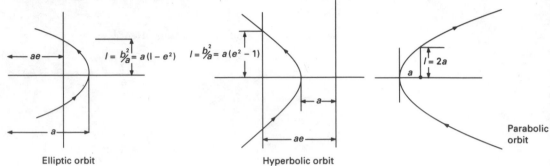

Figure 8.1   Elliptic orbit   Hyperbolic orbit   Parabolic orbit

8.4   A mass orbits under the inverse square law of attraction $f(r) = -m\gamma\hat{r}/r^2$. Derive the three equations for the speed v of m.

$$v^2 = \gamma \left(\frac{2}{r} - \frac{1}{a} \right) \qquad \text{ellipse}$$

$$v^2 = \gamma \left(\frac{2}{r} + \frac{1}{a} \right) \qquad \text{hyperbola}$$

$$v^2 = \frac{2\gamma}{r} \qquad \text{parabola}$$

where a is, in the usual notation, the semi-major axis.

Solution   The equations of motion are, as previously derived,

$$\ddot{r} - r\dot{\theta}^2 = -\gamma/r^2 \qquad \text{(radially)}$$

and

$$r^2\dot{\theta} = h \qquad \text{(transversely – integrated once).}$$

Substituting for $\dot{\theta}$ gives

$$\ddot{r} - \frac{h^2}{r^3} = -\frac{\gamma}{r^2}$$

and multiplying by $\dot{r}$ and integrating with respect to r yields

$$\tfrac{1}{2}\dot{r}^2 + \frac{h^2}{2r^2} = \frac{\gamma}{r} + A \qquad\qquad\qquad \textbf{(8.3)}$$

where A is an arbitrary constant. This equation expresses the conservation of energy per unit mass.

Now $r\dot{\theta}$ is the transverse velocity, so that

$$r\dot{\theta} = r\frac{h}{r^2} = \frac{h}{r}$$

is also the transverse velocity, from which

$$v^2 = \dot{r}^2 + (r\dot{\theta})^2 = \dot{r}^2 + \frac{h^2}{r^2}$$

114

Hence, from Equation (8.3),

$$\tfrac{1}{2}v^2 = \frac{\gamma}{r} + A \qquad\qquad (8.4)$$

For an ellipse, when $r = a(1 - e)$,

$$v = \frac{h}{r} = \frac{h}{a(1 - e)}$$

whence

$$\tfrac{1}{2}\frac{h^2}{a^2(1 - e)^2} = \frac{\gamma}{a(1 - e)} + A$$

Using

$$h^2 = \gamma l = \gamma\, a(1 - e^2)$$

for an ellipse gives

$$A = \frac{\gamma\, a(1 - e^2)}{2a^2(1 - e)^2} - \frac{\gamma}{a(1 - e)}$$

$$= \frac{\gamma}{a(1 - e)} \left(\frac{1 + e}{2} - 1\right)$$

$$= \frac{\gamma}{a(1 - e)} \left(\tfrac{1}{2} e - \tfrac{1}{2}\right) = -\frac{\gamma}{2a}$$

Thus

$$v^2 = \gamma\left(\frac{2}{r} - \frac{1}{a}\right)$$

for an ellipse.

For a hyperbola (near branch) when $r = a(e - 1)$,

$$v\left(= \frac{h}{r}\right) = \frac{h}{a(e - 1)}$$

whence

$$\tfrac{1}{2}\frac{h^2}{a^2(e - 1)^2} = \frac{\gamma}{a(e - 1)} + A$$

Using $h^2 = \gamma l = \gamma\, a(e^2 - 1)$ for a hyperbola gives

$$A = \frac{\gamma\, a(e^2 - 1)}{2a^2(e - 1)^2} - \frac{\gamma}{a(e - 1)}$$

$$= \frac{\gamma}{a(e - 1)} \left[\tfrac{1}{2}(e + 1) - 1\right] = \frac{\gamma}{2a}$$

Thus

$$v^2 = \gamma\left(\frac{2}{r} + \frac{1}{a}\right)$$

for a hyperbola

For a parabola, when $r = a$,

$$v\left(= \frac{h}{r}\right) = \frac{h}{a}$$

so

$$\tfrac{1}{2}\frac{h^2}{a^2} = A + \frac{\gamma}{a}$$

Using $h^2 = \gamma l = 2\gamma a$ for a parabola gives

$$\frac{2\gamma a}{2a^2} = A + \frac{\gamma}{a}$$

or $A = 0$. Thus

$$v^2 = \frac{2\gamma}{r}$$

for a parabola.

8.5 Use the previous example to calculate the escape velocity of a particle from the Earth. Deduce that the velocity required to maintain the particle in a circular orbit is precisely $1/\sqrt{2}$ times the speed of the escaping particle at this distance. (Radius of the Earth = 6370 km.)

Solution   For the particle just to escape, it must have a parabolic orbit. So

$$v^2 = \frac{2\gamma}{r}$$

from Example 8.4, where the force law is $-\gamma/r^2$. Now, at the surface of the Earth, where $r = r_e$, the radius of the Earth,

$$\frac{\gamma}{r_e^2} = g$$

Hence

$$v^2 = \frac{2gr_e^2}{r} \qquad\qquad (8.5)$$

in general, or $v = (2gr_e)^{1/2}$ at $r = r_e$. Inserting $r_e = 6.37 \times 10^6$ m and $g = 9.81$ m s^{-2} gives $v = 1.12 \times 10^4$ m s^{-1} = 11.2 km s^{-1}.

For an elliptical orbit we have

$$v^2 = \gamma\left(\frac{2}{r} - \frac{1}{a}\right)$$

and if this is circular ($r = a$)

$$v^2 = \frac{\gamma}{a} = \frac{gr_e^2}{a}$$

Equation (8.5) at $r = a$ is

$$v^2 = \frac{2gr_e^2}{a}$$

Hence v at the circular orbit is precisely $1/\sqrt{2}$ times the velocity of the escaping particle at the same distance.

8.6 Prove Kepler's laws:
1. Planets move in elliptical orbits about the Sun.
2. The position vector of a planet sweeps out equal areas in equal times.
3. The ratio of the square of the orbital period to the cube of the semi-major axis is the same constant for all planets.

Solution   1. This has already been demonstrated. See Example 8.3, where we saw that, provided the orbit is closed, it is elliptical.

2. The area of the region shown in Fig. 8.2 is $\frac{1}{2}r^2\delta\theta$. Hence the area swept out in time t is

$$\int_0^t \frac{1}{2}r^2 \frac{d\theta}{dt}\, dt = \int_0^t \frac{1}{2}r^2\, \dot\theta dt = \frac{1}{2}ht$$

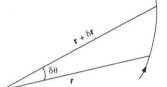

Figure 8.2

Hence planets sweep out equal areas in equal times. The rate is $h/2$, where h is the constant angular momentum.

3. In order to sweep out the entire area we require a time T, where

$$\frac{1}{2}hT = \pi ab \qquad \text{(area of ellipse)}.$$

Now $h^2 = \gamma l = \gamma b^2/a$ (where $-\gamma/r^2$ is the force law and l is the semi-latus rectum of the ellipse). Hence

$$T^2 = \frac{4\pi^2 a^2 b^2}{h^2} = \frac{4\pi^2 a^2 b^2}{\gamma b^2/a} = \frac{4\pi^2 a^3}{\gamma}$$

which implies that

$$\frac{T^2}{a^3} = \frac{4\pi^2}{\gamma}$$

is a constant, which confirms Kepler's third law.

8.7   A satellite is moving in a circular orbit at a height H above the Earth's surface. Find an expression for its orbital speed U.

The firing of retro-rockets reduces the satellite's speed to kU ($0 < k < 1$) and puts the satellite into an elliptical orbit. Show that the satellite will collide with the Earth if

$$k^2 \leq 2R/(2R + H)$$

where R is the radius of the Earth.

(L.U.)

Solution   The equations of motion for the satellite are

$$m(\ddot r - r\dot\theta^2) = -\frac{GM}{r^2}\, m$$

where we can, of course, cancel the mass of the satellite, and

$$r^2\dot\theta = L \qquad \text{(conservation of angular momentum)}.$$

Here G is the gravitational constant and M the mass of the Earth, so that the right-hand side of the first equation expresses Newton's gravitational (inverse square) law. Letting $r = R$, the radius of the Earth, then $-GM/R^2$ is the acceleration (in the $\hat{\mathbf r}$ direction) at the Earth's surface. This is, of course, $-g$ (where $g = 9.81$ m s^{-2}). So $GM = gR^2$.

We shall use this relation to eliminate GM. Hence we can write

$$\ddot r - \frac{L^2}{r^3} = -g\frac{R^2}{r^2} \tag{8.6}$$

117

eliminating $\dot{\theta}$ and substituting for GM. Multiplying this equation by $\dot{r}$ and integrating with respect to t gives

$$\tfrac{1}{2}\dot{r}^2 + \frac{L^2}{2r^2} - \frac{gR^2}{r} = \text{constant} \tag{8.7}$$

This is an energy equation: the first two terms represent the kinetic energy of the satellite (per unit mass), the third term is the potential energy.

Now, we are told that the orbit is circular, at height H, which corresponds to $r = R + H$. The velocity is therefore entirely in the $\hat{\theta}$ direction ($\dot{r} = 0$). Hence $r\dot{\theta} = U$. Also, $r^2\dot{\theta} = L$, and of course $r = R + H$. Eliminating $\dot{\theta}$ gives $U = L/(R + H)$. Putting $\ddot{r} = 0$ and $r = R + H$ in Equation (8.7) leads to

$$- \frac{L^2}{(R + H)^3} = - \frac{gR^2}{(R + H)^2}$$

or

$$L^2 = gR^2(R + H)$$

Therefore

$$U = \frac{L}{R + H} = \left(\frac{gR^2}{R + H} \right)^{1/2}$$

is the required value.

For the second part of the question, U is replaced by kU. Of course, in this case L, the angular momentum of the satellite, is not conserved due to the imposition of retro-rockets. We therefore need to calculate the new value. We are given the velocity kU; hence

$$r\dot{\theta} = kU = k \left(\frac{gR^2}{R + H} \right)^{1/2}$$

Thus the new angular momentum is

$$r^2\dot{\theta} = (R + H)kU = k[gR^2(R + H)]^{1/2} = L$$

We can now use Equation (8.7), the energy equation, which is

$$\tfrac{1}{2}\dot{r}^2 + \frac{k^2gR^2 \, (R + H)}{2r^2} = \frac{gR^2}{r} + A$$

where A is an arbitrary constant. At $r = R + H$, $\dot{r} = 0$; hence

$$0 + \frac{k^2gR^2 \, (R + H)}{2(R + H)^2} = \frac{gR^2}{R + H} + A$$

Subtracting to eliminate A gives

$$\tfrac{1}{2}\dot{r}^2 = gR^2 \left(\frac{1}{r} - \frac{1}{R + H} \right) + \frac{k^2gR^2}{2} \left(\frac{1}{R + H} - \frac{R + H}{r^2} \right)$$

$$= gR^2 \frac{(H + R - r)}{r(R + H)} + \frac{k^2gR^2}{2} \frac{r^2 - (R + H)^2}{r^2(R + H)}$$

or

$$\tfrac{1}{2}\dot{r}^2 = \frac{gR^2}{r^2(R + H)} (H + R - r) \, [r - \tfrac{1}{2}k^2 \, (r + R + H)]$$

At $r = R$, this is

$$\tfrac{1}{2}\dot{r}^2 = \frac{gR^2\,H}{R^2(R + H)} \ [R - \tfrac{1}{2}k^2\,(2R + H)]$$

If this is positive, then the satellite will collide with Earth (otherwise $\dot{r}^2 < 0$ and $r = R$ is never reached). This is so if

$$R \gtrsim \tfrac{1}{2}k^2(2R + H)$$

or

$$k^2 \le \frac{2R}{2R + H}$$

as required.

8.8 A particle moves under the influence of a central force in the orbit $r = \tanh(\theta/\sqrt{2})$. If it is projected from the origin with angular momentum h per unit mass, show that the magnitude of the force is proportional to $1/r^5$ and that the time taken by the particle to move from the point $\theta = 0$ to the point $\theta = \alpha\sqrt{2}$ on its orbit is $\sqrt{2}a^2(\alpha - \tanh \alpha)/h$. (L.U.)

Solution   The orbit is $r = \tanh(\theta/\sqrt{2})$. Differentiating with respect to t gives

$$\dot{r} = a\,\mathrm{sech}^2(\theta/\sqrt{2})\,\frac{1}{\sqrt{2}}\,\dot{\theta}$$

Using the relationship $\mathrm{sech}^2(\theta/\sqrt{2}) = 1 - \tanh^2(\theta/\sqrt{2})$ gives

$$\dot{r} = a\left(1 - \frac{r^2}{a^2}\right)\frac{\dot{\theta}}{\sqrt{2}}$$

$$= \frac{a\dot{\theta}}{\sqrt{2}} - \frac{ha}{\sqrt{2}}$$

since $r^2\dot{\theta} = h$. Therefore

$$\dot{r} = \frac{ah}{r^2\sqrt{2}} - \frac{ha}{\sqrt{2}}$$

(eliminating $\dot{\theta}$). Thus, differentiating again gives

$$\ddot{r} = -\frac{2ah\dot{r}}{r^3\sqrt{2}}$$

Substituting for $\dot{r}$ yields

$$\ddot{r} = -\frac{2ah}{r^3\sqrt{2}}\left(\frac{ah}{r^2\sqrt{2}} - \frac{ah}{a^2\sqrt{2}}\right)$$

so that

$$\ddot{r} = -\frac{a^2h^2}{r^5} + \frac{a^2h^2}{a^2r^3}$$

Hence

$$\ddot{r} - r\dot{\theta}^2 = -\frac{a^2h^2}{r^5}$$

(since $h^2 = r^4\dot\theta^2$). Thus the law is proportional to $1/r^5$, as required. We have that $\dot\theta = h/r^2$, or

$$\dot\theta = \frac{h}{a^2\tanh^2(\theta/\sqrt{2})}$$

on the path itself. Therefore

$$a^2 \int_0^{\alpha\sqrt{2}} \tanh^2(\theta/\sqrt{2})\mathrm{d}\theta = \int_0^t h\mathrm{d}t = ht$$

$$a^2 \int_0^{\alpha\sqrt{2}} [1 - \mathrm{sech}^2(\theta/\sqrt{2})]\mathrm{d}\theta = ht$$

$$a^2[\theta - \sqrt{2}\,\tanh(\theta/\sqrt{2})]_0^{\alpha\sqrt{2}} = ht$$

giving $t = a^2\sqrt{2}(\alpha - \tanh\alpha)/h$, as required.

8.9 A particle of mass m rests on a smooth horizontal table and is attached to a fixed point on the table by a light elastic string of modulus mg and natural length r_0. Initially the string is just taut and the particle is projected along the table in a direction perpendicular to the line of the string with speed $2(\frac{1}{3}gr_0)^{1/2}$. Show that, if r is the length of the string at time t,

$$\ddot r = \frac{4gr_0^3}{3r^3} - \frac{g(r - r_0)}{r_0}$$

Prove that the string will extend until its length is $2r_0$ and that the speed of the particle is then half its initial speed. (L.U.)

Solution Only one force is acting: the tension in the elastic string. (The reaction of the weight on the table exactly balances its weight, hence the motion is purely two-dimensional.) Figure 8.3 displays the situation. The equations of motion in the $\hat r$ and the $\hat\theta$ directions are, respectively,

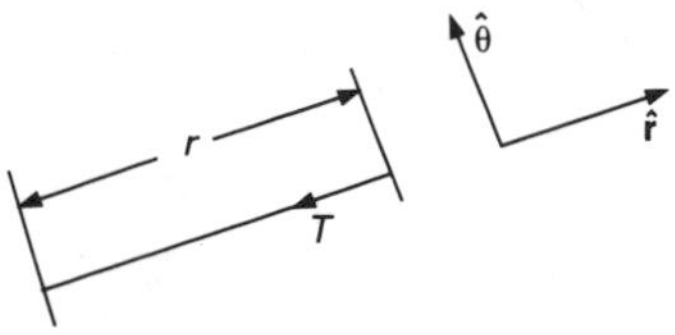

$$m(\ddot r - r\dot\theta^2) = -T$$

and

$$\frac{m}{r}\frac{\mathrm{d}}{\mathrm{d}t}(r^2\dot\theta) = 0$$

Figure 8.3

Now, Hooke's law tells us that the tension in the elastic string is given by

$$T = \text{modulus} \times \text{extension/natural length}$$

which, in the notation of this problem, gives

$$T = \frac{mg(r - r_0)}{r_0}$$

Hence the $\hat r$ equation of motion is, after cancellation of ms,

$$\ddot r - r\dot\theta^2 = -\frac{g}{r_0}(r - r_0) \tag{8.8}$$

The second equation leads to the conservation of angular momentum:

$$r^2\dot\theta = L = \text{constant}$$

Initially, $r\dot\theta = 2(\frac{1}{3}gr_0)^{1/2}$ and $r = r_0$; hence

$$L = 2r_0\,(\tfrac{1}{3}gr_0)^{1/2}$$

We use this to find $\dot\theta$, which is

$$\dot\theta = \frac{2r_0}{r^2}\left(\tfrac{1}{3}gr_0\right)^{1/2}$$

Substituting for $\dot\theta$ in Equation (8.8) gives an equation for r only, namely

$$\ddot r - \frac{4g}{3}\left(\frac{r_0}{r}\right)^3 = -\frac{g}{r_0}(r - r_0)$$

or

$$\ddot r = \frac{4g}{3}\left(\frac{r_0}{r}\right)^3 - \frac{g}{r_0}(r - r_0)$$

as required. We multiply this by $\dot r$ and integrate with respect to t to give

$$\frac{1}{2}\dot r^2 = -\frac{2g}{3}\frac{r_0^3}{r^2} - \frac{g}{r_0}\left(\frac{1}{2}r^2 - rr_0\right) + K \tag{8.9}$$

where K is an arbitrary constant. Initially, $\dot r = 0$ (the velocity is $2\left(\tfrac{1}{3}gr_0\right)^{1/2}$ in the $\hat\theta$ direction) and $r = r_0$; hence

$$0 = -\frac{2g}{3}r_0 - \frac{g}{r_0}\left(\tfrac{1}{2}r_0^2 - r_0^2\right) + K$$

giving

$$0 = -\tfrac{2}{3}gr_0 + \tfrac{1}{2}gr_0 + K$$

or

$$K = \tfrac{1}{6}gr_0$$

Equation (8.9) is thus

$$\frac{1}{2}\dot r^2 = -\frac{2g}{3}\frac{r_0^3}{r^2} - \frac{g}{r_0}\left(\tfrac{1}{2}r^2 - rr_0\right) + \tfrac{1}{6}gr_0$$

We need to find r if $\dot r = 0$. One such value is, of course, $r = r_0$. So we know at least one factor of the right-hand side. In fact, factorising out $r - r_0$ and $r - 2r_0$ gives

$$\tfrac{1}{2}\dot r^2 = -\frac{g}{6r^2}(r - r_0)(r - 2r_0)(3r^2 + 3rr_0 + 2r_0^2)$$

which implies that, at $r = 2r_0$, $\dot r = 0$. Further, for $r > 2r_0$, $\dot r^2$ is negative showing that the particle never gets beyond $r = 2r_0$. Similarly, r is never less than $r = r_0$. Also, at $r = 2r_0$,

$$r\dot\theta = \frac{2r_0}{r}\left(\tfrac{1}{3}gr_0\right)^{1/2} = \frac{2r_0}{2r_0}\left(\tfrac{1}{3}gr_0\right)^{1/2}$$

$$= \left(\tfrac{1}{3}gr_0\right)^{1/2}$$

which is half its initial speed.

8.10 Establish that $h^2 = pv$, where p is the perpendicular distance from the focus to the tangent at the point of the orbit where the velocity is v.

A particle of mass m, which is moving in a circle of radius c under the attractive force γ/r^2

per unit mass, collides and coalesces with a particle of mass λm which is at rest. Show that the orbit of the combined mass is an ellipse with major axis $c\operatorname{cosec}^2\alpha$, latus rectum $4c\cos^2\alpha$ and eccentricity $\cos 2\alpha$, where $\sec^2\alpha = 2(1 + \lambda)^2$.

(L.U.)

Solution There are several ways in which we could solve this problem. We take the opportunity to solve it in a way that introduces some useful concepts. First of all, we draw Fig. 8.4 where S is the focus of the conic. From this figure, $h = r^2\dot\theta = pv$ expresses conservation of angular momentum per unit mass.

If the orbit is circular, then we can use the formula derived for the velocity of a particle moving in an elliptical orbit:

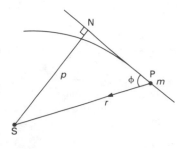

Figure 8.4

$$v^2 = \gamma\left(\frac{2}{r} - \frac{1}{a}\right)$$

(see Example 8.4) and put $r = a = c$ to obtain

$$v^2 = \frac{\gamma}{c}$$

In order that momentum is conserved in the collision,

$$mv + \lambda m.0 = (m + \lambda m)u$$

so that

$$u = \frac{v}{1 + \lambda}$$

is the speed of the composite particle just after collision. The speed in the new conic has the form

$$V^2 = \gamma\left(\frac{2}{r} + K\right)$$

where V is the speed of the composite mass. When $V = u$, $r = c$; thus

$$u^2 = \frac{v^2}{(1 + \lambda)^2} = \gamma\left(\frac{2}{c} + K\right)$$

For a circular orbit, $h^2 = \gamma c = c^2v^2$ since the semi-latus rectum = the perpendicular distance of the orbit from the 'focus' = c, from which $v^2 = \gamma/c$, thus giving

$$K = \frac{1 - 2(1 + \lambda)^2}{c(1 + \lambda)^2}$$

Using the definition of α in the question:

$$\sec^2\alpha = 2(1 + \lambda)^2$$

gives

$$K = -\frac{\tan^2\alpha}{c(1 + \lambda)^2}$$

$$< 0$$

Hence the path is a ellipse.
The major axis is

$$2a = \frac{2c(1 + \lambda)^2}{\tan^2\alpha} = c\operatorname{cosec}^2\alpha$$

Thus

$$a = \frac{c}{2} \operatorname{cosec}^2 \alpha$$

Before the impact we can use $h = pv$ to deduce $h = cv$. Using $h^2 = \gamma l$ before and after the collision, the ratio of the semi-latus rectum before collision $l \, (= c$ since the path is circular) to the semi-latus rectum after the collision L is

$$\frac{l}{L} = \frac{h^2}{H^2} = \frac{c^2 v^2}{c^2 u^2} = (1 + \lambda)^2$$

so that

$$L = \frac{c}{(1 + \lambda)^2} = 2c \cos^2 \alpha$$

Hence the latus rectum $2L = 4c \cos^2 \alpha$.
Finally

$$L = \frac{b^2}{a} = a(1 - e^2)$$

(b = semi-major axis, e is the eccentricity), so that

$$1 - e^2 = \frac{L}{a} = 4\cos^2\alpha \sin^2\alpha = \sin^2 2\alpha$$

and $e = (1 - \sin^2 2\alpha)^{1/2} = \cos 2\alpha$, as required.

8.3 Exercises

8.1 At a certain moment during re-entry, a satellite is moving horizontally in the Earth's atmosphere. The satellite has an acceleration, due to drag, of 18 m s^{-2} opposing its motion, and gravity at this height is 9 m s^{-2}. Determine the angular rate of rotation of its velocity vector at this instant, if its speed is 6000 m s^{-1}.

8.2 A particle P of mass m moves under an attractive force μ/r^2 per unit mass towards a fixed point O, where OP $= r$. If P is projected from a point A with speed (μ/c) perpendicular to OA, where μ and c are positive constants and OA $= 4c/3$, show that the orbit is an ellipse of eccentricity $1/3$, described once in time $4\pi(2c^3/\mu)^{1/2}$.

8.3 Calculate the acceleration due to gravity on Venus, the Moon and Jupiter assuming a Newtonian inverse square law and given the following data:

Venus: mass 4.87×10^{24} kg; radius 6.09×10^6 m

Moon: mass 7.35×10^{22} kg; radius 1.74×10^6 m

Jupiter: mass 1.90×10^{27} kg; radius 7.14×10^7 m

The universal gravitational constant is $G = 6.67 \times 10^{-11}$ SI units.

8.4 Calculate the period of Mercury about the Sun given that the mean distance of the Earth from the Sun is 1.492×10^8 km, and the mean distance of Mercury from the Sun is 5.786×10^7 km.

8.5 A particle P of mass m moves under an attractive force λ/r^3 towards a fixed centre of force O, where λ is constant and r is the distance OP. If P is projected with velocity $5\lambda^{1/2}/4l$ at right angles to OP when OP equals l, show that when P has receded to infinity the radius vector will have turned through an angle of $5\pi/6$.

8.6 A particle at a point P is repelled from a centre of force O with a force n^2r per unit mass (r denotes the distance from O). It is projected from a point distance c from O with velocity nc perpendicular to OP. Show that the orbit is one branch of a rectangular hyperbola.

8.7 A particle of mass m moves under an attractive force μ/r^3 per unit mass. If the particle is projected perpendicularly to the radius with speed V_0 at a distance a from the centre of force, calculate the path. Distinguish between the cases

$$V_0^2 < \frac{\mu}{a^2}, \quad V_0^2 > \frac{\mu}{a^2}$$

8.8 A satellite moves in an elliptic orbit of major axis $2a$ and eccentricity e about the Earth. When at its apogee (furthest point from the Earth), retro-rockets are fired which reduce its speed from V to $(1 - \varepsilon)V$, $\varepsilon << 1$. Ignoring any changes in mass of the rocket, show that the major axis of the elliptical orbit is reduced by

$$4a\varepsilon \, \frac{1 + e}{1 - e}$$

8.9 A particle of mass M is describing a parabolic orbit of latus rectum $4a$ under an inverse square attraction to the focus, when, at a distance na from the focus, it meets and coalesces with a particle of mass m at rest. Show that the composite particle describes an ellipse of latus rectum

$$4a\left(1 + \frac{m}{M}\right)^{-2}$$

and that if $m << M$, the eccentricity of the orbit is approximately

$$\left(1 - \frac{4m}{nM}\right) \qquad \text{(L.U.)}$$

8.10 A comet moves under the gravitational force $m\mu/r^2$ in a hyperbolic orbit of transverse axis $2a$ and eccentricity e. When it is at the point of closest approach to the Earth, it splits into two equal halves. One half carries on in a circular orbit, while the other half flies off on a hyperbolic orbit of eccentricity e'. If U is the speed of the comet before break-up and u the speed of the particle that describes a circular orbit, show that

$$(e + 1)u^2 = U^2$$

and

$$\left(\frac{(e')^2 - 1}{e - 1}\right)^{1/2} = 2(e + 1)^{1/2} - 1$$

8.4 Outline Solutions to Exercises

8.1 The velocity $\mathbf{v} = \dot{x}\hat{\mathbf{i}} + \dot{y}\hat{\mathbf{j}}$, where

$$\dot{x} = 6000 - 18t$$

and

$$\dot{y} = 9t$$

Hence the slope of the satellite's path, dy/dx, is

$$\frac{dy}{dx} = \frac{9t}{6000 - 18t}$$

This is $\tan\theta$, where $\dot{\theta}$ is what is required. Differentiation of

$$\tan\theta = \frac{9t}{6000 - 18t}$$

gives

$$\dot{\theta}\sec^2\theta = \frac{9 \times 6000}{(6000 - 18t)^2}$$

Using $\sec^2\theta = 1 + \tan^2\theta = 1$ at $t = 0$, we obtain $\dot{\theta} = 9/6000$ as the required value.

8.2 Using $\ddot{r} - r\dot{\theta}^2 = -\mu/r^2$, with

$$r^2\dot{\theta} = \frac{4c}{3}\left(\frac{\mu}{c}\right)^{1/2}$$

from which

$$\dot{\theta}^2 = 16\mu c/9r^4$$

gives

$$\dot{r}^2 = \frac{2\mu}{r} - \frac{16\mu c}{9r^2} - \frac{\mu}{2c}$$

Hence

$$v^2 = \dot{r}^2 + (r\dot{\theta})^2 = \dot{r}^2 + \frac{16\mu c}{9r^2} = \frac{2\mu}{r} - \frac{\mu}{2c}$$

i.e. an ellipse, major axis $2c$.

$$h^2 = \frac{16\mu c}{9} = \mu l = \frac{\mu b^2}{a}$$

so that

$$b^2 = \frac{32}{9}c^2$$

Hence $b^2 = a^2(1 - e^2) \Rightarrow e^2 = 1 - \frac{8}{9} = \frac{1}{9}$, i.e. $e = \frac{1}{3}$.

$$\pi ab = \tfrac{1}{2}hT$$

$$\Rightarrow T = \frac{2\pi ab}{h} = 2\pi\frac{3}{4(\mu c)^{1/2}}2c\frac{4\sqrt{2}}{3}c = 4\pi\left(\frac{2c^3}{\mu}\right)^{1/2}$$

8.3 We use

$$mg = \frac{Gmm_1}{R^2}$$

so that

$$g = \frac{Gm_1}{R^2} = 8.76 \text{ m s}^{-2} \text{ for Venus}$$

$$= 1.62 \text{ m s}^{-2} \text{ for the Moon}$$

$$= 24.9 \text{ m s}^{-2} \text{ for Jupiter}$$

8.4 Kepler's third law states that

$$\frac{T^2}{a^3} = \text{constant} = c$$

Assuming a period of 365.25 days,

$$c = \frac{(365.25)^2}{(1.495 \times 10^8)^2}$$

giving, for Mercury, $T^2 = c(5.786 \times 10^7)^3$, from which $T = 88$ days.

8.5 Using $u = 1/r$ and θ as coordinates, we derive (see Example 8.2)

$$\frac{d^2u}{d\theta^2} + u = -\frac{\lambda}{h^2}u$$

Initially,

$$r\dot{\theta} = \frac{5\lambda^{1/2}}{4l}$$

$r = l$; hence

$$h = \frac{5\lambda^{1/2}}{4}$$

and

$$\frac{\lambda}{h^2} = \frac{16}{25}$$

whence

$$\frac{d^2u}{d\theta^2} + \frac{9}{25} u = 0 \Rightarrow u = A\cos\tfrac{3}{5}\theta + B\sin\tfrac{3}{5}\theta$$

Initial conditions give $u = 1/l$, $du/d\theta = 0$; hence $B = 0$, $A = 1/l$. Thus

$$\frac{1}{r} = u = \frac{1}{l} \cos\tfrac{3}{5}\theta$$

As $r \to \infty$, $\cos\tfrac{3}{5}\theta \to 0$. Hence $3\theta/5 \to \pi/2$ or $\theta \to 5\pi/6$, as required.

8.6 Unusually, we solve this in vector form. The equation of motion is $m\ddot{\mathbf{r}} = -mn^2\mathbf{r}$, from which $\mathbf{r} = \mathbf{a}e^{nt} + \mathbf{b}e^{-nt}$, $\mathbf{a}$ and $\mathbf{b}$ vector constants.
  Given

$$\mathbf{r} = \frac{c}{\sqrt{2}} (\hat{\mathbf{i}} + \hat{\mathbf{j}})$$

and

$$\dot{\mathbf{r}} = \frac{nc}{\sqrt{2}} (-\hat{\mathbf{i}} + \hat{\mathbf{j}})$$

at $t = 0$, this leads to $\mathbf{a} = \hat{\mathbf{j}}/\sqrt{2}$, $\mathbf{b} = \hat{\mathbf{i}}/\sqrt{2}$. Thus

$$x = \frac{c}{\sqrt{2}} e^{-nt}, \quad y = \frac{c}{\sqrt{2}} e^{nt}$$

so that $2xy = c^2$, a rectangular hyperbola.

8.7 Defining $u = 1/r$, as in Example 8.3, we obtain

$$\frac{d^2u}{d\theta^2} + u = \frac{\mu u}{h^2}$$

with $aV_0 = h$, so that

$$\frac{d^2u}{d\theta^2} + \left(1 - \frac{\mu}{a^2V_0^2} \right) u = 0$$

(a) If

$$1 - \frac{\mu}{a^2V_0^2} > 0$$

then

$$u = A\cos k\theta + B\sin k\theta = \frac{1}{r}$$

Take $\theta = 0$ when $r = a$. $\dot{r} = 0 \Rightarrow \dot{u} = 0 \Rightarrow B = 0$, so

$$\frac{1}{a} \cos k\theta = \frac{1}{r}$$

$r \to \infty$ when $k\theta \to \pi/2$; hence path $\to \infty$ as $\theta \to \pi/2k$, so

$$k^2 = 1 - \frac{\mu}{a^2V_0^2}$$

See Exercise 8.5: the angle turned through is

$$\frac{\pi}{2[1 - (\mu/a^2V_0^2)]^{1/2}}$$

(b) If

$$1 - \frac{\mu}{a^2V_0^2} < 0$$

then

$$u = \frac{1}{a} \cosh\lambda\theta$$

$$\lambda^2 = \frac{\mu}{a^2V_0^2} - 1 > 0$$

so that $r = a\,\text{sech}\,k\theta$, a spiral.
  In summary: in (a) (where $V_0^2 < \mu/a^2$), the particle tends to infinity asymptotically after it has been turned through an angle $\pi/2k$, and in (b) (where $V_0^2 > \mu/a^2$), the particle tends to infinity along a spiral-like path.

8.8 The first ellipse (see Example 8.4) has speed V given by

$$V^2 = G\left(\frac{2}{r} - \frac{1}{a}\right)$$

at $r = a(1 - e)$ (apogee). After the retro-rockets have fired, V becomes $V(1 - \varepsilon)$:

$$V^2(1 - \varepsilon)^2 = G\left(\frac{2}{r} - \frac{1}{a_1}\right)$$

where a_1 is the new semi-major axis. Dividing gives

$$(1 - \varepsilon)^2 = \frac{2/[a(1 - e)] - (1/a_1)}{2/[a(1 - e)] - (1/a)}$$

or

$$(1 - \varepsilon)^2 \frac{(1 + e)}{a(1 - e)} = \frac{2}{a(1 - e)} - \frac{1}{a_1}$$

from which

$$a_1 \approx a\left(1 + 2\varepsilon\,\frac{1 + e}{1 - e}\right)^{-1}$$

to $O(\varepsilon^2)$. Hence

$$2a - 2a_1 \approx 4a\varepsilon\,\frac{1 + e}{1 - e}$$

as required.

8.9 Conservation of momentum:

$$MU + m.0 = (m + M)V$$

gives

$$V = U\left(1 + \frac{m}{M}\right)^{-1}$$

where V is the speed before coalescing, and U is the speed after coalescing. The parabola implies that

$$v^2 = \frac{2\mu}{r}$$

(see Example 8.4). $r = an$, $v = U$ gives

$$U^2 = \frac{2\mu}{an}$$

The new conic is

$$v^2 = \mu\left(\frac{2}{r} + C\right) = U^2\left(1 + \frac{m}{M}\right)^{-2}$$

at $v = V$. Also, $r = an$; thus

$$V^2 = \frac{2\mu}{an} + C = \frac{2\mu}{an}\left(1 + \frac{m}{M}\right)^{-2}$$

which gives

$$C = \frac{2}{an}\left[\left(1 + \frac{m}{M}\right)^{-2} - 1\right] < 0$$

which is an ellipse.

Let P be the perpendicular distance from the focus to the tangent to the ellipse; then $h = PU$, $H = PV$, where h and H are the angular momenta before and after the collision, respectively. Thus

$$\frac{h}{H} = \frac{U}{V}$$

Since $h^2 = \mu l$, where l is the semi-latus rectum, and for the new conic $H^2 = \mu L$, where L is the new semi-latus rectum,

$$\frac{l}{L} = \frac{h^2}{H^2} = \frac{U^2}{V^2} = \left(1 + \frac{m}{M}\right)^2$$

$$\Rightarrow \qquad L = l\left(1 + \frac{m}{M}\right)^{-2}$$

$l = 2a$, so

$$\text{latus rectum} = 2L = 4a\left(1 + \frac{m}{M}\right)^{-2}$$

as required.

If $m \ll M$:

$$C = \frac{2}{an}\left[\left(1 + \frac{m}{M}\right)^{-2} - 1\right]$$

$$\approx -\frac{4m}{anM}$$

If α is the semi-major axis,

$$\alpha\left(= -\frac{1}{C}\right) = \frac{nMa}{4m}$$

$$L = 2a\left(1 + \frac{m}{M}\right)^{-2} \approx 2a\left(1 - \frac{2m}{M}\right)$$

If β is the semi-minor axis,

$$L = \frac{\beta^2}{\alpha} = \alpha(1 - e^2) = \frac{nMa}{4m}(1 - e^2)$$

Equating, expanding appropriately and retaining only (m/M) terms gives

$$e \approx 1 - \frac{4m}{nM}$$

8.10 In order to solve this problem, we use $h^2 = \mu l$, $h = vp$ and conservation of momentum at break-up. From the latter we deduce that the speeds of the comet, particle 1 (circular orbit) and particle 2 (hyperbolic orbit) are U, u and $2U - u$, respectively. Hence $h_0 a(e - 1)U$, $h_1 = a(e - 1)u$, $h_2 = a(e - 1)(2U - u)$ and $h_0^2 a(e^2 - 1)\mu$, $h_1^2 = a(e^2 - 1)\mu$, $h_2^2 = a[(e')^2 - 1]\mu$ where the subscripts 0, 1 and 2 refer to the comet, particle 1 and particle 2 respectively. By forming the ratio

$$\frac{h_0^2}{h_1^2} = \frac{U^2}{u^2} = \frac{e^2 - 1}{e - 1}$$

we deduce $(e + 1)u^2 = U^2$. From

$$\frac{h_2^2}{h_1^2} = \frac{(2U - u)^2}{u^2} = \frac{(e')^2 - 1}{e - 1}$$

and $U = (e + 1)^{1/2}u$, we find on taking square roots that

$$\left(\frac{(e')^2 - 1}{e - 1}\right) = \frac{2U - u}{u} = 2(e + 1)^{1/2} - 1$$

as required.

9 Rigid Bodies

9.1 Fact Sheet

A rigid body is such that each constituent particle is a fixed distance from every other particle in the body.

If a rigid body is rotating about a fixed axis, then the kinetic energy of rotation is $\frac{1}{2}I\omega^2$, where I is a quantity dependent solely on the geometry of the body called the **moment of inertia**, which is defined by

$$I = \int_V \rho d^2 dV$$

where d is the perpendicular distance of the particle (density ρ, volume dV) from the fixed axis. Table 9.1 gives the value of I for some common body shapes.

Table 9.1

Body, mass M	Moment of inertia
Hollow cylinder, radius a, about axis	Ma^2
Solid cylinder, radius a, about axis	$\frac{1}{2}Ma^2$
Solid sphere, radius a, about a diameter	$\frac{2}{5}Ma^2$
Hollow sphere, radius a, about a diameter	$\frac{2}{3}Ma^2$
Rectangular plate of sides a and b about an axis perpendicular to the plate through the centre of mass	$\frac{1}{12}M(a^2 + b^2)$
Thin rod of length a about an axis perpendicular to the rod through the centre of mass	$\frac{1}{12}Ma^2$

If I_G is the moment of inertia of a rigid body of mass m about an axis through its centre of mass, then the moment of inertia about an axis parallel to the first, but a distance d from it, is given by $I_G + md^2$. This is called the *Theorem of Parallel Axes*.

For a lamina, if I_x and I_y are the moments of inertia of a plane lamina about axes x and y at right angles to each other in the plane of the lamina, then the moment of inertia about an axis z perpendicular to x and y is I_z, where

$$I_z = I_x + I_y$$

This is called the *Perpendicular Axes Theorem*.

Torque The **torque** of a force about O is the quantity

$$\mathbf{\Gamma} = \mathbf{r} \times \mathbf{F}$$

where $\mathbf{r}$ is the position vector of a point on the line of action of $\mathbf{F}$.

In two-dimensional problems it is called the **moment** of the force **F**. The rotational equivalent of Newton's second law is

$$\Gamma = \dot{L}$$

where **L** is the angular momentum of the rigid body. Hence, in words, 'torque = rate of change of angular momentum'. For rolling problems, which are two-dimensional, this takes the convenient non-vector form

$$\text{torque} \;(= \text{moment of force} = aF, \text{ for example}) = I\ddot{\theta}$$

where I is the moment of inertia of the body and θ its angular displacement.

Motion in Three Dimensions

If a body is moving in three dimensions, let I_1, I_2, I_3 be its moments of inertia about the three axes $\hat{\imath}$, $\hat{\jmath}$, $\hat{k}$. Also, suppose the angular velocity $\boldsymbol{\omega}$ has components ω_1, ω_2, ω_3 along $\hat{\imath}$, $\hat{\jmath}$, $\hat{k}$. The angular momentum of the body, **L**, is given by

$$\mathbf{L} = I_1\omega_1\hat{\imath} + I_2\omega_2\hat{\jmath} + I_3\omega_3\hat{k}$$

The rate of change of **L** with respect to t is

$$\frac{d\mathbf{L}}{dt} = \dot{\mathbf{L}} + \boldsymbol{\omega} \times \mathbf{L} = \boldsymbol{\Gamma}$$

where $\boldsymbol{\Gamma}$ is the torque. In component from this is

$$I_1\dot{\omega}_1 - (I_2 - I_3)\omega_2\omega_3 = \Gamma_1$$

$$I_2\dot{\omega}_2 - (I_3 - I_1)\omega_3\omega_1 = \Gamma_2$$

$$I_3\dot{\omega}_3 - (I_1 - I_2)\omega_1\omega_2 = \Gamma_3$$

which are Euler's equations.

If T is the kinetic energy, then it can be shown that

$$\boldsymbol{\Gamma}\cdot\boldsymbol{\omega} = \frac{dT}{dt}$$

9.2 Worked Examples

9.1 Show that an equilateral triangular lamina of mass m and side a and a congruent weightless triangular lamina with equal masses $m/3$ at the mid-points of its sides are equimomental.

Solution In order to show that a system of particles and a lamina are equimomental, we need to show that the principal moments of inertia of both are the same. They obviously both have mass m. Let us consider first the three masses of magnitude $m/3$ placed at the mid-points of the sides. Let the principal axes be through the centre of mass, one perpendicular to the plane, and the other two as shown in Fig. 9.1. The perpendicular distance of each mass from O is $a/3$. Hence the moment of inertia of the three masses about the axis perpendicular to the plane of the triangle is

$$I_z = \frac{m}{3}\left(3\frac{a^2}{9}\right) = \tfrac{1}{9}ma^2$$

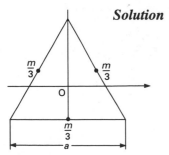

Figure 9.1

From the elementary geometry of the triangle, the other two moments are

$$I_y = \frac{m}{3}\left(2\frac{a^2}{16}\right) = \tfrac{1}{24}ma^2$$

and

$$I_x = \frac{m}{3}\left(\frac{a^2}{12} + \frac{3a^2}{144} + \frac{3a^2}{144}\right) = \frac{ma^2}{24}$$

Consider now the triangular lamina (Fig. 9.2). In order to find the moment of inertia about Oy, we divide the triangle into vertical strips of width δx. Since the length of this strip is $[(a/2) - x]\tan \pi/3$, the moment of inertia is

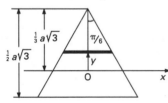

Figure 9.2

$$I_y = 2\rho \int_0^{a/2} x^2 \left(\frac{a}{2} - x\right) \tan\frac{\pi}{3}dx,$$

where ρ is the density, so that

$$\rho \frac{a^2\sqrt{3}}{4} = m$$

Performing the integral gives

$$I_y = \frac{8m}{a^2\sqrt{3}} \int_0^{a/2} \left(\frac{ax^2}{2} - x^3\right) \sqrt{3}dx$$

$$= \frac{8m}{a^2} \left[\frac{ax^3}{6} - \frac{x^4}{4}\right]_0^{a/2}$$

$$= \frac{8m}{a^2} \left(\frac{a^4}{48} - \frac{a^4}{64}\right)$$

$$= ma^2 (\tfrac{1}{6} - \tfrac{1}{8}) = \frac{ma^2}{24}(4 - 3) = \frac{ma^2}{24}$$

This is the same result as obtained previously.

In order to find the moment of inertia about Ox, I_x, we take strips parallel to the base (Fig. 9.3). The length of the strip is $2[(a\sqrt{3}/3) - y]\tan \pi/6$. Hence the moment of inertia is

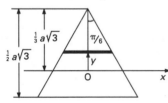

Figure 9.3

$$I_x = \frac{8m}{a^2\sqrt{3}} \int_{-a\sqrt{3}/3}^{a\sqrt{3}/3} y^2 \left(\frac{a\sqrt{3}}{3} - y\right) \tan\frac{\pi}{6}dy$$

$$= \frac{8m}{3a^2} \left[\frac{y^3 a\sqrt{3}}{9} - \frac{y^4}{4}\right]_{-a\sqrt{3}/3}^{a\sqrt{3}/3}$$

$$= \frac{8m}{3a^2} \left(\frac{a^4}{27} - \frac{a^4}{36} + \frac{a^4}{9 \times 24} + \frac{a^4}{9 \times 64}\right)$$

$$= \frac{ma^2}{24}$$

which also corresponds to the previous result.

Hence the two systems have the same principal moments of inertia by the perpendicular axes theorem. They are therefore equimomental.

9.2 Show that the moment of inertia of a regular hexagonal lamina about any axis in the plane of the lamina through its centre is the same, and find its value.

Solution In order to solve this problem, we need to develop some notation. Figure 9.4 shows the hexagon and a general line through its centre. Also shown is the angle θ, made by the axis with the line FC.

The hexagon may be considered to be composed of six equilateral triangles of side $2a$. We now construct an *equimomental system* for the hexagon as follows. An equilateral triangular laminate of mass m has the same moment of inertia and centre of mass as three masses of $m/3$ placed at the mid-points of a congruent weightless triangle (see previous example). Hence the hexagon can be replaced by the system shown in Fig. 9.4, that is masses $m/18$ at the mid-points of AB, BC, CD, DE, EF and masses $m/9$ at the mid-points of OA, OB, OC, OD, OE and OF.

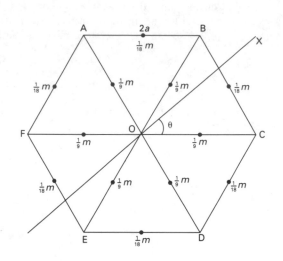

Figure 9.4

In order to calculate the total moment of inertia of the hexagonal lamina about the axis, we need to find the perpendicular distance of the twelve masses from the axis. Using the geometry of the hexagon we see that the expressions in Table 9.2 give the perpendicular distances of the masses from the axis OX. The mass on a particular side is referred to by the side itself, so that, for example 'BC' denotes the mass $m/18$ at its mid-point and OC denotes the mass $m/9$ at its mid-point.

Table 9.2

Mass	Perpendicular distance from OX
OF and OC	$a \sin \theta$
OE and OB	$a \sin \left(\dfrac{\pi}{3} - \theta \right)$
OA and OD	$a \sin \left(\dfrac{\pi}{3} + \theta \right)$
EF and BC	$a\sqrt{3} \sin \left(\theta - \dfrac{\pi}{6} \right)$
ED and AB	$a\sqrt{3} \sin \left(\theta - \dfrac{\pi}{2} \right)$
DC and AF	$a\sqrt{3} \sin \left(\theta + \dfrac{\pi}{6} \right)$

Using the fact that the moment of inertia is $\Sigma \frac{1}{2}(\text{mass})(\text{perpendicular distance})^2$ we obtain the following expression for the moment of inertia of the hexagon about OX:

$$I = \frac{2ma^2}{9} \left[\sin^2\theta + \sin^2 \left(\frac{\pi}{3} - \theta \right) + \sin^2 \left(\frac{\pi}{3} + \theta \right) \right] + 2m \, 3a^2 \frac{m}{18} \left[\sin^2 \left(\theta - \frac{\pi}{6} \right) \right.$$

$$\left. + \sin^2 \left(\theta + \frac{\pi}{6} \right) + \sin^2 \left(\theta - \frac{\pi}{2} \right) \right]$$

130

$$= \frac{2ma^2}{9}\left(\sin^2\theta + 2\sin^2\frac{\pi}{3}\cos^2\theta + 2\cos^2\frac{\pi}{3}\sin^2\theta\right) + \frac{ma^2}{3}\left(2\sin^2\frac{\pi}{6}\cos^2\theta\right.$$

$$\left. + 2\cos^2\frac{\pi}{6}\sin^2\theta + \cos^2\theta\right)$$

$$= \frac{2ma^2}{9}(\tfrac{1}{2}\sin^2\theta + \tfrac{3}{2}\cos^2\theta + \sin^2\theta) + \frac{ma^2}{3}(\tfrac{1}{2}\cos^2\theta + \tfrac{3}{2}\sin^2\theta + \cos^2\theta)$$

so that

$$I = ma^2\,(\tfrac{1}{3}\sin^2\theta + \tfrac{1}{3}\cos^2\theta + \tfrac{1}{2}\cos^2\theta + \tfrac{1}{2}\sin^2\theta)$$

$$= ma^2\,(\tfrac{5}{6}\sin^2\theta + \tfrac{5}{6}\cos^2\theta)$$

$$= \frac{5ma^2}{6}$$

Hence the moment of inertia of the hexagonal lamina of side $2a$ is $5ma^2/6$ about *any* axis through its centre in its plane. This is perhaps a surprising result; it is not true for all other regular polygons.

9.3 Prove the theorem of parallel axes, and use it to determine the moment of inertia of a solid, uniform hemisphere of radius a and mass m about an axis parallel to the flat base through the centre of mass. Find also the moment of inertia about a parallel axis tangential to the hemisphere.

Solution Proof of parallel axes theorem: let I_G be the moment of inertia of an arbitrarily shaped body about an axis OG through the centre of mass (see Fig. 9.5). Then by definition

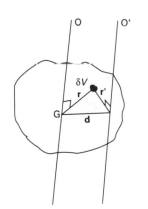

$$I_G = \int_v \rho r^2 dV$$

where the integration is taken over the volume. The moment of inertia about an axis parallel to OG but a distance d from it is

$$I = \int_v \rho(r')^2 dV$$

However

$$(\mathbf{r}')^2 = \mathbf{r}^2 + \mathbf{d}^2 + 2|\mathbf{r}|\,|\mathbf{d}|\cos\theta$$

$$= \mathbf{r}^2 + \mathbf{d}^2 + 2\mathbf{r}\cdot\mathbf{d}$$

Figure 9.5

Hence

$$\int_v \rho(\mathbf{r}')^2 dV = \int_v \rho(\mathbf{r}^2 + \mathbf{d}^2 + 2\mathbf{r}\cdot\mathbf{d})dV$$

$$= \int_v \rho\mathbf{r}^2 dV + \mathbf{d}^2\int_v \rho dV + 2\mathbf{d}\int_v \rho\mathbf{r}dV$$

The last integral is zero since $\mathbf{r}$ is the position vector of the centre of mass and this integral expresses the distance G is from the centre of mass (zero, since G *is* the centre of mass!).

$$\int_v \rho dV = m$$

by definition, and

$$\int_v \rho\mathbf{r}^2 dV = I_G$$

Hence $I = I_G + m\mathbf{d}^2$ which proves the parallel axes theorem.

First of all, we need to determine the moment of inertia of a hemisphere about a diameter in its base. To do this we draw Fig. 9.6, and perform the integration. For convenience we use spherical polar coordinates r, θ, ϕ, as shown. Mass:

$$m = \tfrac{2}{3}\pi\rho a^3$$

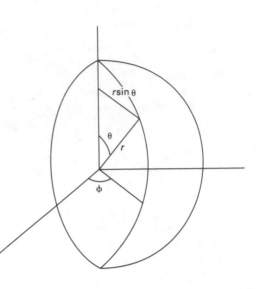

Figure 9.6

Moment of inertia:

$$I = \int_0^\pi \int_0^\pi \int_0^a \rho (r \sin\theta)^2 r^2 \sin\theta \; dr d\theta d\phi$$

$$= \pi\rho \frac{a^5}{5} \int_0^\pi \sin^3\theta \; d\theta$$

$$= \frac{4\pi\rho a^5}{15} = \tfrac{2}{5}ma^2$$

Using the parallel axis theorem, and the fact that the centre of mass of a hemisphere is a distance $3a/8$ from the flat surface, the required moment of inertia parallel to the flat surface but through the centre of mass, I_G is given by

$$I = I_\mathrm{G} + m(\tfrac{3}{8}a)^2$$

Using $I = \tfrac{2}{5}ma^2$ gives

$$I_\mathrm{G} = ma^2(\tfrac{2}{5} - \tfrac{9}{64}) = \tfrac{83}{320}ma^2$$

If I_T is the moment of inertia about a tangent which is a distance $5a/8$ from the centre of mass, then

$$I_\mathrm{T} = \tfrac{83}{320}ma^2 + m(\tfrac{5}{8}a)^2 = \tfrac{25}{80}ma^2$$

9.4 A solid uniform sphere is rolling on the inside of a fixed hollow sphere, the two centres being always in the same vertical plane. Show that the smaller sphere will make complete revolutions if, when it is in its lowest position, the reaction on it is greater than 34/7 times its own weight.

Solution Let b be the radius of the fixed hollow sphere, and a the radius of the solid sphere. Figure 9.7 displays the motion in the general position. θ and ϕ are defined as in the diagram (A and A' are coincident at the bottom of the hollow sphere where $\phi = \theta = 0$). Hence

$$a(\phi + \theta) = b\theta$$

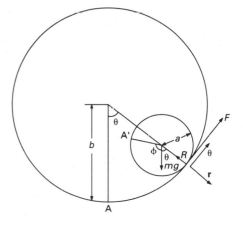

Figure 9.7

so that

$$\phi = \frac{\theta}{a}(b - a)$$

Although we will need to consider R, the reaction, let us first calculate an energy equation. The kinetic energy (KE) of the small sphere is

$$\tfrac{1}{2}I\omega^2 + \tfrac{1}{2}mv^2$$

where $I = \tfrac{2}{5}ma^2$, $\omega = \dot{\phi}$ and $v = a\omega = a\dot{\phi}$. Thus

$$\text{KE} = \tfrac{1}{2}\,\tfrac{2}{5}\,ma^2\dot{\phi}^2 + \tfrac{1}{2}ma^2\dot{\phi}^2 = \tfrac{7}{10}ma^2\dot{\phi}^2 = \tfrac{7}{10}m(b - a)^2\dot{\theta}^2$$

The potential energy (PE) is $mg(b - a)(1 - \cos\theta)$, taking A on the level of zero potential. Hence conservation of energy gives

$$\tfrac{7}{10}m(b - a)^2\dot{\theta}^2 + mg(b - a)(1 - \cos\theta) = \text{constant} \qquad \textbf{(9.1)}$$

With $\hat{r}$ and $\hat{\theta}$ as defined in Fig. 9.5, the radial equation of motion is

$$m(\ddot{r} - r\dot{\theta}^2) = -R + mg\cos\theta$$

With $r = b - a = \text{constant}$ this gives

$$R = m(b - a)\dot{\theta}^2 + mg\cos\theta \qquad \textbf{(9.2)}$$

For complete revolutions, $R \geq 0$ at $\theta = \pi$, so that

$$m(b - a)\dot{\theta}^2 - mg \geq 0$$

or

$$\dot{\theta}^2 \geq g/(b - a)$$

(at $\theta = \pi$). In order to obtain a limiting value, the *least* value of R required, we put $\dot{\theta}^2 = g/(b - a)$ when $\theta = \pi$. Using in Equation (9.1)

$$\tfrac{7}{10}m(b - a)^2\frac{g}{(b - a)} + 2mg(b - a) = \text{constant}$$

gives the constant on the right-hand side of Equation (9.1) as $\tfrac{27}{10}mg\,(b - a)$, so that this equation becomes

$$\tfrac{7}{10}m(b - a)^2\dot{\theta}^2 + mg(b - a)(1 - \cos\theta) = \tfrac{27}{10}mg\,(b - a)$$

which means, at $\theta = 0$ (point A), where we put $\dot{\theta} = \dot{\theta}_A$,

$$\tfrac{7}{10}m(b - a)^2\dot{\theta}_A^2 = \tfrac{27}{10}mg\,(b - a)$$

or

$$\dot{\theta}_A^2 = \frac{27g}{7(b - a)}$$

is the least possible value of $\dot{\theta}_A$.

Now, at $\theta = 0$, from Equation (9.2), the corresponding least possible value of R_A is given by

$$R_A = m(b - a)\dot{\theta}_A^2 + mg$$

$$= m(b - a)\frac{27g}{7(b - a)} + mg$$

$$= \tfrac{34}{7}mg$$

Hence R_A, the reaction at A, must be at least 34/7 times its weight in order for complete revolutions to be made.

9.5   A uniform solid sphere is slightly displaced from its position of unstable equilibrium at the topmost point of a fixed sphere and it then rolls on this sphere. Show that slipping must occur before θ, which is the angle between the line connecting the centres of the spheres with the vertical, attains the value $\cos^{-1}(10/17)$.

Solution   Figure 9.8 displays the situation at the general angle θ. Let the radii of the fixed and rolling spheres be a and b respectively, and the mass of the rolling sphere be m. Let the angular velocity of the rolling sphere be ω. Then, since the spheres remain in contact, $b\omega = (a + b)\,\dot{\theta}$.

If N and F are the normal reaction and frictional force, respectively, then the equation of motion in the $\hat{\theta}$ direction need not concern us, but the equation of motion in the direction perpendicular to this is

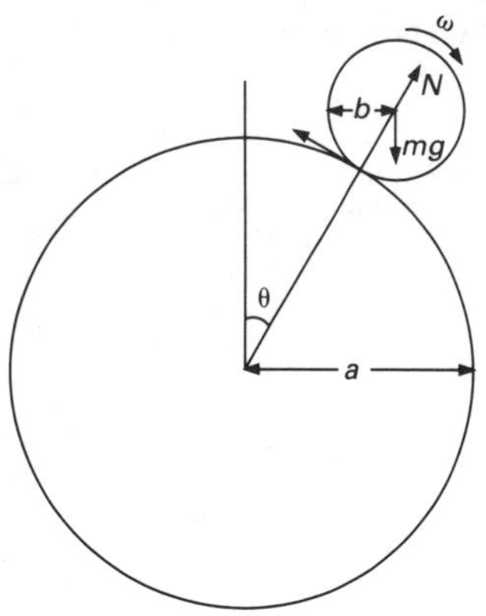

$$N - mg\cos\theta = -m(a + b)\dot{\theta}^2 \qquad (= m(\ddot{r} - r\dot{\theta}^2))$$

Although there is a frictional force, it does no work; hence mechanical energy is conserved. If we take $\theta = 0$ as zero potential, then total energy $= 0$ at the top. For general angle θ, the kinetic energy is given by

$$\text{KE} = \text{KE of centre of mass} + \text{KE relative to centre of mass}$$

$$= \tfrac{1}{2}mb^2\omega^2 + \tfrac{1}{2}(\tfrac{2}{5}mb^2)\omega^2$$

$$= \tfrac{7}{10}mb^2\omega^2 = \tfrac{7}{10}m(a + b)^2\dot{\theta}^2$$

and

$$\text{PE} = -mg(a + b)(1 - \cos\theta)$$

Hence

$$\tfrac{7}{10}m(a + b)^2\dot{\theta}^2 - mg(a + b)(1 - \cos\theta) = 0$$

Now,

$$N = mg\cos\theta - m(a + b)\dot{\theta}^2$$

but

Figure 9.8

134

$$\dot{\theta}^2 = \frac{10g(1 - \cos\theta)}{7(a + b)}$$

Hence

$$N = mg\cos\theta - \tfrac{10}{7}mg(1 - \cos\theta)$$

$$= mg(\tfrac{17}{7}\cos\theta - \tfrac{10}{7})$$

Now $N > 0$ if $\cos\theta > \frac{10}{17}$, i.e. $\theta > \cos^{-1}(10/17)$. Since $N = 0$ when $\theta = \cos^{-1}(10/17)$, slippage, which happens when $F = \mu N$ (and $F > 0$) must happen when $\theta < \cos^{-1}(10/17)$.

9.6 A perfectly rough sphere of radius a rolls on a horizontal plane with linear velocity v, the direction of its motion being perpendicular to a vertical face of a fixed inelastic rectangular block of height $a/5$. Show that the sphere can mount the block without losing contact at any stage if

$$\tfrac{7}{18}ag < v^2 < \tfrac{49}{45}ag$$

Solution   Figure 9.9 displays the situation just as the ball hits the block. Just before the moment of impact, the ball is rolling on the floor, and A is the instantaneous centre of rotation. Just after impact the ball is rotating about B. If ω_1 is the angular velocity of the rolling ball (before striking the block) then $v = a\omega_1$. Also, the angular momentum of the sphere about B is the sum of the quantities 'angular momentum of the centre of mass' $= mv(a - a/5)$ and 'angular momentum relative to the centre of mass' $= \tfrac{2}{5}ma^2\omega_1$. Using $v = a\omega_1$, this sum is

$$mv\left(\frac{4a}{5}\right) + \tfrac{2}{5}mav = \tfrac{6}{5}mav$$

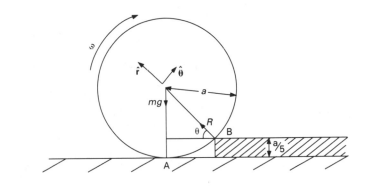

Figure 9.9

After hitting the block, the angular momentum of the sphere is

$$\tfrac{2}{5}ma^2\omega + ma^2\omega = \tfrac{7}{5}ma^2\omega$$

where ω is the (new) angular velocity of the sphere. Since angular momentum is conserved, these quantities are equal, we thus have

$$\tfrac{6}{5}mav = \tfrac{7}{5}ma^2\omega$$

or

$$\omega = \frac{6v}{7a} \tag{9.3}$$

The smallest allowable value of v is that which will enable the ball to mount the brick, but to lose all its momentum in doing so. This can be solved using energy as follows. The kinetic energy at impact is equal to $\tfrac{1}{2}I\omega^2$. This has to be converted to potential energy $mga/5$. Therefore

135

$$\frac{1}{2}I\omega^2 > \frac{mga}{5}$$

so

$$\frac{1}{2}\,\frac{7}{5}ma^2\left(\frac{6v}{7a}\right)^2 > \frac{mga}{5}$$

from which

$$v^2 > \frac{10}{7}\,\frac{49}{36}\,\frac{1}{5}ga = \frac{7}{18}ga$$

The reader may wish to follow through from the equation arising from considering *torque = rate of change of momentum* about B. This gives

$$\frac{7}{5}ma^2\ddot{\theta} = -mg\cos\theta\, a$$

Multiplying by $\dot{\theta}$ and integrating, and evaluating the constant of integration by letting $\dot{\theta} = \omega$ when $\theta = \sin^{-1}\left(\frac{4}{5}\right)$ leads to the following equation for $\dot{\theta}$:

$$\frac{7}{10}a\dot{\theta}^2 = \frac{7}{10}a\omega^2 + \frac{4g}{5} - g\sin\theta$$

Demanding that $\dot{\theta}^2 > 0$ when $\theta = \pi/2$ gives $v^2 > \frac{7}{18}ga$, as before.

If v is too large, the sphere 'bounces back' from the corner of the block. Thus if we can find an expression for the reaction R at B, the maximum value of v would be that which enabled R to be positive and non-zero. Taking radial coordinates r, θ as shown, centred at B (*not* centred at the centre of the sphere – it is accelerating!), the radial equation of motion is

$$m(\ddot{r} - r\dot{\theta})^2 = R - mg\sin\theta$$

Since $r = a$ = const., this gives

$$R = m(g\sin\theta - a\dot{\theta}^2)$$

At $\theta = \sin^{-1}\left(\frac{4}{5}\right)$, $\dot{\theta} = \omega$; hence

$$R = m\left(\frac{4g}{5} - a\omega^2\right)$$

Thus we require $(4g/5) - a\omega^2 > 0$ for the sphere not to leave B. Using $\omega = 6v/7a$ this gives

$$\left(\frac{6v}{7a}\right)^2 < \frac{4g}{5a}$$

or

$$v^2 < \frac{4}{5}\,\frac{49}{36}ag = \frac{49}{45}ag$$

Hence for the sphere to be able to mount the block

$$\frac{7}{18}ag < v^2 < \frac{49}{45}ag$$

as required.

9.7 A solid sphere of radius a rolls down a rough plane which is at an angle of $\pi/6$ to the horizontal. On the plane is an inelastic spike of height $a/2$ protruding at right angles to the plane. How far up the plane does the sphere have to be released in order to ensure that the ball mounts the spike?

Solution   See Fig. 9.10. Suppose that the speed of the sphere is u just as it hits the spike. Before impact,

$$\text{moment of momentum} = mu(a - \tfrac{1}{2}a) + \tfrac{2}{5}ma^2\left(\frac{u}{a}\right)$$

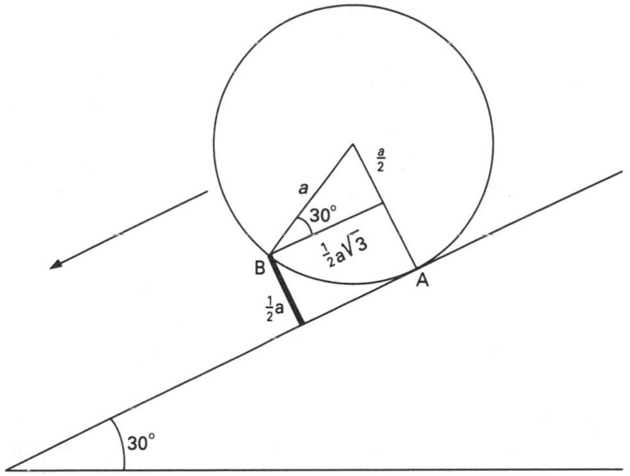

Figure 9.10

After impact,

$$\text{moment of momentum} = \tfrac{7}{5}ma^2\omega$$

In order to conserve the moment of momentum, or angular momentum, these two are equal, hence

$$\tfrac{7}{5}ma^2\omega = \tfrac{1}{2}mua + \tfrac{2}{5}mau = \tfrac{9}{10}mau$$

or

$$\omega = \tfrac{9}{7}\,\tfrac{5}{10}\frac{u}{a} = \frac{9u}{14a}$$

In order to solve the next part of the question, we use the principle of conservation of energy. The height the ball has to climb $= a(1-\cos 30°) = (a/2)(2 - \sqrt{3})$. The gain in PE required is thus $(mga/2)(2 - \sqrt{3})$.

$$\text{KE of ball} = \tfrac{1}{2}\,\tfrac{7}{5}ma^2\omega^2 = \tfrac{7}{10}ma^2\omega^2 > \frac{mga}{2}(2 - \sqrt{3})$$

$\therefore$

$$\omega^2 > \frac{5g}{7a}(2 - \sqrt{3})$$

which is

$$\omega^2 = \frac{81u^2}{196a^2} > \frac{5g}{7a}(2 - \sqrt{3})$$

so that

$$u^2 > \frac{5 \times 196}{81 \times 7}ag(2 - \sqrt{3})$$

If the ball starts a distance x up the plane, then it has fallen a distance $x/2$ ($= x\sin 30°$). Therefore

$$\tfrac{1}{2}I\omega^2\left(= \tfrac{1}{2}I\frac{u^2}{a^2}\right) = \frac{mgx}{2}$$

137

Thus

$$x = \frac{Iu^2}{g} = \frac{7}{5} \frac{5 \times 196}{81 \times 7} a(2 - \sqrt{3}) = \frac{196}{81} a(2 - \sqrt{3})$$

Hence if x exceeds $\frac{196}{81} a(2 - \sqrt{3})$, the ball will surmount the blade.

9.8 Obtain Euler's equations for the motion of a rigid body having principal moments of inertia A, B, C at a point O fixed in a Newtonian frame of reference. If gravity and the reaction at O are the only forces acting, show that the vertical is a possible axis of steady rotation when its direction cosines l, m, n and the coordinates a, b, c of the centre of mass referred to the principal axes at O satisfy the equation

$$\frac{a}{l}(B - C) + \frac{b}{m}(C - A) + \frac{c}{n}(A - B) = 0$$

provided none of l, m, n vanish.

(L.U.)

Solution Let d/dt denote differentiation with respect to axes fixed in space, and $\partial/\partial t$ denote differentiating with respect to axes which are moving. Hence for any vector variable **A**,

$$\frac{d\mathbf{A}}{dt} = \frac{\partial \mathbf{A}}{\partial t} + \boldsymbol{\omega} \times \mathbf{A}$$

where the moving axes have angular velocity $\boldsymbol{\omega}$. Letting $\mathbf{A} = \mathbf{h}$, the angular momentum, gives

$$\frac{d\mathbf{h}}{dt} = \frac{\partial \mathbf{h}}{\partial t} + \boldsymbol{\omega} \times \mathbf{h}$$

However, $\boldsymbol{\Gamma} = d\mathbf{h}/dt$ where $\boldsymbol{\Gamma}$ is the torque about the fixed point O. We now write this in terms of coordinates. Let $\boldsymbol{\Gamma} = (L, M, N)$ and we know that $\mathbf{h} = (A\omega_1, B\omega_2, C\omega_3)$, where $\boldsymbol{\omega} = (\omega_1, \omega_2, \omega_3)$. Since A, B and C, the principal moments of inertia, are constant (for a rigid body),

$$\frac{d\mathbf{h}}{dt} = (A\dot{\omega}_1, B\dot{\omega}_2, C\dot{\omega}_3)$$

Hence

$$\boldsymbol{\Gamma} = \frac{\partial \mathbf{h}}{\partial t} + \boldsymbol{\omega} \times \mathbf{h}$$

gives

$$(L, M, N) = (A\dot{\omega}_1, B\dot{\omega}_2, C\dot{\omega}_3) + \begin{vmatrix} \hat{\mathbf{i}} & \hat{\mathbf{j}} & \hat{\mathbf{k}} \\ \omega_1 & \omega_2 & \omega_3 \\ A\omega_1 & B\omega_2 & C\omega_3 \end{vmatrix}$$

Thus

$$L = A\dot{\omega}_1 - (B - C)\omega_2\omega_3$$

$$M = B\dot{\omega}_2 - (C - A)\omega_3\omega_1$$

and

$$N = C\dot{\omega}_3 - (A - B)\omega_1\omega_2$$

These are Euler's equations of motion.

If l, m, n are the direction cosines of $\boldsymbol{\omega}$, we have

$$\boldsymbol{\omega} = \omega(l\hat{\mathbf{i}} + m\hat{\mathbf{j}} + n\hat{\mathbf{k}})$$

If $\boldsymbol{\omega}$ is vertical, then

$$\mathbf{g} = g(l\hat{\mathbf{i}} + m\hat{\mathbf{j}} + n\hat{\mathbf{k}})$$

The torque, $\boldsymbol{\Gamma}$, is given by

$$\boldsymbol{\Gamma} = \mathbf{r} \times \mathbf{F}$$

where $\mathbf{r}$ is the position vector, relative to O, of the point where the force $\mathbf{F}$ acts. Hence

$$\mathbf{r} = a\hat{\mathbf{i}} + b\hat{\mathbf{j}} + c\hat{\mathbf{k}}$$

and

$$\mathbf{F} = M_0\mathbf{g}$$

where M_0 is the mass of the body. Therefore $\boldsymbol{\Gamma} = \mathbf{r} \times \mathbf{F}$ is $(L, M, N) = (a,b,c) \times M_0(l,m,n)$ so that

$$L = M_0g(bn - cm)$$

$$M = M_0g(cl - an)$$

and

$$N = M_0g(am - bl)$$

For steady rotation, $\dot{\boldsymbol{\omega}} = \mathbf{0}$; hence Euler's equations become

$$M_0g(bn - cm) = (C - B)\omega_2\omega_3 = (C - B)\omega^2mn \qquad \textbf{(9.4)}$$

$$M_0g(cl - an) = (A - C)\omega_3\omega_1 = (A - C)\omega^2nl \qquad \textbf{(9.5)}$$

and

$$M_0g(am - bl) = (B - A)\omega_1\omega_2 = (B - A)\omega^2ml \qquad \textbf{(9.6)}$$

Forming Equation (9.4) $\times$ a + Equation (9.5) $\times$ b + Equation (9.6) $\times$ c eliminates M_0g, since the left-hand side becomes

$$M_0g(abn - acm + bcl - ban + cam - cbl) = 0$$

Hence

$$amn(C - B) + bnl(C - A) + cml(A - B) = 0$$

or, dividing by lmn, since none of l, m or n is zero, gives

$$\frac{a}{l}(B - C) + \frac{b}{m}(C - A) + \frac{c}{n}(B - A) = 0$$

as required.

9.9   A uniform rectangular lamina is in deep space and can rotate freely about its centre O. The lamina ABCD is such that $BC = AB\sqrt{2}$. Initially it is rotating with angular velocity Ω about a line through O perpendicular to AB and at an angle of $\pi/6$ with the plane of the rectangle. Find the components of angular velocity about the principal axes at O at a time t.

Solution   Define axes x, y and z such that Ox and Oy are embedded in the lamina and Oz is at right angles to it (Fig. 9.11). We need to determine the moment of inertia of the lamina about Ox, Oy and Oz. Call these I_x, I_y and I_z. If $AB = CD = a$, $AD = BC = a\sqrt{2}$, then

$$I_x = \frac{Ma^2}{3}, \qquad I_y = \frac{M(a\sqrt{2})^2}{3} = \frac{2Ma^2}{3}$$

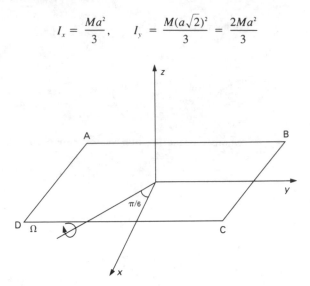

Figure 9.11

and by the perpendicular axes theorem $I_z = I_x + I_y = Ma^2$. Given that the axis of rotation is in the xz-plane, at angle $\pi/6$ with Ox, if ω_1, ω_2, and ω_3, denote the components of Ω in the x, y and z directions, respectively, then

$$\omega_1 = \Omega \cos \frac{\pi}{6} = \Omega \frac{\sqrt{3}}{2}$$

$$\omega_2 = 0$$

and

$$\omega_3 = \Omega \sin \frac{\pi}{6} = \frac{\Omega}{2}$$

The quantity $\mathbf{L} = I_x \omega_1 \, \hat{\mathbf{i}} + I_y \omega_2 \, \hat{\mathbf{j}} \, I_z \omega_3 \, \hat{\mathbf{k}}$ is the angular momentum. Hence

$$L^2 = I_x^2 \omega_1^2 + I_y^2 \omega_2^2 + I_z^2 \omega_3^2$$

$$= (\tfrac{1}{9} \cdot \tfrac{3}{4} + \tfrac{4}{9} \cdot 0 + 1 \cdot \tfrac{1}{4}) \, M^2 a^4 \Omega^2$$

so

$$L^2 = (\tfrac{1}{12} + \tfrac{1}{4}) \, M^2 a^4 \Omega^2 = M^2 a^4 \Omega^2 / 3$$

Also T, the total kinetic energy, is

$$T = \tfrac{1}{2}(I_x \omega_1^2 + I_y \omega_2^2 + I_z \omega_3^2)$$

$$= \tfrac{1}{2}(\tfrac{1}{3} \cdot \tfrac{3}{4} + \tfrac{2}{3} \cdot 0 + 1 \cdot \tfrac{1}{4}) \, M a^2 \omega^2$$

so

$$T = Ma^2 \omega^2 / 4$$

In order to find out what ω_1, ω_2 and ω_3 are subsequently, we solve Euler's equations under zero force, which are

$$I_x \dot{\omega}_1 - (I_y - I_z) \omega_2 \omega_3 = 0$$

$$I_y \dot{\omega}_2 - (I_z - I_x) \omega_1 \omega_3 = 0$$

and

$$I_z\dot{\omega}_3 - (I_x - I_y)\omega_1\omega_2 = 0$$

These become

$$\dot{\omega}_1 = -\omega_2\omega_3 \tag{9.7}$$

$$2\dot{\omega}_2 = 2\omega_3\omega_1 \tag{9.8}$$

and

$$3\dot{\omega}_3 = \omega_1\omega_2 \tag{9.9}$$

respectively. Hence Equation (9.7) $\times$ ω_1 $-$ Equation (9.9) $\times$ ω_3 gives

$$\dot{\omega}_1\omega_1 - 3\dot{\omega}_3\omega_3 = 0$$

Integrating gives

$$\omega_1^2 - 3\omega_3^2 = K_1 = 0$$

since, when $t = 0$, $\omega_1 = \Omega\sqrt{3}/2$ and $\omega_3 = \Omega/2$. Hence

$$\omega_1 = \sqrt{3}\omega_3$$

From Equations (9.7) and (9.8), $\omega_1^2 + \omega_2^2 = K_2$, and, initially, $\omega_1 = \Omega\sqrt{3}/2$, $\omega_2 = 0$ giving $K_2 = \frac{3}{4}\Omega^2$; hence

$$4(\omega_1^2 + \omega_2^2) = 3\Omega^2$$

Equation (9.8) is thus

$$\dot{\omega}_2 = \frac{\omega_1}{3}\omega_1 = \tfrac{1}{3}\omega_1^2 = \tfrac{1}{3}\left(\frac{3\Omega^2}{4} - \omega_2^2\right)$$

or

$$\frac{d\omega_2}{dt} = \left(\frac{\Omega^2}{4} - \frac{\omega_2^2}{3}\right)$$

Hence

$$\int \frac{d\omega}{\frac{3}{4}\Omega^2 - \omega_2^2} = \tfrac{1}{3}\int dt$$

or

$$\frac{2}{\sqrt{3}}\tanh^{-1}\left(\frac{2\omega_2}{\Omega\sqrt{3}}\right) = \tfrac{1}{3}t + K_3$$

with $K_3 = 0$ since $\omega_2 = 0$ when $t = 0$. Thus

$$\omega_2 = \frac{\Omega\sqrt{3}}{2}\tanh\left(\frac{t}{2\sqrt{3}}\right)$$

Substituting back,

$$\omega_1^2 = \frac{3\Omega^2}{4} - \omega_2^2 = \frac{3\Omega^2}{4}\left[1 - \tanh^2\left(\frac{t}{2\sqrt{3}}\right)\right]$$

141

or

$$\omega_1 = \frac{\Omega\sqrt{3}}{2}\operatorname{sech}\left(\frac{t}{2\sqrt{3}}\right)$$

and finally

$$\omega_3 = \frac{1}{\sqrt{3}}\omega_1 = \frac{\Omega}{2}\operatorname{sech}\left(\frac{t}{2\sqrt{3}}\right)$$

9.10 A top is spinning about an axis of symmetry. Let the angle between the vertical and this axis be a constant α. Show that the top precesses with a constant angular velocity (steady procession).

Solution For this problem, we have to work with axes that are moving with the top. The rate of change of angular momentum with respect to fixed axes is

$$\dot{\mathbf{L}} + \boldsymbol{\omega} \times \mathbf{L}$$

where $\boldsymbol{\omega}$ is the angular velocity of the axes that move with the top. Since the top itself is spinning, it is convenient to separate out the spin of the top and any movement of the axes. Hence we let

$$\boldsymbol{\omega} = \omega_1\hat{\mathbf{e}}_1 + \omega_2\hat{\mathbf{e}}_2 + \omega_3\hat{\mathbf{e}}_3$$

and

$$\boldsymbol{\Omega} = \Omega\hat{\mathbf{e}}_3$$

where Ω is the angular velocity of the top due to its spin alone and $\hat{\mathbf{e}}_3$ is the unit vector along the axis of symmetry of the top. The trio $\hat{\mathbf{e}}_1$, $\hat{\mathbf{e}}_2$ and $\hat{\mathbf{e}}_3$ form a right-handed system of mutually orthogonal unit vectors. Figure 9.12 shows the situation in which $\hat{\mathbf{k}}$ is the fixed vertical axis, and α is the angle between $\hat{\mathbf{k}}$ and $\hat{\mathbf{e}}_3$. We are given that α is a constant.

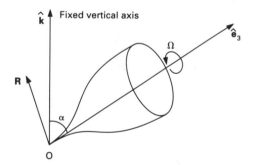

Figure 9.12

The torque, $\boldsymbol{\Gamma}$, of the top about O is $a\hat{\mathbf{e}}_3 \times (-mg\hat{\mathbf{k}})$ where a is the distance of the centre of mass of the top from O, the fixed point about which the top pivots. Since the axes $\hat{\mathbf{e}}_1$ and $\hat{\mathbf{e}}_2$ have not been specified precisely, except of course that with $\hat{\mathbf{e}}_3$ they form a right-handed system, without loss of generality we can let $\hat{\mathbf{e}}_1$ be in the direction of $\hat{\mathbf{e}}_3 \times \hat{\mathbf{k}}$. In fact,

$$\hat{\mathbf{k}} = (\hat{\mathbf{k}} \cdot \hat{\mathbf{e}}_1)\hat{\mathbf{e}}_1 + (\hat{\mathbf{k}} \cdot \hat{\mathbf{e}}_2)\hat{\mathbf{e}}_2 + (\hat{\mathbf{k}} \cdot \hat{\mathbf{e}}_3)\hat{\mathbf{e}}_3$$

$$= \sin\alpha\,\hat{\mathbf{e}}_2 + \cos\alpha\,\hat{\mathbf{e}}_3$$

Thus

$$\boldsymbol{\Gamma} = mga\sin\alpha\hat{\mathbf{e}}_1$$

Hence, Euler's equations of motion for the spinning top are

$$A\dot{\omega}_1 + (C - A)\omega_2\omega_3 + C\omega_2\Omega = mga\sin\alpha$$

$$A\dot{\omega}_2 + (A - C)\omega_1\omega_3 - C\omega_1\Omega = 0$$

and

$$\dot{\omega}_3 + \dot{\Omega} = 0$$

where A is the moment of inertia of the top about $\hat{e}_1$ and $\hat{e}_2$ (axi-symmetry), and C is the moment of inertia of the top about $\hat{e}_3$. Since α is a constant and $\hat{e}_2$ is in the plane of the fixed axis and $\hat{e}_3$, we have $\omega_1 = 0$. Thus the second equation becomes $\dot{\omega}_2 = 0$, which implies that $\omega_2 = $ constant. That is, $\dot{\theta}_2$ (where $\omega_2 = d\theta_2/dt$ and θ_2 is the angle between $\hat{e}_2$ and a (fixed) horizontal axis $\hat{j}$) is constant. This means that θ_2 increases at a steady rate, which is the meaning of a top precessing at a constant angular velocity (steady precession).

9.11   A top is spinning such that its axis of symmetry is at a constant angle α to the vertical. Let ϕ be the angle swept through by the projection of the spin axis on to the horizontal table. Show that there are two possible speeds of precession provided

$$C^2\Omega_0^2 > 4\,Amga\cos\alpha$$

In this inequality, A and C are the moments of inertia perpendicular to and along the axis of the top through its contact point with the ground respectively, Ω_0 is the total angular velocity of the top about the vertical, α is the angle between the axis of the top and the vertical, mg is the weight of the top and a is the distance between the centre of mass and its fulcrum. Find these two frequencies for very large values of Ω_0.

Solution   From the previous question, Euler's equation of motion for the top are

$$A\dot{\omega}_1 + (C - A)\omega_2\omega_3 + C\omega_2\Omega = mga\sin\alpha \qquad \textbf{(9.10)}$$

$$A\dot{\omega}_2 + (A - C)\omega_1\omega_3 - C\omega_1\Omega = 0$$

$$\dot{\omega}_3 + \dot{\Omega} = 0$$

using the same notation. Integrating the last equation with respect to time yields

$$\omega_3 + \Omega = \Omega_0$$

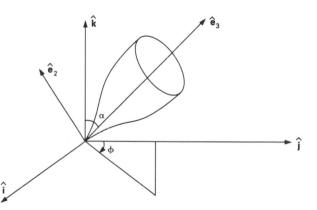

Figure 9.13

From the previous problem, since α is a constant, $\omega_1 = 0$; hence $\omega_2 = $ constant. Now, ϕ is the angle on the horizontal plane swept out by the axis (see Fig. 9.13). Therefore

$$\omega_2 = \dot{\phi}\sin\alpha, \qquad \omega_3 = \dot{\phi}\cos\alpha$$

and, with $\omega_1 = 0$, Equation (9.10) becomes

$$(C - A)\dot{\phi}^2 \cos\alpha \sin\alpha + C\dot{\phi} \sin\alpha(\Omega_0 - \dot{\phi} \cos\alpha) = mga \sin\alpha,$$

which simplifies to

$$A\dot{\phi}^2 \cos\alpha - C\Omega_0\dot{\phi} + mga = 0$$

This quadratic has real roots provided

$$C^2\Omega_0^2 > 4 \, Amga \cos\alpha$$

as required. The roots are

$$\dot{\phi} = \frac{C\Omega_0 \pm (C^2\Omega_0^2 - 4 \, Amga \cos\alpha)^{1/2}}{2A \cos\alpha}$$

and for large value of Ω_0,

$$(C^2\Omega_0^2 - 4 \, Amga \cos\alpha)^{1/2} \approx C\Omega_0\left(1 - \frac{2 \, Amga \cos\alpha}{C^2\Omega_0^2}\right)$$

hence

$$\dot{\phi} \approx \frac{C\Omega_0}{A \cos\alpha}, \qquad \frac{mga}{C\Omega_0}$$

9.12   The gyrocompass is a device that enables an aircraft to detect true north. Explain its operation.

Solution   Let O represent a point on the Earth's surface with latitude λ. We abandon our usual practice and let axes $\hat{\mathbf{k}}$ and $\hat{\mathbf{j}}$ be horizontal, with $\hat{\mathbf{k}}$ making an angle θ with the north–south line of longitude through O (Fig. 9.14). If $\hat{\mathbf{i}}$ is the local vertical, then the rotation of the Earth $\mathbf{\Omega}$ expressed in terms of $\hat{\mathbf{i}}$, $\hat{\mathbf{j}}$ and $\hat{\mathbf{k}}$ is

$$\mathbf{\Omega} = \Omega(\hat{\mathbf{i}} \sin\lambda - \hat{\mathbf{j}} \cos\lambda \sin\theta + \hat{\mathbf{k}} \cos\lambda \cos\theta)$$

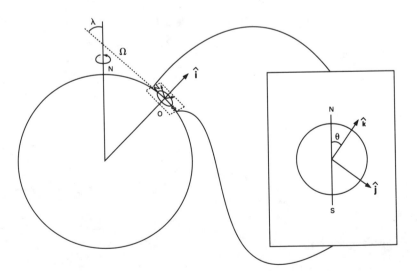

Figure 9.14

If $\mathbf{\omega}_a$ is the angular velocity of the axes, then

$$\mathbf{\omega}_a = \hat{\mathbf{i}}(\Omega \sin\lambda - \dot{\theta}) - \hat{\mathbf{j}}\Omega \cos\lambda \sin\theta + \hat{\mathbf{k}}\Omega \cos\lambda \cos\theta$$

since $\dot\theta$ represents the rotation of the $\hat{\mathbf{j}}$–$\hat{\mathbf{k}}$ plane which is in the $-\hat{\mathbf{i}}$ direction; hence

$$\boldsymbol{\omega}_a = \boldsymbol{\Omega} - \hat{\mathbf{i}}\dot\theta$$

The device called a gyrocompass consists of a flywheel which is maintained in a horizontal position, spinning with a large angular velocity compared to the rotation of the Earth. Hence the angular velocity of the flywheel is $\boldsymbol{\omega}$, where

$$\boldsymbol{\omega} = \hat{\mathbf{i}}(\Omega \sin\lambda - \dot\theta) - \hat{\mathbf{j}}\Omega \cos\lambda \sin\theta + \hat{\mathbf{k}}s$$

where s ($\gg \Omega$) is actually ($\Omega \cos\lambda + s'$), s' being the locally induced enhanced $\hat{\mathbf{k}}$ component of angular velocity due to the flywheel. The angular momentum of the flywheel is thus $\mathbf{L}$, where

$$\mathbf{L} = \hat{\mathbf{i}}A(\Omega \sin\lambda - \dot\theta) - \hat{\mathbf{j}}A\Omega \cos\lambda \sin\theta + \hat{\mathbf{k}}Cs$$

A, A and C are the principal moments of inertia of the flywheel along $\hat{\mathbf{i}}$, $\hat{\mathbf{j}}$ and $\hat{\mathbf{k}}$ respectively. Now, for the axis to be maintained in the horizontal plane a couple $M\hat{\mathbf{j}}$ needs to be applied. Euler's equations are

$$M\hat{\mathbf{j}} = \dot{\mathbf{L}} + \boldsymbol{\omega}_a \times \mathbf{L}$$

$$= -\hat{\mathbf{i}}A\ddot\theta - \hat{\mathbf{j}}A\Omega\dot\theta \cos\lambda \cos\theta + \hat{\mathbf{k}}C\dot{s} + \hat{\mathbf{i}}\Omega\cos\lambda \sin\theta(A\Omega \cos\lambda \cos\theta - Cs)$$

$$+ \hat{\mathbf{j}}(\Omega \sin\lambda - \dot\theta)(A\Omega \cos\lambda \cos\theta - Cs)$$

This immediately implies that the coefficients of $\hat{\mathbf{i}}$ and $\hat{\mathbf{k}}$ are zero. Hence s = constant and also

$$-A\ddot\theta + \Omega \cos\lambda \sin\theta(A\Omega \cos\lambda \cos\theta - Cs) = 0$$

This can be simplified once it is assumed that $s \gg \Omega$, i.e.

$$\ddot\theta + \frac{\Omega sC}{A} \cos\lambda \sin\theta = 0$$

This, for small angles θ, is simple harmonic motion of period

$$2\pi \left(\frac{A}{s\Omega C \cos\lambda}\right)^{1/2}$$

Since the flywheel oscillates about $\theta = 0$, it can be used to estimate true north. This is the principle of the gyrocompass.

9.3 Exercises

9.1 Show that the moment of inertia of an equilateral triangular lamina of side $2a$ about any axis in the plane of the lamina through the centre of mass is $\frac{1}{6}ma^2$.

9.2 Prove the perpendicular axes theorem. Hence find the moments of inertia of a rectangular plate, side $2a \times 2b$, about the three axes of symmetry.

9.3 Find the moment of inertia of a right circular cone, height h and base radius a, about the axis of symmetry.

9.4 A body which has moment of inertia I and mass m is able to roll in a vertical plane inside a fixed hollow cylinder of radius a. It is given a speed u at the bottom, and it rolls without slipping. The rolling body is axi-symmetric and its circle of contact with the outer cylinder has radius b. Find conditions on u such that:

(a) the inner body just reached the top,
(b) the inner body completes revolutions.

Determine these conditions for a solid cylinder and a solid sphere.

9.5 A sphere, of radius a, is projected up an inclined plane with velocity V and angular velocity Ω in the sense which would cause it to roll up. If $V > a\Omega$ and the coefficient of friction is $> \frac{2}{7}\tan\alpha$, show that the sphere will cease to ascend at the end of a time

$$\frac{5v + 2a\Omega}{5g \sin\alpha}$$

where α is the inclination of the plane.

9.6 A space station with moment of inertia I about its axis of symmetry is moving in deep space. An alien of mass m has landed on the space station and crawls around the axis of symmetry in a complete circle of radius a. Find the angle turned through by the station if, initially, it had zero angular velocity. (Assume that m is much smaller than the mass of the space station.)

9.7 A uniform sphere rolls without slipping on a rough turntable rotating about a fixed vertical axis with constant angular velocity Ω. Show that the centre of the sphere describes a circle about another fixed vertical axis with angular velocity $2\Omega/7$.

9.8 A body can move about its centre of mass which is fixed. The principal moments of inertia about the centre of mass are in the ratio 6:3:1 and the corresponding components of the initial angular velocity are 1:0:3. show that a time t later the angular velocity about the principal axis is $-n\sqrt{5}\tanh(nt\sqrt{5})$, where n is the initial value of the angular velocity of the body about the first axis. Hence find the other two angular velocities. Show also that kinetic energy is conserved.

9.9 A top has an axis of symmetry OG and it spins with the end O of its axis on a rough horizontal table. The mass of the top is M and its moments of inertia about OG and about any axis through O perpendicular to OG are C and A respectively. By considering $d\hat{\mathbf{i}}/dt = \boldsymbol{\omega} \times \hat{\mathbf{i}}$, where $\hat{\mathbf{i}}$ is a unit vector along OG and $\boldsymbol{\omega}$ is the angular velocity of the top, show that

$$\boldsymbol{\omega} = \hat{\mathbf{i}} \times \frac{d\hat{\mathbf{i}}}{dt} + n\hat{\mathbf{i}}$$

and that the angular momentum of the top about O is

$$\mathbf{H} = A\hat{\mathbf{i}} \times \frac{d\hat{\mathbf{i}}}{dt} + Cn\hat{\mathbf{i}}$$

Deduce that if $\mathbf{z}$ is the unit vector in the direction of the upward vertical and h is the distance of the centre of mass of the top from O, then

$$A\hat{\mathbf{i}} \times \frac{d^2\hat{\mathbf{i}}}{dt^2} + C\frac{d}{dt}(n\hat{\mathbf{i}}) = -Mgh\hat{\mathbf{i}} \times \mathbf{z}$$

and n is a constant.

Show that steady motion is possible with the axis of the top vertical or with a precessional motion $\hat{\mathbf{i}} \cdot \mathbf{z} = \cos\alpha$ and $d\hat{\mathbf{i}}/dt = \Omega\mathbf{z} \times \hat{\mathbf{i}}$, where α and Ω are constants satisfying

$$A\Omega^2\cos\alpha - Cn\Omega + Mgh = 0 \qquad \text{(L.U.)}$$

9.10 The Earth is an oblate spheroid. C and A are respectively the moment of inertia about the polar axis of symmetry and the moment of inertia about any axis in the equatorial plane perpendicular to it, and measurements show that $C - A = 0.003\,27A$. Show that the period of precession is about 306 days. Neglect all interactive gravitational effects from the Sun and Moon.
(L.U.)

9.4 Outline Solutions to Exercises

9.1 Using notation as given in Fig. 9.15, the perpendicular distance of m_1, m_2 and m_3 from the line OX are $l\cos\theta$, $l\cos(\pi/3 - \theta)$ and $l\sin(\pi/6 - \theta)$, respectively, where l is 1/3 of the length of the median, i.e. $l = a/\sqrt{3}$.

If $m_1 = m_2 = m_3 = \frac{1}{3}m$, the system is equimomental to the triangular lamina (see Example 9.1)

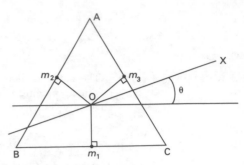

Figure 9.15

$$\text{Moment of inertia} = \frac{ma^2}{9}\left[\cos^2\left(\frac{\pi}{6} - \theta\right) + \sin^2\left(\frac{\pi}{6} - \theta\right)\right.$$
$$\left. + \cos^2\theta\right] = \frac{ma^2}{6}$$

9.2 Figure 9.16 shows an arbitrary plate, origin and x- and y-axes, together with an element $dxdy$. If r is the distance from $dxdy$ to the origin O, then

$$I_z = \int_{\text{plate}} r^2\rho\,dxdy = \int_{\text{plate}} x^2\rho\,dxdy + \int_{\text{plate}} y^2\rho\,dxdy$$

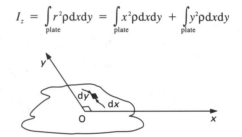

Figure 9.16

These integrals are I_x and I_y respectively. This proves $I_z = I_x + I_y$, the perpendicular axes theorem.

For a rectangular plate,

$$I_x = \rho\int_{-b}^{b} 2ay^2\,dy = \frac{4ab^3}{3}\rho = \frac{mb^2}{3}$$

and

$$I_y = \rho\int_{-a}^{a} 2bx^2\,dx = \frac{4a^3b}{3}\rho = \frac{ma^2}{3}$$

Hence $I_z = (m/3)(a^2 + b^2)$.

9.3 Using the notation of Fig. 9.17, with cylindrical polar coordinates

$$I = \int_0^{2\pi}\int_0^{h}\int_0^{(a/h)(h-z)} \rho R^3\,dR\,dz\,d\theta$$

since

$$\tan\alpha = \frac{a}{h} = \frac{R}{h - z}$$

this gives

$$I = \frac{\pi a^4 h\rho}{10}$$

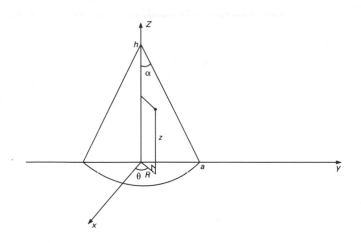

Figure 9.17

Since mass $m = \frac{1}{3}\pi a^2 h \rho$, $I = \frac{3}{10}ma^2$.

9.4 Adopting the notation of Fig. 9.18, where O and O' coincide when the smaller body is at the bottom, then $a\theta = b\phi$. Also, the principle of conservation of energy gives

$$\frac{1}{2}m(a - b)^2\dot{\theta}^2 + \frac{1}{2}I(\dot{\phi} - \dot{\theta})^2 + mg(a - b)(1 - \cos\theta) = C$$

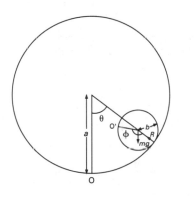

Figure 9.18

At the bottom, $\theta = 0$ and $(a - b)\dot{\theta} = u$, which implies

$$(\dot{\phi} - \dot{\theta}) = \left(\frac{a}{b} - 1\right)\dot{\theta} = \frac{u}{b} \qquad (\text{at } \theta = 0)$$

Hence

$$C = \frac{1}{2}mu^2 + \frac{1}{2}I\frac{u^2}{b^2}$$

In order to just reach the top, $\dot{\theta} = 0$ at $\theta = \pi$; hence

$$2mg(a - b) = \frac{1}{2}mu^2 + \frac{1}{2}I\frac{u^2}{b^2}$$

So

$$u^2 \geq \frac{4mg(a - b)b^2}{mb^2 + I}$$

The radial equation of motion is

$$-m(a - b)\dot{\theta}^2 = -R + mg\cos\theta$$

If $R = 0$ at $\theta = \pi$, we require $\dot{\theta}^2 = g/(a - b)$. Inserting this into the energy equation gives

$$\frac{1}{2}mg(a - b) + \frac{1}{2}I\frac{(a - b)}{b^2}g + 2mg(a - b) = \frac{1}{2}mu^2 + \frac{1}{2}I\frac{u^2}{b^2}$$

from which we deduce that

$$u^2 \geq \left(\frac{I + 5mb^2}{I + mb^2}\right)g(a - b)$$

For a solid cylinder, $I = \frac{1}{2}mb^2$, and hence the two conditions are

$$u^2 \geq \frac{8}{3}g(a - b)$$

and

$$u^2 \geq \frac{11}{3}g(a - b)$$

For a solid sphere, $I = \frac{2}{5}mb^2$, and hence the two conditions are

$$u^2 \geq \frac{20}{7}g(a - b)$$

and

$$u^2 \geq \frac{27}{7}g(a - b)$$

respectively.

9.5 Adopting the notation of Fig. 9.19, we derive the following equations:

$$R = mg\cos\alpha$$

and

$$F - mg\sin\alpha = m\ddot{x}$$

from Newton's laws, and

$$-mga\sin\alpha = \frac{2}{5}ma^2\dot{\omega} + m\dot{v}a \qquad \textbf{(9.11)}$$

from *torque = rate of change of momentum* about the point of contact of the sphere with the plane.

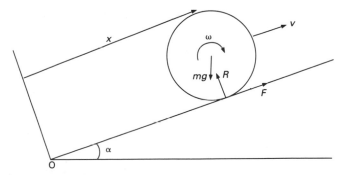

Figure 9.19

If $v = a\omega$, the sphere rolls; $\ddot{x} = -\frac{5}{7}g\sin\alpha$ and

$$\mu > \frac{F}{R} = \frac{2}{7}\tan\alpha$$

If $v > a\omega$, the sphere slips. If we integrate Equation (9.11) we obtain

$$\tfrac{2}{5}ma^2\Omega + mVa - mgta\sin\alpha = \tfrac{2}{5}ma^2\omega + mva$$

If the sphere stops, then $v\,(= a\omega) = 0$; hence

$$t = \frac{2a\Omega + 5V}{5g\sin\alpha}$$

as required.

9.6 As the alien crawls, the space station moves under it in such a way that no net angular momentum is created. The alien crawls what it considers is a complete circle, but in fact it is $(2\pi - \theta)$, where θ is the angle turned through by the station. As it is crawling, if $\dot\phi_1$ is the angular velocity of the space station, and $\dot\phi_2$ the angular velocity of the alien, then by the conservation of angular momentum,

$$I\dot\phi_1 = ma^2\dot\phi_2$$

Integrating gives $I\phi_1 = ma^2\phi_2$, defining $\phi_1 = \phi_2 = 0$ as the alien lands. Now, $\phi_1 = 2\pi - \theta$ when $\phi_2 = \theta$; hence

$$\theta = \frac{2\pi ma^2}{ma^2 + I}$$

We need to assume no change in the axis of symmetry of the space station, or in its centre of mass. Hence the necessity of the assumption regarding m.

9.7 The sphere is shown in Fig. 9.20. Newton's laws (treating the sphere as a particle) give

$$R = mg, \qquad m\ddot y = F_2, \qquad m\ddot x = F_1 \qquad \textbf{(9.12)}$$

if the angular velocities about x, y, z are ω_1, ω_2, ω_3 respectively. *Torque = rate of change of angular momentum* gives

$$0 = I\dot\omega_3 \Rightarrow \omega_3 = \text{constant}$$

$$\left.\begin{array}{l} -aF_2 = I\dot\omega_1 \\[2mm] aF_1 = I\dot\omega_2 \end{array}\right\} \qquad \textbf{(9.13)}$$

Since the turntable rotates with angular velocity Ω, and A is an instantaneous centre,

$$\left.\begin{array}{l} \Omega x = -\dot y + \omega_1 a \\[2mm] \Omega y = \dot x + \omega_2 a \end{array}\right\} \qquad \textbf{(9.14)}$$

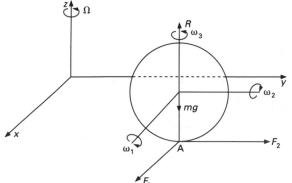

Figure 9.20

148

Eliminating F_1 and F_2 from Equations (9.12) and (9.13), with $I = \tfrac{2}{5}ma^2$, gives

$$\tfrac{2}{5}a\dot\omega_1 + \ddot y = 0$$

and

$$\tfrac{2}{5}a\dot\omega_2 - \ddot x = 0$$

from which

$$7a\dot\omega_1 = 5\Omega\dot x$$

and

$$7a\dot\omega_2 = 5\Omega\dot y$$

Integrating and then substituting for ω_1 and ω_2 in Equations (9.14) gives

$$\left.\begin{array}{l} 7\dot y = A - 2\Omega x \\[2mm] 7\dot x = 2\Omega y + B \end{array}\right\} \qquad \textbf{(9.15)}$$

so

$$(\dot x,\, \dot y) = \left(\frac{2\Omega}{7}x + k_1,\ \frac{2\Omega}{7}y + k_2\right)$$

i.e. angular velocity $2\Omega/7$ about another vertical axis. (In fact, Equations (9.15) mean that the sphere moves in a circle.)

9.8 We use Euler's equations of motion, which become

$$3\dot\omega_1 = \omega_2\omega_3, \qquad 3\dot\omega_2 = -5\omega_3\omega_1, \qquad \dot\omega_3 = 3\omega_1\omega_2$$

Eliminating ω_2 from the first and last gives

$$9\dot\omega_1\omega_1 = \dot\omega_3\omega_3 \Rightarrow 3\omega_1 = \omega_3$$

Similarly,

$$5\omega_3^2 + 9\omega_2^2 = 45n^2$$

and

$$\dot\omega_2^2 = \omega_2^2 - 5n^2$$

so that

$$\omega_2 = -n\sqrt5\,\tanh(nt\sqrt5)$$

Substituting back;

$$\omega_3 = 3n\,\text{sech}(nt\sqrt5)$$

$$\omega_1 = n\,\text{sech}(nt\sqrt5)$$

$$T = \frac{k}{2}(6\omega_1^2 + 3\omega_2^2 + \omega_3^2) = \frac{15k}{2}n^2$$

which is constant. Hence kinetic energy is conserved.

9.9 The top is shown in Fig. 9.21, which also gives the notation. $(\hat{\mathbf i}, \hat{\mathbf j}, \hat{\mathbf k})$ is a right-handed triad, with $\hat{\mathbf j}$ in the plane of $\hat{\mathbf z}$ and $\hat{\mathbf i}$.

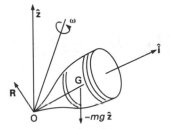

Figure 9.21

We are given $d\hat{\mathbf{i}}/dt = \dot{\boldsymbol{\omega}} \times \hat{\mathbf{i}}$; hence $\dot{\boldsymbol{\omega}} = \lambda\hat{\mathbf{i}} + \mu\hat{\mathbf{j}}$, ($\lambda$, μ constants). Thus

$$\boldsymbol{\omega} \times \hat{\mathbf{i}} = \mu\hat{\mathbf{j}} \times \hat{\mathbf{i}} = \mu\hat{\mathbf{k}} = \frac{d\hat{\mathbf{i}}}{dt}$$

whence

$$\mu\hat{\mathbf{j}} = \mu\hat{\mathbf{k}} \times \hat{\mathbf{i}} = -\mu\hat{\mathbf{i}} \times \hat{\mathbf{k}} = \hat{\mathbf{i}} \times \frac{d\hat{\mathbf{i}}}{dt}$$

which gives

$$\boldsymbol{\omega} = n\hat{\mathbf{i}} + \hat{\mathbf{i}} \times \frac{d\hat{\mathbf{i}}}{dt}$$

as required (writing $\lambda = n$). Since

$$\mathbf{H} = C\omega_1\hat{\mathbf{i}} + A\omega_2\hat{\mathbf{j}}$$

this is

$$\mathbf{H} = Cn\hat{\mathbf{i}} + A\hat{\mathbf{i}} \times \frac{d\hat{\mathbf{i}}}{dt}$$

as required. *Torque = rate of change of angular momentum* gives

$$mgh\hat{\mathbf{z}} \times \hat{\mathbf{i}} = \frac{d}{dt}(\mathbf{H}) = C\frac{d}{dt}(n\hat{\mathbf{i}}) + A\hat{\mathbf{i}} \times \frac{d^2\hat{\mathbf{i}}}{dt^2} \quad \textbf{(9.16)}$$

as required.

$$\frac{d}{dt}(n\hat{\mathbf{i}}) = n\frac{d\hat{\mathbf{i}}}{dt} + \hat{\mathbf{i}}\frac{dn}{dt}$$

but taking the scalar product of Equation (9.16) with $\hat{\mathbf{i}}$ gives $dn/dt = 0$; hence $n = $ constant. If $d\hat{\mathbf{i}}/dt = 0$ and $\hat{\mathbf{z}} = \hat{\mathbf{i}}$, Equa-

tion (9.16) is satisfied; hence steady motion with the top's axis vertical is possible.

Writing

$$\frac{d\hat{\mathbf{i}}}{dt} = \boldsymbol{\omega} \times \hat{\mathbf{i}} = \Omega\hat{\mathbf{z}} \times \hat{\mathbf{i}}$$

gives

$$\frac{d^2\hat{\mathbf{i}}}{dt^2} = \frac{d}{dt}(\Omega\hat{\mathbf{z}} \times \hat{\mathbf{i}}) = \Omega\hat{\mathbf{z}} \times \frac{d\hat{\mathbf{i}}}{dt} = \Omega\hat{\mathbf{z}} \times (\Omega\hat{\mathbf{z}} \times \hat{\mathbf{i}})$$

$$= \Omega^2\cos\alpha\hat{\mathbf{z}} - \Omega^2\hat{\mathbf{i}} \qquad (\hat{\mathbf{i}}\cdot\hat{\mathbf{z}} = \cos\alpha)$$

Thus Equation (9.16) becomes

$$mgh\hat{\mathbf{z}} \times \hat{\mathbf{i}} = Cn\Omega\hat{\mathbf{z}} \times \hat{\mathbf{i}} + A\Omega^2\cos\alpha\hat{\mathbf{i}} \times \hat{\mathbf{z}}$$

which is satisfied as long as

$$A\Omega^2\cos\alpha - Cn\Omega + mgh = 0$$

(Note: Nutation – the periodic but small variation in α – is not discussed in this text.)

9.10 The Earth is assumed to be entirely free of forces and couples; hence Euler's equations in free space apply:

$$A\dot{\omega}_1 + (C - A)\omega_2\omega_3 = 0$$

$$A\dot{\omega}_2 + (A - C)\omega_3\omega_1 = 0$$

and

$$A\dot{\omega}_3 + (A - A)\omega_1\omega_2 = 0$$

Hence $\omega_1 = n = $ constant, where ω_1 is the rotation about the polar axis (ω_1 and ω_2 are rotations about equatorial axes). Solving for ω_2 gives

$$\ddot{\omega}_2 + \left(\frac{C - A}{A}\right)^2 n^2\omega_2 = 0$$

a period of

$$\frac{2\pi A}{n(C - A)} = \frac{A}{C - A} \text{ days} \qquad \text{(since } n = 2\pi \text{ radians per day)}$$

$$= 306 \text{ days}$$

(In fact, by judicious choice of time origin $\omega_1 = k\cos\lambda t$, $\omega_2 = k\sin\lambda t$ and $A^2\lambda^2 = (C - A)^2n^2$.)

10 Energy, Impulse and Stability

10.1 Fact Sheet

Energy If a force $\mathbf{F}$ is conservative, then $\nabla = \times \mathbf{F} = \mathbf{0}$, so that there exists a potential energy function V such that $\mathbf{F} = -\nabla V$.

The kinetic energy of a particle is $\frac{1}{2} mv^2$, where m is the mass and v the speed. The kinetic energy of a rigid body is T, where

$$T = \tfrac{1}{2} mV_G^2 + \tfrac{1}{2} I\omega^2$$

V_G = speed of the centre of mass

ω = angular speed of the body

I = moment of inertia of the body about the axis of rotation

In a conservative system, the equations of motion can be integrated once to give

$$T + V = \text{constant}$$

The **work done** by a force $\mathbf{F}$ moving a unit mass along a path C is the line integral

$$\int_C \mathbf{F} \cdot d\mathbf{r}$$

Also, work done = change in kinetic energy.

The **power** is the rate of working of a force $\mathbf{F}$ and is given by $\mathbf{F} \cdot \mathbf{v}$, where $\mathbf{v}$ is velocity.

Impulse For a rigid body, we can use

$$\text{Impulse} = \text{change in momentum}$$

for the centre of mass of the body. However, we can also use the relation

Moment of impulse = moment of inertia × impulsive change in angular velocity

When the axis of a rotating body is suddenly changed, the angular momentum parallel to the new axis is conserved.

Stability At a static equilibrium state, the velocity of the mass is zero. Hence the energy equation is

$$V = \text{constant},$$

or

$$\frac{dV}{dq} = 0$$

where q is one of the coordinates that describe the motion (usually q is x or θ).

If ε denotes the displacement or **angular** displacement of a mass from equilibrium, then if ε is sufficiently small,

$$\ddot{\varepsilon} + k\varepsilon = 0$$

The equilibrium position is **stable** if $k > 0$ and **unstable** if $k < 0$. If $k = 0$ then the equilibrium point needs to be investigated from first principles. k is proportional to the second derivative of V in single degree of freedom systems.

These ideas are generalised in the next chapter.

10.2 Worked Examples

10.1 If a force $\mathbf{F}$ is such that $\mathbf{F} = -\nabla V$, where V is a potential function, and T is the kinetic energy, show that

$$T + V = \text{constant}$$

Solution Consider the expression

$$\int_C \mathbf{F} \cdot d\mathbf{r} \tag{10.1}$$

where C is any curve. Using Newton's second law,

$$\mathbf{F} = m\ddot{\mathbf{r}}$$

substituting for $\mathbf{F}$ in Equation (10.1) yields

$$\int_C \mathbf{F} \cdot d\mathbf{r} = \int_C m\ddot{\mathbf{r}} \cdot d\mathbf{r}$$

$$= \int_C m\ddot{\mathbf{r}} \cdot \frac{d\mathbf{r}}{dt} \, dt$$

so that

$$\int_C \mathbf{F} \cdot d\mathbf{r} = \int_C \frac{m}{2} \frac{d}{dt} (\dot{\mathbf{r}})^2 dt$$

$$= [\tfrac{1}{2} m\dot{\mathbf{r}}^2]_C$$

$$= [T]_C \tag{10.2}$$

which represents the change of kinetic energy as the curve C is traversed. Also:

$$\int_C \mathbf{F} \cdot d\mathbf{r} = \int_C -\nabla V \cdot d\mathbf{r}$$

$$= -\int_C dV \qquad \text{(since } \nabla V \cdot d\mathbf{r} = dV \text{ by the chain rule)}$$

$$= -[V]_C \tag{10.3}$$

From Equations (10.2) and (10.3), we see that

$$[T + V]_C = 0$$

However, the curve C is entirely arbitrary; therefore $T + V = $ constant (since its change along an arbitrary curve is always zero).

10.2 Use the conservation of energy to calculate the escape velocity from the Earth's gravitational attraction in metres per second. (Radius of the Earth $= 6.4 \times 10^6$ m, mass of the Earth $= 6.0 \times 10^{24}$ kg, $G = 6.7 \times 10^{-11}$ SI units.)

Solution The (attractive) force of a particle of mass m towards the centre of the Earth, of mass M, is

$$\mathbf{F} = -\frac{mMG}{r^2} \hat{\mathbf{r}}$$

That is, $\mathbf{F}$ has potential Ω where $\mathbf{F} = -\nabla\Omega$ so that $\Omega = -mMG/r$. The conservation of energy thus gives

$$-\frac{mMG}{r} + \tfrac{1}{2} mv^2 = Am \qquad \text{(a constant).}$$

Now, when $r = R$, the radius of the Earth, $v = V$ (the initial velocity of the particle). Hence, cancelling m, the energy equation yields

$$MG \left(\frac{1}{r} - \frac{1}{R} \right) = \tfrac{1}{2}(v^2 - V^2) \qquad\qquad \textbf{(10.4)}$$

We now let $r = R + h$, where h is the height of the particle above the Earth's surface, and rearrange Equation (10.4) to give

$$v^2 = V^2 - \frac{2MGh}{R(R + h)}$$

so that

$$v = \left(V^2 - \frac{2MG}{(R^2/h) + R} \right)^{1/2}$$

Hence, as $h \to \infty$ we obtain

$$v = \left(V^2 - \frac{2MG}{R} \right)^{1/2}$$

For the velocity v to remain real, we must have the initial velocity of the particle V exceeding $2MG/R$, i.e.

$$V^2 > \frac{2MG}{R}$$

Hence $(2MG/R)^{1/2}$ is the required escape velocity. Inserting the values of M, G and R gives the Earth's escape velocity as 1.12×10^4 m s^{-1} (about 7 miles per second). (Compare this with Example 8.5.)

10.3 Three particles A, B, C, each of mass m, lie in a straight line on a smooth horizontal table. They are connected by taut, inextensible strings of length a. The middle particle is given an impulse that moves it with initial velocity u perpendicular to the line of the strings. If 2θ denotes the angle ABC, find the subsequent angular velocity of the string AB, and show that A and C will eventually collide with relative speed $2u/\sqrt{3}$. What will be the velocities of A, B and C when the particles are once more in a straight line? (Take the coefficient of restitution as e.)

Solution The position of the particles in the general case is shown in Fig. 10.1. Let v_1 be the velocities of A, B

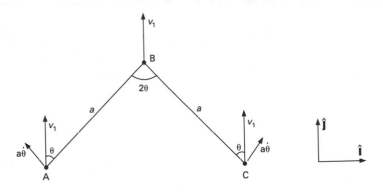

Figure 10.1

and C in the $\hat{\mathbf{j}}$ direction. Also, there will be an additional rotation $-\dot{\theta}$ of A and C about B. This is negative because θ is decreasing. We shall solve this problem by using the conservation of energy and the conservation of momentum. The velocities of A, B and C at time t are as follows:

A: $-a\dot{\theta}\cos\theta\,\hat{\mathbf{i}} + (v_1 + a\dot{\theta}\sin\hat{\theta})\mathbf{j}$

B: $v_1\hat{\mathbf{j}}$

C: $+a\dot{\theta}\cos\theta\hat{\mathbf{i}} + (v_1 + a\dot{\theta}\sin\hat{\theta})\mathbf{j}$

Conservation of momentum gives

$$mu = 3mv_1 + 2ma\dot{\theta}\sin\theta \tag{10.5}$$

Conservation of energy gives

$$\tfrac{1}{2}mu^2 = \tfrac{1}{2}m[v_1^2 + 2(a\dot{\theta}\cos\theta)^2 + 2(v_1 + a\dot{\theta}\sin\theta)^2]$$

which simplifies to

$$u^2 = 3v_1^2 + 4v_1a\dot{\theta}\sin\theta + 2a^2\dot{\theta}^2 \tag{10.6}$$

Squaring Equation (10.5) after first cancelling m gives

$$u^2 = 9v_1^2 - 12av_1\dot{\theta}\sin\theta + 4a^2\dot{\theta}^2\sin^2\theta \tag{10.7}$$

Multiplying Equation (10.6) by 3 gives

$$3u^2 = 9v_1^2 + 12v_1a\dot{\theta}\sin\theta + 6a^2\dot{\theta}^2$$

which, using Equation (10.7) to eliminate v_1 gives

$$2u^2 = 6a^2\dot{\theta}^2 - 4a^2\dot{\theta}^2\sin^2\theta$$

or

$$\dot{\theta}^2 = \frac{u^2}{a^2(3 - 2\sin^2\theta)} = \frac{u^2}{a^2(2 + \cos 2\theta)}$$

Hence the angular velocity of AB is

$$-\frac{u}{a(2 + \cos 2\theta)^{1/2}}$$

(it is negative since θ is decreasing).

When $\theta = 0$, A and C collide. A travels at $a\dot{\theta}\,\hat{\mathbf{i}}$ and C travels at $-a\dot{\theta}\,\hat{\mathbf{i}}$, where $\dot{\theta} = u/a\sqrt{3}$. After impact, their velocities are $-eu\hat{\mathbf{i}}/\sqrt{3}$ and $eu\hat{\mathbf{i}}/\sqrt{3}$, respectively. There is a loss of energy after the impact, and the new total energy is obtained by adding all the contributions:

$$\tfrac{1}{2}m\left[\left(\frac{u}{3}\right)^2 + \left(\frac{-eu}{\sqrt{3}}\right)^2 + \left(\frac{u}{3}\right)^2 + \left(\frac{u}{3}\right)^2 + \left(\frac{eu}{\sqrt{3}}\right)^2\right]$$

$$= \tfrac{1}{6}mu^2(1 + 2e^2)$$

The velocities of A, B and C are now as follows:

A: $\quad -a\dot{\theta}\cos\theta\hat{\mathbf{i}} + (v_2 + a\dot{\theta}\sin\theta)\hat{\mathbf{j}}$

B: $\quad v_2\,\hat{\mathbf{j}}$

C: $\quad a\dot{\theta}\cos\theta\hat{\mathbf{i}} + (v_2 + a\dot{\theta}\sin\theta)\hat{\mathbf{j}}$

where v_2 is the (new) velocity of B. The equations of conservation of energy and momentum are now

$$\tfrac{1}{6}mu^2\,(1 + 2e^2) = \tfrac{1}{2}m(3v_2^2 + 4v_2 a\dot{\theta}\sin\theta + 2a^2\dot{\theta}^2)$$

and

$$mu = 3mv_2 + 2ma\dot{\theta}\sin\theta$$

from which we can eliminate v_2 in a similar fashion to v_1:

$$\frac{u^2}{3}(1 + 2e^2) = 3v_2^2 + 4v_2 a\dot{\theta}\sin\theta + 2a^2\dot{\theta}^2$$

$$u^2 = 9v_2^2 + 12v_2 a\dot{\theta}\sin\theta + 4a^2\dot{\theta}^2\sin^2\theta$$

The second of these equations minus three times the first gives

$$-2u^2e^2 = 4a^2\dot{\theta}^2\sin^2\theta - 6a^2\dot{\theta}^2$$

so that

$$\dot{\theta} = \frac{eu}{a(2 + \cos 2\theta)^{1/2}}$$

(this time it is positive).

When $2\theta = \pi$, $\dot{\theta} = eu/a$ and the particles are in a straight line once more. The velocities of A, B and C are given by:

A: $\quad v_2 + eu$

B: $\quad v_2$

C: $\quad v_2 + eu$

Since $u = 3v_2 + 2a\dot{\theta}\sin\theta$, with $\theta = \pi/2$ this implies

$$u = 3v_2 + 2eu$$

or

$$v_2 = \frac{u}{3}(1 - 2e)$$

so that the velocities of A and C are both $(u/3)(1 + e)$.

10.4 The power output of the engine of a car is given in kW by

$$P = Ane^{-nk}$$

where n is the engine speed in r.p.m. and A and k are constants. The maximum output of 50 kW occurs at 4000 r.p.m. In top gear, 5000 r.p.m. corresponds to 100 km h^{-1}. Obtain the shortest time for the car to accelerate from 50 km h^{-1} to 120 km h^{-1} in top gear if its mass is 1000 kg.

Solution There are several interesting points about this problem. Unusually for a mathematical mechanics example, we need to take care with units. We also make use of *power equals force times speed*.
We are given that

$$P = Ane^{-nk}$$

and that maximum power occurs at $n = 4000$ r.p.m. (revs per minute). For an extreme value,

$$\frac{dP}{dn} = 0$$

Hence, differentiating,

$$Ae^{-nk} - Anke^{-nk} = 0$$

or

$$n = \frac{1}{k}$$

Since

$$\frac{d^2P}{dn^2} = 2kAe^{-nk} + Ak^2ne^{-nk} < 0$$

when $n = 1/k = 4000$ this is clearly a maximum. Hence $k = 1/4000$ ($= 60/4000$ in SI units).
In the next part of the problem, we convert everything to SI units. One kW is 1000 W which is 1000 N m s^{-1}. This gives

$$50\,000 = A\,\frac{4000}{60}\,e^{-1}$$

so that

$$A = 750e$$

In top gear, the number of revolution of the engine is directly proportional to the speed of the car. Hence we can write

$$n = \alpha v$$

where α is a constant. Working in SI units, when $n = 5000/60$ r.p.s.

$$v = 100\,\frac{1000}{3600}\ \text{m s}^{-1}$$

Hence

$$\frac{500}{6} = \alpha\,\frac{1000}{36}$$

giving $\alpha = 3$. The power, written in terms of v in SI units, is thus

$$P = 3Ave^{-3vk}$$

Hence the force exerted by the engine is F, where

$$F = \frac{P}{v} = 3\,Ae^{-3vk}\ \text{N}$$

Using Newton's second law, we thus obtain

$$3Ae^{-3vk} = m\,\frac{\mathrm{d}v}{\mathrm{d}t}$$

where m is the mass of the car and we have neglected any resistance. Separating and integrating gives

$$\frac{m}{3A}\int e^{3vk}\,\mathrm{d}v = \int \mathrm{d}t \tag{10.8}$$

The limits of the left-hand integral are given by 120 km h^{-1} and 50 km h^{-1} (converted to m s^{-1} of course):

$$120\ \text{km h}^{-1} = \frac{100}{3}\ \text{m s}^{-1}$$

and

$$50\ \text{km h}^{-1} = \frac{500}{36}\ \text{m s}^{-1}$$

When $v = 100/3$

$$3vk = 100k = 100\,\frac{1}{4000}\,60 = \tfrac{3}{2}$$

When $v = 50/36$

$$3vk = \frac{50}{12}\,k = \frac{50}{12}\,\frac{1}{4000}\,60 = \tfrac{5}{8}$$

Hence Equation (10.8), on integrating between these limits, gives

$$\frac{m}{3A}\,\frac{1}{3k}\left[e^{3/2} - e^{5/8}\right] = T$$

where T is the required time taken. Inserting the values $m = 1000$ kg, $A = 750e$ and $k = 60/4000 = 3/200$ gives

$$T = \frac{1000}{3.750e}\,\frac{200}{3.3}\left(e^{3/2} - e^{5/8}\right) = T$$

which gives $T = 9.5$ s.

Take care with units in this type of problem.

10.5 A rigid body is initially at rest in equilibrium but subject to an impulse J. The perpendicular distance of the line of action of J from the centre of mass of the body is a. Show that $Ja = I\omega$ where ω is the instantaneous angular velocity of the mass, and I is its moment of inertia about its centre of mass.

Solution The rigid body is shown in Fig. 10.2. Now the torque applied to the body in time δt about G is given by Fa, where $F\delta t = J$, and F is the (extremely large) force applied over the (extremely small) time interval δt.

Using *torque = rate of change of angular momentum,*

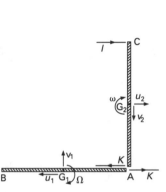

Figure 10.2

$$aF = I \times \text{rate of change in angular velocity}$$

$$= I\frac{\omega}{\delta t}$$

since the body acquires an angular velocity ω in the time δt. Hence

$$\frac{aJ}{\delta t} = \frac{I\omega}{\delta t}$$

or

$$aJ = I\omega$$

as required.

10.6 Two equal uniform rods, AB and AC, freely jointed at A, are placed on a smooth table so as to be at right angles. The rod AC is struck by a blow at C in a direction perpendicular to the rod; show that the resulting velocities of the mid-points of AB and AC are in the ratio 2:7.

Solution Let the velocities of the mid-points of AB and AC be as shown in Fig. 10.3, and let the angular velocities of AB and AC be Ω and ω respectively. Also, let the impulse at C be I, and the impulsive reaction at C be **k** (see Fig. 10.3). We use *Impulse = change in momentum* together with *Torque = rate of change of angular momentum* for AB and AC. We also assume both rods are of mass m.

For AC conservation of momentum parallel to AC gives $mv_2 = 0$. *Impulse = change in momentum* perpendicular to AC gives

$$I - K = mu_2 \tag{10.9}$$

Figure 10.3

Taking moments about G_2 (the centre of mass of AC) gives

$$Ia + Ka = \tfrac{1}{3}ma^2\omega \tag{10.10}$$

since $\tfrac{1}{3}ma^2$ is the moment of inertia, and ω is the (instantaneous) angular velocity of AC.

For AB conservation of momentum perpendicular to AB gives $0 = mv_1$. *Impulse = change in momentum* parallel to AB gives

$$K = -mu_1 \tag{10.11}$$

Taking moments about G_1 (the centre of mass of AB) gives

$$0 = \tfrac{1}{3}ma^2\Omega$$

again since $\tfrac{1}{3}ma^2$ is the moment of inertia, and Ω is the (instantaneous) angular velocity of AB. Straightaway from these six equations we can see that

$$v_2 = v_1 = \Omega = 0$$

Eliminating K from Equations (10.9) and (10.11) gives

$$I = m(u_2 - u_1) \tag{10.12}$$

Using Equations (10.11) and (10.12) in Equation (10.10) gives

$$ma(u_2 - 2u_1) = \tfrac{1}{3}ma^2\omega$$

or

$$u_2 - 2u_1 = \tfrac{1}{3}a\omega \tag{10.13}$$

Now, we also have that, at A, the velocities of both rods must be equal, so that

$$u_2 - a\omega = -u_1$$

or

$$u_2 + u_1 = a\omega \qquad\qquad (10.14)$$

Subtracting Equation (10.13) from Equation (10.14) yields

$$3u_1 = \tfrac{2}{3}\, a\omega$$

or

$$u_1 = \tfrac{2}{9}\, a\omega$$

Now $u_2 = a\omega - u_1$, so

$$u_2 = a\omega - \tfrac{2}{9}\, a\omega = \tfrac{7}{9}\, a\omega$$

Hence

$$u_1 : u_2 = \tfrac{2}{9}\, a\omega : \tfrac{7}{9}\, a\omega = 2 : 7$$

which is the ratio required.

10.7 A rigid body of mass m is at rest. It receives a blow along a line which is a perpendicular distance x from the centre of mass. Show that there are points in the rigid body which are not set in motion. Discuss this with reference to cricket/baseball and snooker/pool.

Solution Let the body have centre of mass at G, and the impulse be J, as illustrated in Fig. 10.4. Using *impulse = change in momentum*, if the body (to be precise, the centre of mass of the body) begins moving with velocity v, then $J = mv$. Since the line of the impulse J is a perpendicular distance x from G, i.e. PG, a turning moment will also be applied to the body. If the body begins to rotate with angular velocity ω, then $Jx = I\omega$.

If we consider the motion of a point A on the line PG produced a distance a from G, then it will have speed $v - a\omega$. This speed will be zero if $v = a\omega$. Eliminating J from the above equations gives

$$mvx = I\omega$$

Hence $v = a\omega$ implies

$$a = \frac{v}{\omega} = \frac{I}{mx}$$

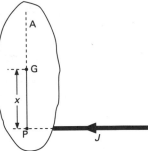

Figure 10.4

The point (strictly, line of points perpendicular to the plane of Fig. 10.4) at which this occurs is sometimes referred to as the **centre of percussion** of the body under the impulse.

If a cricket or baseball bat is struck by an impulse (due to the ball) a distance x from the centre, and we take the bat as being a rod of length $2a$ held at the end, then we ask the question, 'What is the value of x such that the held end does not move?'. In this problem, $I = \tfrac{1}{3} ma^2$ and GA $= a$. Hence

$$a = \frac{v}{\omega} = \tfrac{1}{3} m \frac{a^2}{x}$$

or

$$x = \tfrac{1}{3} a.$$

A point $\tfrac{2}{3}$ of the way along the bat is referred to as 'the meat of the bat' by cricketers and is the ideal place to strike a ball, as there is no reaction at the held end. In reality of course, since the bat is not held at the end but some little way down, one might expect x to be a little less than this value. On the other hand, the bat is not a rod, the handle being flimsier than the blade; hence perhaps $x = a/3$ is more or less correct.

If a snooker or pool ball strikes the cushion, there should be no reaction at the point of contact between the ball and the table. Figure 10.4 can thus be considered upside down, with A on the bottom of a sphere, and the line of J above G. For a solid sphere, $I = \frac{2}{5}ma^2$. Thus for no reaction at A,

$$a = \frac{v}{\omega} = \frac{2a^2}{5x}$$

or $x = \frac{2}{5}a$. This means that, for balls of radius a, the ideal height of the cushion in snooker or pool is $7a/5$ above the floor of the table. For any height other than this the balls will jump as they hit the cushion. Hence always use the correct size balls for the size of a pool/snooker table!

10.8 A cube is rotating with angular velocity ω about a diagonal **d**. A side, not intersecting **d**, is clamped and **d** simultaneously released. What is the new angular velocity of the cube about this side?

Solution Let the cube have side $2a$, and let x-, y- and z-axes be defined as in Fig. 10.5, where AB is the side that is clamped. The direction cosines of ω are $(1/\sqrt{3}, 1/\sqrt{3}, 1/\sqrt{3})$. The angular momentum of the cube about **d** is $\mathbf{h} = I\omega$. The component of **h** in the y-direction is h_y, where

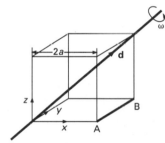

Figure 10.5

$$h_y = \frac{2}{3}ma^2 \frac{\omega}{\sqrt{3}} = \frac{2}{3\sqrt{3}}ma^2\omega$$

Now, as AB is clamped, the angular momentum in the y-direction is conserved. Of course, the other two components, h_x and h_z are not conserved. It is the fact that h_x and h_z (both also equal to $(2/3\sqrt{3})ma^2\omega$) become instantaneously zero as AB is clamped that gives the impulsive jerk or shock that arises as a result of this clamping. In the y-direction, after AB is clamped and becomes the new axis, the new angular velocity is Ω, say. The angular momentum about AB is, using the parallel axes theorem

$$[\tfrac{2}{3}ma^2 + m(a\sqrt{2})^2]\Omega = (\tfrac{2}{3} + 2)ma^2\Omega = \tfrac{8}{3}ma^2\Omega$$

This component of angular momentum is conserved; hence

$$\tfrac{8}{3}ma^2\Omega = \frac{2}{3\sqrt{3}}ma^2\omega$$

giving

$$\Omega = \frac{\omega}{4\sqrt{3}}$$

10.9 A small bead of mass m is thrown so that it slides around the inside of a smooth hemispherical bowl of radius a. If ω is the angular velocity of the bead (considered a particle) show that the circular path of the bead is at a depth of g/ω^2 below the rim of the bowl. Show further that the period of small oscillation of the bead about this path is

$$2\pi \left(\frac{a \cos \alpha}{g(1 + 3\cos^2 \alpha)} \right)^{1/2}$$

where 2α is the angle subtended by the diameter of the bead's path at the centre of the circle that forms the rim of the hemisphere.

Solution Figure 10.6 shows the bead of mass m and its circular path on the hemispherical bowl. Since the bowl is smooth, we can find an energy equation. Take the bottom of the bowl as the level of zero potential; then the potential energy (PE) of the bead, using θ as shown in Fig. 10.6, is $mga(1 - \cos \theta)$.

159

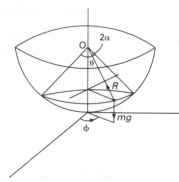

Figure 10.6

The velocity of the bead is $(a \sin \theta)\dot{\phi}$ along the circular path $\theta = $ constant and $a\dot{\theta}$ meridionally ($\phi = $ constant) if the bead is displaced from this circular path. The kinetic energy (KE) of the bead is thus

$$\tfrac{1}{2}(a^2\dot{\theta}^2 + a^2 \sin^2\theta\dot{\phi}^2)$$

Demanding that KE + PE is a constant thus leads to the equation

$$\tfrac{1}{2}ma^2(\dot{\theta}^2 + \sin^2\theta\dot{\phi}^2) + mga(1 - \cos\theta) = K \tag{10.15}$$

Consider the angular momentum of the bead in the $\hat{\phi}$ direction. The only forces acting, R and mg, are perpendicular to $\hat{\phi}$; hence the torque in the $\hat{\phi}$ direction is zero. The angular momentum in the $\hat{\phi}$ direction is thus constant, which implies that

$$ma^2\sin^2\theta\hat{\dot{\phi}} = h = \text{constant}$$

On the circular path, $\theta = \alpha = $ constant, and $\dot{\phi} = \omega$, giving

$$\sin^2\theta\dot{\phi} = \sin^2\alpha\ \omega$$

Hence

$$\dot{\phi} = \frac{\omega\sin^2\alpha}{\sin^2\theta}$$

Substituting for $\dot{\phi}$ in Equation (10.15) gives

$$\tfrac{1}{2}ma^2\left(\dot{\theta}^2 + \frac{\omega^2\sin^4\alpha}{\sin^2\theta}\right) + mga(1 - \cos\theta) = K \tag{10.16}$$

In order to investigate the stability (or otherwise) of the bead, we differentiate Equation (10.16) with respect to t and treat θ as being close to α. Differentiating in this way gives

$$a\ddot{\theta} - \frac{a\omega^2\ \sin^4\alpha}{\sin^3\theta}\ \cos\theta + g\sin\theta = 0 \tag{10.17}$$

The equilibrium value of θ occurs when $\ddot{\theta} = 0$ ($\theta = \alpha$), whence Equation (10.18) becomes

$$-\frac{a\omega^2\sin^4\alpha}{\sin^3\alpha}\ \cos\alpha + g\sin\alpha = 0$$

or

$$\sin\alpha(-a\omega^2\cos\alpha + g) = 0$$

giving

$$a\omega^2\cos\alpha = g \qquad (\alpha \neq 0)$$

Hence, the depth of the bead below O, $a\cos\alpha$, is g/ω^2. Substituting $g/\cos\alpha$ for $a\omega^2$ in Equation (10.17) gives

$$a\ddot{\theta} - \frac{g\sin^4\alpha\ \cos\theta}{\cos\alpha\ \sin^3\theta} + g\sin\theta = 0$$

We are now in a position to put $\theta = \alpha + \varepsilon$ and consider ε to be small. This gives $\ddot{\theta} = \ddot{\varepsilon}$;

$$\cos\theta = \cos(\alpha + \varepsilon) \approx \cos\alpha - \varepsilon\sin\alpha \qquad \text{to } O(\varepsilon^2)$$

and

$$\sin\theta = \sin(\alpha + \varepsilon) \approx \sin\alpha + \varepsilon\cos\alpha \qquad \text{to } O(\varepsilon^2)$$

Hence

$$\frac{\sin^4\alpha\,\cos\theta}{\cos\alpha\,\sin^3\theta} \approx \frac{\sin^4\alpha(\cos\alpha - \varepsilon\sin\alpha)}{\cos\alpha(\sin\alpha + \varepsilon\cos\alpha)^3}$$

$$= \frac{\sin^4\alpha\,\cos\alpha}{\cos\alpha\,\sin^3\alpha}\left(1 - \varepsilon\frac{\sin\alpha}{\cos\alpha}\right)\left(1 + \varepsilon\frac{\cos\alpha}{\sin\alpha}\right)^{-3}$$

$$= \sin\alpha\left(1 - \varepsilon\frac{\sin\alpha}{\cos\alpha} - 3\varepsilon\frac{\cos\alpha}{\sin\alpha} + O(\varepsilon^2)\right)$$

Thus, for small values of ε

$$a\ddot{\varepsilon} - g\sin\alpha\left[1 - \varepsilon\left(\frac{\sin\alpha}{\cos\alpha} + \frac{3\cos\alpha}{\sin\alpha}\right)\right] + g(\sin\alpha + \varepsilon\cos\alpha) = 0$$

or

$$a\ddot{\varepsilon} + \varepsilon g\left(\frac{\sin^2\alpha}{\cos\alpha} + 3\cos\alpha + \cos\alpha\right) = 0$$

whence

$$a\ddot{\varepsilon} + \frac{\varepsilon g}{\cos\alpha}(1 + 3\cos^2\alpha) = 0$$

which is periodic motion, of period

$$2\pi\left(\frac{a\cos\alpha}{g(1 + 3\cos^2\alpha)}\right)$$

10.10 A rectangular picture of mass m hangs from a smooth nail O by an inextensible string of length $2a$, tied to two points A and B symmetrically placed on the upper edge, a distance a apart. The picture has depth $2d$ and the centre of gravity lies at the point of intersection of the diagonals of the picture. Discuss the equilibrium of the picture.

Solution In Fig. 10.7 the picture is shown hanging from the nail. The angle made by its upper edge with the horizontal is θ. The reaction R of the string AOB on the nail at O is equal to the weight W of the picture (plus string). Therefore G is directly below O. The two tensions in the strings OA, OB are equal since the nail is smooth. Thus the angles that the two parts of the string, OA and OB, make with the vertical, OG, must be equal (resolving horizontally).

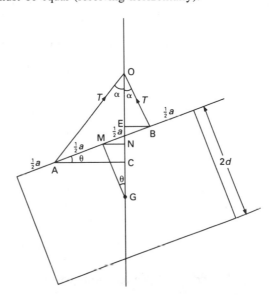

Figure 10.7

The potential energy of the picture is proportional to the distance OG. Therefore if OG is a maximum or minimum, the picture will be in equilibrium. We use trigonometry in order to obtain an expression for OG in terms of one variable (θ). To do this, we find two expressions for OG in terms of θ and α, then eliminate α. Denote by M the mid-point of AB. Elementary trignometry gives

$$OG = OC + NG - NC$$
$$= OA \cos\alpha + d\cos\theta - \tfrac{1}{2} a \sin\theta$$

Also

$$OG = OE + NG + EN$$
$$= OB \cos\alpha + d\cos\theta + \tfrac{1}{2} a \sin\theta$$

Adding these two expressions gives

$$2OG = (OA + OB) \cos\alpha + 2d\cos\theta$$

or

$$OG = a\cos\alpha + d\cos\theta$$

(since OA + OB = 2a). Also, since BE + AC = AB $\cos\theta$ we have

$$(OA + OB)\sin\alpha = a\cos\theta$$

so that

$$2\sin\alpha = \cos\theta$$

Hence

$$\cos\alpha = \tfrac{1}{2} (4 - \cos^2\theta)^{1/2}$$

We can now express OG solely in terms of θ as follows:

$$OG = d\cos\theta + \tfrac{1}{2} a(4 - \cos^2\theta)^{1/2}$$

The potential energy function is gOG; thus

$$V(\theta) = gd\cos\theta + \tfrac{1}{2} ga(4 - \cos^2\theta)^{1/2}$$

To find the equilibrium positions, we set $V'(\theta) = 0$:

$$-gd \sin\theta + \tfrac{1}{4} ga(4 - \cos^2\theta)^{-1/2} \, 2 \cos\theta \, \sin\theta = 0$$

i.e.

$$g\sin\theta\left(-d + \frac{a\cos\theta}{2(4 - \cos^2\theta)^{1/2}}\right) = 0$$

where, of course, $0 \leq \theta \leq \pi/2$. The roots of this equation in this range are

$$\theta = 0, \qquad \cos^{-1}[4d/(4d^2 + a^2)^{1/2}]$$

provided $4d/(4d^2 + a^2)^{1/2} \leq 1$, i.e. $d < a\sqrt{3}/6$.

Let us investigate the stability of these two positions. First, take $\theta = 0$. Since

$$V(\theta) = gd\cos\theta + \tfrac{1}{2}ga(4 - \cos^2\theta)^{1/2}$$

near $\theta = 0$, we may write $\cos\theta \approx 1 - \tfrac{1}{2} \varepsilon^2$ (ε is a small number). This gives

$$V(\theta) = g(d + \tfrac{1}{2}a\sqrt{3}) + \tfrac{1}{2}g\varepsilon^2(\tfrac{1}{2}a - d)$$

Since $a > 2d\sqrt{3}$, $\tfrac{1}{2}a - d = d\sqrt{3} - d > 0$. Hence the coefficient of $\varepsilon^2 > 0$ and the equilibrium position is stable.

For $\theta = \theta_0$,

$$\cos\theta_0 = 4d/(a^2 + 4d^2)^{1/2}$$

This time we let $\theta = \theta_0 + \varepsilon$, where ε is small, so that

$$\cos\theta \approx (1 - \tfrac{1}{2}\varepsilon^2)\cos\theta_0 - \varepsilon\sin\theta_0$$

This gives

$$V(\theta) = V(\theta_0 + \varepsilon) = gd\cos\theta_0 + \tfrac{1}{2}ga(4 - \cos^2\theta_0)^{1/2} + \varepsilon\left(-gd\sin\theta_0 + \frac{ga\sin\theta_0\cos\theta_0}{2(4 - \cos^2\theta_0)^{1/2}}\right)$$

$$+ \varepsilon^2\left(-\tfrac{1}{2}gd\cos^2\theta_0 - \frac{ag\sin^2\theta_0}{4(4 - \cos^2\theta_0)} - \frac{ag\sin^2\theta_0\cos^2\theta_0}{16(4 - \cos^2\theta_0)^2}\right)$$

to terms in ε^2. Since $4 - \cos^2\theta_0 = 4a^2/(a^2 + 4d^2)$, we see that the coefficient of ε is zero (as required). Moreover, all the terms in the coefficient of ε^2 are negative definite. Hence θ_0 is an unstable equilibrium point.

10.3 Exercises

10.1 A smooth fixed sphere of radius a stands on a horizontal plane and a particle is slightly displaced from rest at its highest point. Show that the horizontal distance from the point of contact of the sphere with the plane to the point where the particle strikes the plane is $5a(\sqrt{5} + 4\sqrt{2})/27$.   (L.U.)

10.2 An alternative definition of *conservative* is that the work done by the force $\mathbf{F}$ is independent of the path. Show that, using this definition, $\nabla \times \mathbf{F} = \mathbf{0}$. Hence establish whether or not the following fields are conservative, and for those that are find the potential function.

(a) $-\dfrac{\mu\hat{\mathbf{r}}}{r^2}$, (b) $\mathbf{r}$, (c) $(\mathbf{a}\cdot\mathbf{r})\mathbf{r}$, (d) $(\mathbf{a}\cdot\mathbf{r})\mathbf{a}$, (e) $\mathbf{a} \times \mathbf{r}$,

(f) $(3x^2y,x^3 + z^3,3yz^2)$

where $\mathbf{r} = (x,y,z)$ and $\mathbf{a}$ is a constant vector.

For case (f), calculate the work done in moving a unit mass from the point $(1,1,1)$ to the point $(2,4,8)$ along the cubic $x = t$, $y = t^2$, $z = t^3$.

10.3 A particle moves along the x-axis under the action of a force $-\mu/x^2$ ($\mu > 0$) per unit mass in the x-direction. Initially $\dot{x} > 0$. Establish the energy equation in the form

$$\tfrac{1}{2}\dot{x}^2 = E + \frac{\mu}{x}$$

where E is a constant.

(a) Show that if $E = -\mu/2a$ ($a > 0$), the particle comes to rest and then falls into the origin. By writing $x = a(1 + \cos\theta)$ obtain t in terms of θ.
(b) If $E = 0$, show that

$$x^{3/2} = 3(\mu/2)^{1/2}t + K$$

(c) If $E = \mu/2a$, write $x = a(\cosh\phi - 1)$ to obtain t in terms of ϕ.

10.4 A particle of mass 2 kg is initially at a distance 3 m from the origin along the positive x-axis, and has velocity 2 m s^{-1} parallel to the positive direction of the y-axis. The particle moves under the influence of a force of magnitude $48/r^2$ N directed towards the origin. Show that in the motion

$$\dot{r}^2 = -12 + \frac{48}{r} - \frac{36}{r^2}$$

and determine the path of the mass.

10.5 A lorry of weight W kg can generate power P and has a maximum speed of u m s^{-1} on level ground, but v m s^{-1} on an up-slope α. If the power and resistance remain unchanged, prove that

$$uvW\sin\alpha = P(u - v)$$

10.6 A uniform circular disc can move in its own plane and is rotating with angular velocity ω about a point A on the circumference. It is suddenly seized at a point B diametrically opposite to A which is simultaneously released. Find the new angular velocity of the disc.

10.7 A ruler, considered inelastic, is falling vertically without rotation. It is inclined to the vertical and hits a smooth peg one third along its length from the upper end. Show that at impact the lower end begins to fall vertically.

10.8 AB and CD are two equal and similar rods connected by a string BC, AB, BC and CD form three sides of a square. The point A of the rod AB is struck a blow in a direction perpendicular to the rod; show that the initial velocity of A is seven times that of D.

10.9 A smooth semi-circular wire is fixed in a vertical plane with the diameter vertical. A bead of weight w slides on the wire and is connected to the topmost point of the wire by a light spring of modulus $2w$ and natural length equal to the diameter of the wire. A constant horizontal force of magnitude $2w$ in the plane of the wire and outwards from the diameter acts on the bead. Show that there is a position of stable equilibrium in which the spring makes an angle $\pi/6$ with the vertical, and find the period of small oscillations about this position if the diameter of the wire is d.

10.10 A smooth right circular cone of angle 2α is fixed with its axis vertical and its vertex downwards. A particle A of mass m is held in contact with the smooth inner surface of the cone at a height h above the vertex and is connected with a second particle B of mass $mk\cos\alpha$ by a light inextensible string which passes through a small hole in the vertex. If A is then projected horizontally along the surface of the cone with speed $(2gh)^{1/2}$, show that z, the height of A above the vertex at time t, satisfies the equation

$$(1 + k\cos\alpha)z^2\dot{z}^2\sec^2\alpha = 2g[-(1 + k)z^3 + (2 + k)hz^2 - h^3]$$

Deduce that if $k = 5$ the motion of A always lies between two horizontal circles. Determine the position of these circles.

(L.U.)

10.4 Outline Solutions to Exercises

10.1 The particle slides down the sphere until the reaction vanishes. Since

$$m(\ddot{r} - r\dot{\theta}^2) = R - mg\cos\theta$$

and also $r = a$, $R = 0$ when

$$\dot{\theta}^2 = \frac{g}{a}\cos\theta \qquad \textbf{(10.18)}$$

Using energy,

$$PE = -mag(1 - \cos\theta)$$

$$KE = \tfrac{1}{2}m(a\dot{\theta})^2$$

and $PE + KE = 0$ on taking the top of the sphere as zero potential. Hence

$$\dot{\theta}^2 = 2\frac{g}{a}(1 - \cos\theta) \qquad \textbf{(10.19)}$$

Comparing Equations (10.18) and (10.19) gives $\cos\theta = \frac{2}{3}$, $\sin\theta = \frac{1}{3}\sqrt{5}$. Hence the distance the mass needs to fall as a projectile is $5a/3$.

At the point of leaving the sphere, the horizontal and vertical velocities are

$$a\dot{\theta}\cos\theta = \frac{2}{3}\left(\frac{2ag}{3}\right)^{1/2}$$

and

$$a\dot{\theta}\sin\theta = \frac{1}{3}\left(\frac{10ag}{3}\right)^{1/2}$$

respectively. We now use the well-known projectile equations. In order to reach the ground, i.e. fall $5a/3$ in a time t:

$$\frac{5}{3}a = \frac{t}{3}\left(\frac{10ag}{3}\right)^{1/2} + \frac{1}{2}gt^2$$

so

$$t = (10 - \sqrt{10})\left(\frac{a}{27g}\right)^{1/2}$$

Thus the horizontal distance travelled as a projectile is

$$a\frac{2}{3}\sqrt{\frac{2}{3}}(10 - \sqrt{10})\frac{1}{\sqrt{27}} = \frac{a}{27}(20\sqrt{2} - 2\sqrt{20})$$

Add to this $(a/3)\sqrt{5}$, the horizontal distance from the vertical diameter of the sphere to the projection point to obtain the total horizontal distance:

$$h = \frac{a}{27}(20\sqrt{2} - 2\sqrt{20} + 9\sqrt{5}) = \frac{5a}{27}(\sqrt{5} + 4\sqrt{2})$$

10.2 We are given that if $\mathbf{F}$ is conservative then the work done in moving a mass under $\mathbf{F}$ from A to B is independent of the path. Take two such paths (see Fig. 10.8). Then

$$\int_{C_1}\mathbf{F}\cdot d\mathbf{r} = \int_{C_2}\mathbf{F}\cdot d\mathbf{r}$$

or

$$\int_C\mathbf{F}\cdot d\mathbf{r} = 0$$

where $C = C_1 - C_2$. Hence

$$\int_S\nabla\times\mathbf{F}\cdot d\mathbf{S} = 0$$

using Stokes' theorem (or Green's theorem on the plane). This is zero for every S, hence $\nabla\times\mathbf{F} = \mathbf{0}$ everywhere. Since $\nabla\times\mathbf{F} = \mathbf{0}$; there exists a value ϕ such that $\mathbf{F} = \nabla\phi$, so a potential function exists.

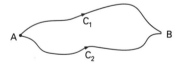

Figure 10.8

To those familiar with curvilinear coordinates, for (a) and (b), $\nabla\times\mathbf{F} = \mathbf{0}$ using spherical polar coordinates (trivially). Otherwise: (a)

$$\mathbf{F} = -\mu\left(\frac{x}{r^3}, \frac{y}{r^3}, \frac{z}{r^3}\right)$$

$$\nabla\times\mathbf{F} = -\mu\left[\frac{\partial}{\partial y}\left(\frac{z}{r^3}\right) - \frac{\partial}{\partial z}\left(\frac{y}{r^3}\right), \frac{\partial}{\partial z}\left(\frac{x}{r^3}\right) - \frac{\partial}{\partial x}\left(\frac{z}{r^3}\right),\right.$$

$$\left.\frac{\partial}{\partial x}\left(\frac{y}{r^3}\right) - \frac{\partial}{\partial y}\left(\frac{x}{r^3}\right)\right]$$

$$= 3\mu\left(\frac{yz}{r^5} - \frac{zy}{r^5}, \frac{zx}{r^5} - \frac{xz}{r^5}, \frac{yx}{r^5} - \frac{xy}{r^5}\right) = 0$$

and integration reveals that $\phi = -\mu/r$.

(b) $\mathbf{F} = (x, y, z) \Rightarrow \nabla \times \mathbf{F} = 0$ and $\phi = \frac{1}{2}r^2$.

(c) $\mathbf{F} = (\mathbf{a}\cdot\mathbf{r})\mathbf{r}$

$$\nabla \times \mathbf{F} = \nabla \times [(a_1 x + a_2 y + a_3 z)x, (a_1 x + a_2 y + a_3 z)y,$$
$$(a_1 x + a_2 y + a_3 z)z]$$

$$= (a_2 z - a_3 y, a_3 x - a_1 z, a_1 y - a_2 x) = \mathbf{a} \times \mathbf{r} \neq 0$$

(d) $\mathbf{F} = (\mathbf{a}\cdot\mathbf{r})\mathbf{a} = (a_1 x + a_2 y + a_3 z)\mathbf{a}$

$$\Rightarrow \nabla \times \mathbf{F} = (a_2 a_3 - a_3 a_2, a_3 a_1 - a_1 a_3, a_1 a_2 - a_2 a_1) = 0$$

$$\phi = \frac{1}{2}a_1^2 x^2 + \frac{1}{2}a_2^2 y^2 + \frac{1}{2}a_3^2 z^2 + a_1 a_2 xy + a_1 a_3 xz + a_2 a_3 yz$$

(e) $\mathbf{F} = \mathbf{a} \times \mathbf{r} = (a_2 z - a_3 y, a_3 x - a_1 z, a_1 y - a_2 x)$ so

$$\nabla \times \mathbf{F} = (a_1 + a_1, a_2 + a_2, a_3 + a_3) = 2\mathbf{a} \neq 0$$

(f) $\mathbf{F} = (3x^2 y, x^3 + z^3, 3yz^2)$

$$\nabla \times \mathbf{F} = (3z^2 - 3z^2, 0 - 0, 3x^2 - 3x^2) = 0$$

so

$$\frac{\partial\phi}{\partial x} = 3x^2 y$$

$$\frac{\partial\phi}{\partial y} = x^3 + z^3$$

and

$$\frac{\partial\phi}{\partial z} = 3yz^2$$

from which

$$\phi = x^3 y + z^3 y = y(x^3 + z^3)$$

For case (f), since $\mathbf{F}$ is conservative the work done is independent of the path and is $\phi_B - \phi_A$, where $B = (2, 4, 8)$ and $A = (1, 1, 1)$, so work done $= 4(8 + 512) - 1(1 + 1) = 2078$ N m.

10.3 From

$$m\ddot{x} = -\frac{m\mu}{x^2}$$

cancel ms, multiply by $\dot{x}$ and integrate (constant of integration E) to obtain

$$\frac{1}{2}\dot{x}^2 = E + \frac{\mu}{x}$$

(a) If $E = \mu/2a$ then $\dot{x}^2 = (\mu/2ax)(2a - x)$ and x must lie between $x = 0$ and $x = 2a$ (otherwise $\dot{x}^2 < 0$). This is typical of 'orbit' problems with negative total energy. As $x \to 0$, $\dot{x} \to \infty$ and the particle 'falls into' $x = 0$. Writing $x = a(1 + \cos\theta)$ so that $2a - x = a(1 - \cos\theta)$ we obtain

$$\dot{x}^2 = \frac{\mu}{a}\left(\frac{1 - \cos\theta}{1 + \cos\theta}\right).$$

Also,

$$\frac{dx}{dt} = \frac{dx}{d\theta}\frac{d\theta}{dt} = -a\sin\theta\frac{d\theta}{dt}$$

Hence

$$\dot{x}^2 = a^2(1 - \cos^2\theta)\dot{\theta}^2$$

Substituting for $\dot{x}^2$ gives

$$a^2(1 + \cos^2\theta)^2\left(\frac{d\theta}{dt}\right)^2 = \frac{\mu}{a}$$

so that

$$a\int(1 + \cos\theta)d\theta = \left(\frac{\mu}{a}\right)^{1/2}t + C_1$$

on integrating, or

$$a(\theta + \sin\theta) = t\left(\frac{\mu}{a}\right)^{1/2} + C_1$$

Thus

$$t = (\theta + \sin\theta)\left(\frac{a^3}{\mu}\right)^{1/2} + C$$

If $t = 0$ when $\theta = 0$, $C = 0$ and $x = a(1 + \cos\theta)$, $t = (\theta + \sin\theta)(a^3/\mu)^{1/2}$ give the parametric equations of a slightly distorted cycloid (unless $a^3 = \mu$, in which case it is a true cycloid).

(b) $\dot{x}^2 = \dfrac{2\mu}{x}$

or

$$\frac{dx}{dt} = \left(\frac{2\mu}{a}\right)^{1/2}$$

or

$$\frac{2}{3}x^{3/2} = t(2\mu)^{1/2} + \text{constant}$$

so

$$x^{3/2} = 3\left(\frac{\mu}{2}\right)^{1/2}t + K$$

as required.

(c) If $E = \mu/2a$, then $\dot{x}^2 = (\mu/ax)(2a + x)$. With $x = a(\cosh\phi - 1)$ the algebra is very similar to part (a). Completing the algebra gives

$$t = \left(\frac{a^3}{\mu}\right)^{1/2}(\sinh\phi - \phi) + C'$$

As $t \to \infty$, in this case $\dot{x} \to (\mu/a)^{1/2}$ and the particle moves to infinity at a rate which tends to this constant value.

10.4 The potential energy $V(r)$ due to the force $-48/r^2$ is its negative integral, $-48/r$. The energy equation is thus

$$\frac{1}{2}\cdot 2 \cdot v^2 - \frac{48}{r} = \text{constant}$$

In polar coordinates,

$$v^2 = \dot{r}^2 + (r\dot{\theta})^2$$

For a central force (see Chapter 8) $r^2\dot{\theta} = h = $ constant. Hence

$$\dot{r}^2 + \frac{h^2}{r^2} - \frac{48}{r} = \text{constant} \qquad (10.20)$$

Initially, $r = 3$, $r\dot{\theta} = 2$, $\dot{r} = 0$, giving $h = 6$, whence $v^2 = 4$ and the constant on the right of Equation (10.20) is $4 - 48/3 = -12$. Equation (10.20) is thus

$$\dot{r}^2 + \frac{36}{r} - \frac{48}{r^2} = -12 \qquad (10.21)$$

as required.

To find the extent of the orbit, set $\dot{r} = 0$

$$r^2 - 4r + 3 = 0$$

$$(r - 3)(r - 1) = 0$$

So r lies between 1 and 3.

To find the path, write $u = 1/r$ so that $\dot{\theta} = u^2 h$, $\dot{r}^2 = h^2 (du/d\theta)^2$. Equation (10.21) thus gives

$$h^2 \left(\frac{du}{d\theta}\right)^2 = -12 + 48u - 36u^2$$

or, with $h = 6$

$$3 \left(\frac{du}{d\theta}\right)^2 = -1 + 4u - 3u^2$$

$$= \tfrac{1}{3} [1 - (3u - 2)^2]$$

whence

$$3 \frac{du}{d\theta} = [1 - (3u - 2)^2]^{1/2}$$

which integrates to

$$\sin^{-1} (3u - 2) = \theta + \varepsilon$$

or

$$\frac{3}{r} = 2 + \sin(\theta + \varepsilon)$$

an ellipse with eccentricity $1\sqrt{2}$, semi-latus rectum $3\sqrt{2}$.

10.5 We use *power = force × velocity*. On the level, if μ is the coefficient of friction then

$$P = Fu$$

where F is the frictional force. $R = W$, where R is the reaction and $F = \mu R$, so

$$P = \mu u W$$

On the slope, the force downwards is $W \sin \alpha + F$. Hence

$$P = (W \sin \alpha + F)v$$

$$= W v \sin \alpha + \frac{Pv}{u}$$

giving $uvW \sin \alpha = P(u - v)$, as required.

10.6 Figure 10.9 shows the disc and the points about which it revolves. The change in angular momentum = moment of impulse about A. Applying this ($I = \frac{1}{2} ma^2$), gives

$$\tfrac{1}{2}ma^2\omega + ma^2\omega - \tfrac{1}{2}ma^2\Omega - ma^2\Omega = 2ma\omega a$$

from which $3\omega - 3\Omega = 4\omega$ or $\Omega = -\omega/3$ is the new angular velocity.

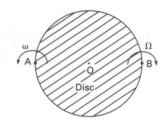

Figure 10.9

10.7 Figure 10.10 shows the ruler. The entire ruler falls with speed v. Its moment of inertia about its centre of mass is $\frac{1}{3}ma^2$ if its length is $2a$ and mass is m. If the impulse is I then impulse = change in momentum about the centre of mass gives

$$I\tfrac{1}{3}a = \tfrac{1}{3}ma^2\omega$$

Also, $I = mV$, where V is the speed of the ruler imparted by the blow in the same direction as I. At the end marked A, apart from the speed v downwards, there is no other velocity since $V = a\omega$. Hence the lower end (A) falls vertically.

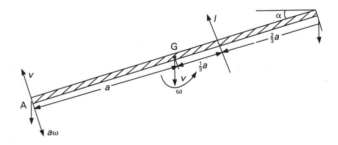

Figure 10.10

10.8 Adopting the notation of Fig. 10.11, at the instant A is struck, BC goes taut, tension T. All motion will be parallel to BC, and the centres of mass G_1 and G_2 will move with speeds u and v respectively. Thus

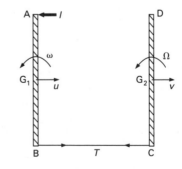

Figure 10.11

and

$$T - I = mu$$

$$-T = mv$$

Moments about G_1:

$$Ia + Ta = \tfrac{1}{3}ma^2\omega$$

Moments about G_2:

$$-Ta = \tfrac{1}{3}ma^2\Omega$$

Eliminating I and T from these four equations gives

$$3v = a\Omega$$

and

$$-u - 2v = \tfrac{1}{3}a\omega$$

The speed of B is $u + a\omega$ = speed of C = $v + a\Omega$. Hence

$$u - 3(u + 2v) = v + 3v$$

so

$$-2u = 10v \quad \text{or} \quad u = -5v.$$

$$\text{Speed of A} = a\omega - u = -3u - 6v - u$$

$$= (-6 + 20)v = 14v$$

$$\text{Speed of D} = a\Omega - v = 3v - v = 2v$$

Thus the speed of A is seven times that of D.

10.9 Figure 10.12 shows the physical situation. N is the normal reaction of the wire on the bead. $T = 2w(1 - \cos\theta)$, where T is the tension in the spring and θ is the angle the spring makes with the vertical. The equations of motion are

$$\frac{w}{g}(\ddot{r} - r\dot{\theta}^2) = w\cos\theta + 2w\sin\theta + T - N\cos\theta \quad \textbf{(10.22)}$$

and

$$\frac{w}{gr}\frac{d}{dt}(r^2\dot{\theta}) = -w\sin\theta + 2w\cos\theta - N\sin\theta$$

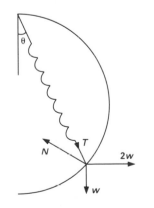

Figure 10.12

$r = d\cos\theta$, hence $\dot{r} = -d\sin\theta\dot{\theta}$ and $\ddot{r} = -d\cos\theta\dot{\theta}^2 - d\sin\theta\ddot{\theta}$. Obviously, for equilibrium, $\dot{\theta} = 0$ and $\ddot{\theta} = 0$, from which

$$0 = w\cos\theta + 2w\sin\theta + 2w(1 - \cos\theta) - N\cos\theta$$

$$0 = -w\sin\theta + 2w\cos\theta - N\sin\theta$$

giving

$$N = 2w\cot\theta - w$$

and hence

$$0 = 2\sin^2\theta + 2\sin\theta - 2 + 2\sin^2\theta$$

so that $\sin\theta = \tfrac{1}{2}, -1$, from which the only sensible root is $\theta = \pi/6$, as required.

Near $\theta = \pi/6$, $\cos\theta = \sqrt{3}/2 - \varepsilon/2$, $\sin\theta = \tfrac{1}{2} + (\sqrt{3}/2)\varepsilon$; hence $r = d\cos\theta = d\sqrt{3}/2 - (d/2)\varepsilon$.

Equation (10.22) with these values of θ etc. becomes

$$\frac{w}{g}(-2d\cos\theta\dot{\theta}^2 - d\sin\theta\ddot{\theta}) = w\cos\theta + 2w\sin\theta$$
$$+ 2w(1 - \cos\theta) - N\cos\theta$$

or

$$\frac{d}{4g}\ddot{\varepsilon} = 3\sqrt{3}\varepsilon \quad \text{where} \quad \theta = \frac{\pi}{6} + \varepsilon, \; \varepsilon << 1$$

giving a period of $\pi(d/3g\sqrt{3})^{1/2}$.

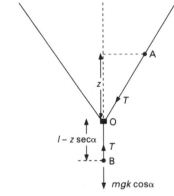

Figure 10.13

10.10 Let the length of the string be l, so that the setup is as shown in Fig. 10.13. Take the orifice O as the origin, and $\dot{\theta}$, the angular velocity of particle A, into the paper. Conservation of momentum gives

$$(z\tan\alpha)^2\dot{\theta} = c$$

$$\text{PE} = mgz - mk(l - z\sec\alpha)\cos\alpha$$

$$\text{KE} = \tfrac{1}{2}mk\cos\alpha(z\sec\alpha)^2 + \tfrac{1}{2}m(z\tan\alpha)^2\dot{\theta}^2 + \tfrac{1}{2}m(\dot{z}\sec\alpha)^2$$

Initially, $z = h$, $\dot{\theta}h\tan\alpha = (2gh)^{1/2}$ and $\dot{z} = 0$, so that $c = (2gh^3)^{1/2}\tan\alpha$. Demanding that total energy = constant thus gives

$$gzk + gz + \tfrac{1}{2}\dot{z}^2k\sec\alpha + \tfrac{1}{2}2gh^3\frac{1}{z^2} + \tfrac{1}{2}\dot{z}^2\sec^2\alpha = gh(2 + k)$$

which, when rearranged, gives the required equation.

With $k = 5$, the right-hand side is $2g(6z - h)(h^2 - z^2)$. In order for the roots to be positive $\tfrac{1}{6}h \leq z \leq h$, so A lies between the circles $z = h/6$ and $z = h$.

Topic Guide

Generalised Force
Lagrangian
Euler's Equation
Ignorable Coordinate
Normal Modes in Holonomic
Systems

11 Lagrangian Dynamics

11.1 Fact Sheet

If a dynamical system is completely described by a set of scalar coordinates $q_1, q_2, \ldots, q_k$, then a constraint which can be written

$$\phi(q_1, q_2, \ldots, q_n, t) = 0$$

is called **holonomic**. $(q_1, q_2, \ldots, q_n)$ are called the **generalised coordinates**. If all the constraints are holonomic and no subset of its coordinates specifies the system completely then n is the **number of degrees of freedom** of the system.

If the coordinates q_i have associated velocities $\dot{q}_1$, then the kinetic energy

$$T = T(q_1, q_2, \ldots, q_n, \dot{q}_1, \dot{q}_2, \ldots, \dot{q}_n)$$

If V is the potential energy, which is a function of $(q_1, q_2, \ldots, q_n, t)$, but not of the generalised velocities $(q_1, \dot{q}_2, \ldots, q_n)$, then the Lagrangian L is defined by

$$L = T - V$$

If there are n particles, with the force on the jth particle being $\mathbf{F}_j$ and its position vector being $\mathbf{r}_j$, then we define

$$Q_j = \sum_{j=1}^{n} \mathbf{F}_j \cdot \frac{\partial \mathbf{r}_j}{\partial q_i}$$

as the **generalised force** on the ith particle. The infinitesimal displacement δq_i is called the virtual displacement of the ith particle. Then for a conservative holonomic system, for each particle

$$Q_t = -\frac{\partial V}{\partial q_i}$$

Also, for a conservative holonomic system,

$$\frac{\mathrm{d}}{\mathrm{d}t}\left(\frac{\partial L}{\partial \dot{q}_i}\right) - \frac{\partial L}{\partial q_i} = 0 \qquad \text{for all } i = 1,2,\ldots,n$$

For a non-conservative system,

$$\frac{\mathrm{d}}{\mathrm{d}t}\left(\frac{\partial T}{\partial \dot{q}_i}\right) - \frac{\partial T}{\partial q_i} = Q_i \qquad \text{for all } i = 1,2,\ldots,n$$

A cautionary note: Despite their appearance, Lagrange's equations in the form introduced here cannot solve all dynamics problems. For example, consider the following general problem types: (a) masses connected over pulleys and (b) beads sliding on wires that are rotating. In case (a), Lagrange's equations can never determine the tensions in the strings. In case (b), Lagrange's equations can never determine the reaction between the bead and the wire. Both are internal forces. Note also that, despite the smoothness of the wire, in case (b) energy is not conserved because the revolving wire transfers energy to the bead *without* it slowing (see Exercise 11.3, for which this may be regarded as a hint!). This is an example of constrained motion, further discussion of which is outside the scope of this text. See treatises on analytical dynamics, e.g. Woodhouse (1987).

11.2 Worked Examples

11.1 If $\dot{r} = \mathbf{r}(q_1, q_2, \ldots, q_n, t)$, show that

$$\frac{\partial \dot{\mathbf{r}}}{\partial \dot{q}_i} = \frac{\partial \mathbf{r}}{\partial q_i}$$

for any $1 \le i \le n$.

Solution If $\dot{r} = \mathbf{r}(q_1, q_2, \ldots, q_n, t)$ then by the chain rule

$$\frac{d\mathbf{r}}{dt} = \dot{\mathbf{r}} = \frac{\partial \mathbf{r}}{\partial q_1}\frac{dq_1}{dt} + \frac{\partial \mathbf{r}}{\partial q_2}\frac{dq_2}{dt} + \ldots + \frac{\partial \mathbf{r}}{\partial q_n}\frac{dq_n}{dt} + \frac{\partial \mathbf{r}}{dt}$$

or

$$\dot{\mathbf{r}} = \frac{\partial \mathbf{r}}{\partial q_1}\dot{q}_1 + \frac{\partial \mathbf{r}}{\partial q_2}\dot{q}_2 + \ldots + \frac{\partial \mathbf{r}}{\partial q_n}\dot{q}_n + \frac{\partial \mathbf{r}}{dt}$$

Differentiating this expression with respect to $\dot{q}_1$ gives

$$\frac{\partial \dot{\mathbf{r}}}{\partial \dot{q}_i} = \frac{\partial \mathbf{r}}{\partial q_i}$$

as required. This relationship can be regarded loosely as 'cancellation of the dots'.

11.2 If W is the work done by displacing a system having generalised coordinates $q_1, q_2, \ldots, q_n$ by increments $dq_1, dq_2, \ldots, dq_n$, show that $Q_i = \partial W/\partial q_i$, where Q_i is the generalised force.

Solution Let the n particles of the system have position vectors $\mathbf{r}_1, \mathbf{r}_2, \ldots, \mathbf{r}_n$. Let the force on the ith particle be $\mathbf{F}_i$; then the work done by displacing the ith particle $d\mathbf{r}_i$ must be

$$\sum_{i=1}^{n} \mathbf{F}_i \cdot d\mathbf{r}_i$$

Thus

$$dW = \sum_{i=1}^{n} \mathbf{F}_i \cdot d\mathbf{r}_i$$

However, by the chain rule

$$d\mathbf{r}_i = \sum_{j=1}^{n} \frac{\partial \mathbf{r}_i}{\partial q_j} dq_j$$

so that

$$dW = \sum_{j=1}^{n}\sum_{i=1}^{n} \mathbf{F}_i \frac{\partial \mathbf{r}_i}{\partial q_j} dq_j$$

Now, by definition, the generalised force Q_j is

$$Q_j = \sum_{i=1}^{n} \mathbf{F}_i \cdot \frac{\partial \mathbf{r}_i}{\partial q_j}$$

Hence

$$dW = \sum_{j=1}^{n} Q_j dq_j \qquad (11.1)$$

Now, since $W = W(q_1, q_2, \ldots, q_n)$, by the chain rule

$$dW = \frac{\partial W}{\partial q_1} dq_1 + \frac{\partial W}{\partial q_2} dq_2 + \ldots + \frac{\partial W}{\partial q_n} dq_n$$

$$= \sum_{j=1}^{n} \frac{\partial W}{\partial q_j} dq_j \qquad (11.2)$$

Subtracting Equation (11.1) from Equation (11.2) gives

$$\sum_{j=1}^{n} \left(\frac{\partial W}{\partial q_j} - Q_j \right) dq_j = 0$$

Since the dq_j are independent coordinates, we have that

$$Q_j = \frac{\partial W}{\partial q_j}$$

(or $Q_i = \partial W / \partial q_i$ since j is a dummy variable), as required.

11.3 Establish Lagrange's equations in the form

$$\frac{d}{dt} \left(\frac{\partial L}{\partial \dot{q}_i} \right) - \frac{\partial L}{\partial q_i} = 0$$

for conservative holonomic systems.

Solution The Lagrangian L is defined as $T - V$, where T is the kinetic energy and V the potential energy. Now,

$$T = \sum_{i=1}^{n} (\tfrac{1}{2} m_i \dot{\mathbf{r}}_i^2)$$

so that differentiating with respect to $\dot{q}_j$ gives

$$\frac{\partial T}{\partial q_j} = \sum_{i=1}^{n} m_i \frac{\partial \dot{\mathbf{r}}_i}{\partial q_j} \cdot \dot{\mathbf{r}}_i$$

$$= \sum_{i=1}^{n} m_i \frac{\partial \mathbf{r}_i}{\partial q_j} \cdot \dot{\mathbf{r}}_i$$

(by Example 11.1). Also,

$$\frac{\partial T}{\partial q_j} = \sum_{i=1}^{n} m_i \frac{\partial \dot{\mathbf{r}}_i}{\partial q_j} \cdot \dot{\mathbf{r}}_i$$

Newton's second law applied to the ith particle is

$$\mathbf{F}_i = m_i \ddot{\mathbf{r}}_i$$

Hence

$$\mathbf{F}_i \cdot \frac{\partial \mathbf{r}_i}{\partial q_j} = m_i \ddot{\mathbf{r}}_i \cdot \frac{\partial \mathbf{r}_i}{\partial q_j} \qquad \textbf{(11.3)}$$

using the elementary differentiation rule

$$\frac{\mathrm{d}}{\mathrm{d}t}\left(\dot{\mathbf{r}}_i \cdot \frac{\partial \mathbf{r}_i}{\partial q_j}\right) = \ddot{\mathbf{r}}_i \cdot \frac{\partial \mathbf{r}_i}{\partial q_j} + \dot{\mathbf{r}}_i \cdot \frac{\mathrm{d}}{\mathrm{d}t}\left(\frac{\partial \mathbf{r}_i}{\partial q_j}\right)$$

the right-hand side of Equation (11.3) is thus

$$m_i \ddot{\mathbf{r}}_i \cdot \frac{\partial \mathbf{r}_i}{\partial q_j} = m_i \frac{\mathrm{d}}{\mathrm{d}t}\left(\dot{\mathbf{r}}_i \cdot \frac{\partial \mathbf{r}_i}{\partial q_j}\right) - m_i \dot{\mathbf{r}}_i \cdot \frac{\mathrm{d}}{\mathrm{d}t}\left(\frac{\partial \mathbf{r}_i}{\partial q_j}\right)$$

We have already seen that

$$\frac{\partial \mathbf{r}_i}{\partial q_j} = \frac{\partial \dot{\mathbf{r}}_i}{\partial \dot{q}_j}$$

(Example 11.1). Also,

$$\frac{\mathrm{d}}{\mathrm{d}t}\left(\frac{\partial \mathbf{r}_i}{\partial q_j}\right) = \frac{\partial \dot{\mathbf{r}}_i}{\partial q_j}$$

assuming the order of differentiation can be reversed. Thus Equation (11.3) is

$$\mathbf{F}_i \cdot \frac{\partial \mathbf{r}_i}{\partial q_j} = m_i \frac{\mathrm{d}}{\mathrm{d}t}\left(\dot{\mathbf{r}}_i \cdot \frac{\partial \dot{\mathbf{r}}_i}{\partial \dot{q}_j}\right) - m_i \dot{\mathbf{r}}_i \cdot \frac{\partial \dot{\mathbf{r}}_i}{\partial q_j} \qquad \textbf{(11.4)}$$

We have seen that Q_j, the generalised force, is defined by

$$Q_j = \sum_{i=1}^{n} \mathbf{F}_i \cdot \frac{\partial \mathbf{r}_i}{\partial q_j}$$

For conservative forces, $\mathbf{F}_i$ is $-\mathrm{grad}V_i$, so that

$$\mathbf{F}_i \cdot \mathrm{d}\mathbf{r}_i = -\mathrm{d}V_i$$

Hence

$$Q_i \mathrm{d}q_j = \sum_{i=1}^{n} -\frac{\partial V_i}{\partial q_j}\,\mathrm{d}q_j = -\mathrm{d}V$$

$$\therefore \quad Q_i = -\frac{\mathrm{d}V}{\mathrm{d}q_j}$$

We have already noted that

$$T = \sum_{i=1}^{n} \tfrac{1}{2} m_i \dot{\mathbf{r}}_i^2$$

and so

$$\frac{\partial T}{\partial \dot{q}_j} = \sum_{i=1}^{n} m_i \dot{\mathbf{r}}_i \cdot \frac{\partial \dot{\mathbf{r}}_i}{\partial \dot{q}_j}$$

Differentiating T with respect to q_j gives

$$\frac{\partial T}{\partial q_j} = \sum_{i=1}^{n} m_i \dot{\mathbf{r}}_i \cdot \frac{\partial \dot{\mathbf{r}}_i}{\partial q_j}$$

Hence the summation of Equation (11.5) over all the particles yields

$$-\frac{\partial V}{\partial q_j} = \frac{\mathrm{d}}{\mathrm{d}t}\left(\frac{\partial T}{\partial \dot{q}_j}\right) - \frac{\partial T}{\partial q_j} \qquad \textbf{(11.5)}$$

Recalling that $L = T - V$ and that $V = V(q_1, q_2, \ldots, q_n, t)$, so that $\partial V/\partial \dot{q}_j = 0$, we can write Equation (11.5) as

$$\frac{\mathrm{d}}{\mathrm{d}t}\left(\frac{\partial L}{\partial \dot{q}_j}\right) - \frac{\partial L}{\partial q_j} = 0 \qquad i = 1, 2, \ldots, n$$

These are Lagrange's equations.

As a corollary, we see that for a non-conservative system, Equation (11.4) summed over all particles is

$$Q_j = \frac{\mathrm{d}}{\mathrm{d}t}\left(\frac{\partial T}{\partial \dot{q}_j}\right) - \frac{\partial T}{\partial q_j} \qquad j = 1, 2, \ldots, n$$

which are also Lagrange's equations, but for a non-conservative system.

11.4   Establish Euler's equations for the three-dimensional motion of a rigid body about a fixed point by using Lagrange's equations.

Solution   Let the principal moments of inertia about the three axes be A, B and C. Also, let the angular velocities be ω_1, ω_2 and ω_3 respectively so that the kinetic energy T is

$$T = \tfrac{1}{2}\left(A\omega_1^2 + B\omega_2^2 + C\omega_3^2\right)$$

We now need to express ω_1, ω_2 and ω_3 in terms of coordinates. The coordinates we use are the Euler angles θ, ϕ and ψ. These are depicted in Fig. 11.1.

In order to make sense of Fig. 11.1, consider (a) a rotation about the z-axis of magnitude $\dot{\psi}$. Then freeze ψ and consider (b) which is a rotation of magnitude $\dot{\theta}$ about the (moved) x-axis. Finally freeze θ and consider (c) a rotation of magnitude $\dot{\phi}$ about the (moved again) y-axis. ω_1, ω_2 and ω_3 are the angular velocities about the positions of x, y and z as depicted in (a). With just $\dot{\psi}$ present, the angular velocities about the x-axis, y-axis and z-axis are simply 0, 0 and $\dot{\psi}$ respectively. Looking at Fig. 11.1(b), where now both x-axis and y-axis have rotated through ψ, the rotation about the x-axis with angular velocity $\dot{\theta}$ imparts no extra component about the z-axis. However (remembering we are considering motion relative to x, y and z as depicted in (a)), we have $\dot{\theta}\cos\psi$ along the x-axis and $\dot{\theta}\sin\psi$ along the y-axis. The final rotation, $\dot{\phi}$, about the y-axis may be quite difficult to see. It is best considered in component form. First of all, $\dot{\phi}$ will have

Figure 11.1

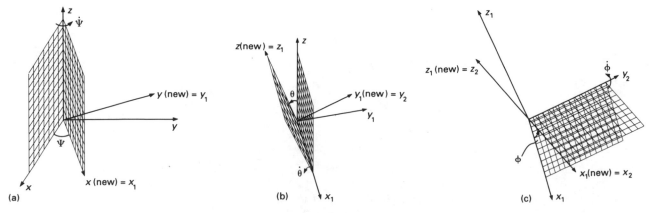

(a)   (b)   (c)

component $\dot\phi\sin\theta$ in the (Fig. 11.1(a)) z-direction. The component at right angles, $\dot\phi\cos\theta$, is in the z–y plane, making an angle ψ with the old y-axis. Hence $-\dot\phi\cos\theta\sin\psi$ and $\dot\phi\cos\theta\cos\psi$ will be x- and y-components, respectively. Summing these up we obtain

$$\omega_1 = \dot\theta\cos\psi - \dot\phi\cos\theta\sin\psi$$

$$\omega_2 = \dot\theta\sin\psi + \dot\phi\cos\theta\cos\psi$$

and

$$\omega_3 = \dot\psi + \dot\phi\sin\theta$$

as the three angular velocities referred to θ, ϕ and ψ (called the **Euler angles**). Thus the kinetic energy T is given by

$$T = \tfrac{1}{2}[A(\dot\theta\cos\psi - \dot\phi\cos\theta\sin\psi)^2 + B(\dot\theta\sin\psi - \dot\phi\cos\theta\cos\psi)^2 + C(\dot\psi + \dot\phi\sin\theta)^2]$$

The partial derivative of T with respect to ψ is given by

$$\frac{\partial T}{\partial\psi} = A(\dot\theta\cos\psi - \dot\phi\cos\theta\sin\psi)(-\dot\theta\sin\psi - \dot\phi\cos\theta\cos\psi) + B(\dot\theta\sin\psi - \dot\phi\cos\theta\cos\psi)(\dot\theta\cos\psi - \dot\phi\cos\theta\sin\psi)$$

$$= A\omega_1(\omega_2) + B\omega_2\omega_1$$

$$= (B - A)\omega_1\omega_2$$

and

$$\frac{\partial T}{\partial\dot\psi} = C(\dot\psi + \dot\phi\sin\theta) = C\omega_3$$

Using Lagrange's equation

$$\frac{\mathrm{d}}{\mathrm{d}t}\left(\frac{\partial T}{\partial\dot\psi}\right) - \frac{\partial T}{\partial\psi} = Q_z$$

we obtain

$$C\dot\omega_3 - (B - A)\omega_1\omega_2 = Q_z$$

where Q_z is the generalised force corresponding to a small rotation of ψ, and so represents the torque. We have thus derived the third Euler equation. We can deduce that

$$B\dot\omega_2 - (A - C)\omega_1\omega_3 = Q_y$$

and

$$A\dot\omega_1 - (C - B)\omega_2\omega_3 = Q_x$$

by cyclically permuting the rules of θ, ϕ, ψ.

(The sceptics may smell a rat, since these two Euler equations cannot be deduced directly from Lagrange's equations for θ and ϕ. However, they can be deduced from specific linear combinations of them. In fact, it is because we *started* by rotating about the z-axis ($\dot\psi$) that the ψ Lagrange equation led directly to Euler's third (ψ) equation. Re-doing the whole problem twice over, starting with θ and then starting with ϕ would explicitly derive the other Euler equations. The above symmetry argument is both justifiable, and a lot quicker!)

11.5 A particle is projected horizontally with a velocity u along the inner surface of a smooth fixed sphere of radius a. The initial depth below the centre is h_1. Assuming that the particle never leaves the surface of the sphere, show that the subsequent orbit lies between the depths h_1 and h_2, where h_1 is a root of the equation

$$2gx^2 + u^2x + u^2h_1 - 2ga^2 = 0$$

Show also that the particle rises initially if

$$u^2h_1 > g(a^2 - h_1^2) \qquad\qquad \text{(L.U.)}$$

Solution This is another example of a problem that can be solved directly using Newton's laws, but is elegantly tackled using Lagrange's equations.

The particle moves on the inner surface of the sphere of radius a. It is therefore desirable to use spherical polar coordinates. The zonal (horizontal) velocity of the particle is $a\dot{\phi}\sin\theta$ and its azimuthal (vertical) velocity is $a\dot{\theta}$, as shown in Fig. 11.2. The kinetic energy of the particle is T where

$$T = \tfrac{1}{2}ma^2 \sin^2\theta \; \dot{\phi}^2 + \tfrac{1}{2}ma^2\dot{\theta}^2$$

The potential energy V is, using a simple trigonometry,

$$V = -mga\cos\theta$$

($\theta = \pi/2$ is the level of zero potential). The Lagrangian is thus given by

$$L = \tfrac{1}{2}ma^2 \sin^2\theta \; \dot{\phi}^2 + \tfrac{1}{2}ma^2\dot{\theta}^2 + mga\cos\theta$$

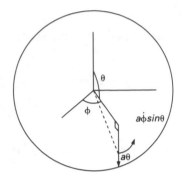

Figure 11.2

Notice that the variable ϕ does not occur in V. This is an example of what is sometimes called an **ignorable coordinate**. Lagrange's equation for ϕ is

$$\frac{\mathrm{d}}{\mathrm{d}t}\left(\frac{\partial L}{\partial \dot{\phi}}\right) = 0$$

which integrates immediately to give

$$\frac{\partial L}{\partial \dot{\phi}} = \text{constant}$$

from which

$$a^2\sin^2\theta\dot{\phi} = \text{constant} = A \qquad\qquad \textbf{(11.6)}$$

This is the conservation of angular momentum.

The energy equation is

$$\tfrac{1}{2}m(a^2\sin^2\theta\dot{\phi}^2 + a^2\dot{\theta}^2) - mga\cos\theta = B \qquad\qquad \textbf{(11.7)}$$

Initially, $\dot{\theta} = 0$, $a\sin\theta \; \dot{\phi} = u$ and $\cos\theta = h_1/a$. Substituting these values into Equation (11.6) yields

$$a^2\sin^2\theta\dot{\phi} = a(a\sin\theta\dot{\phi})\sin\theta$$
$$= au(1 - h_1^2/a^2)^{1/2} = u(a^2 - h_1^2)^{1/2} = A$$

Similarly, Equation (11.7) yields

$$\tfrac{1}{2}m(u^2 + 0) - mgh_1 = B$$

Making $\tfrac{1}{2}ma^2\dot{\theta}^2$ the subject of Equation (11.7) as well as writing $\dot{\phi}^2$ in terms of θ through

$$\dot{\phi}^2 = u^2(a^2 - h_1^2)/a^4\sin^4\theta$$

gives

$$\tfrac{1}{2}a^2\dot{\theta}^2 = g(a\cos\theta - h_1) + \tfrac{1}{2}u^2 - \tfrac{1}{2}a^2\sin^2\theta\,\frac{u^2(a^2 - h_1^2)}{a^4\sin^4\theta}$$

$$= \frac{1}{a^2\sin^2\theta}(a\cos\theta - h_1)[ga^2\sin^2\theta - \tfrac{1}{2}u^2(h_1 + a\cos\theta)]$$

If $x = a\cos\theta$, then we write

$$a^2\dot{\theta}^2 = \frac{2}{a^2\sin^2\theta}(x - h_1)[g(a^2 - x^2) - \tfrac{1}{2}u^2(x + h_1)]$$

Hence $a\dot{\theta} = 0$ when $x = h_1$ (the initial condition) and when

$$g(a^2 - x^2) - \tfrac{1}{2}u^2(x + h_1) = 0$$

or

$$2gx^2 + u^2x + u^2h_1 - 2ga^2 = 0 \qquad\qquad (11.8)$$

Lagrange's equation for the θ coordinate is

$$\frac{\mathrm{d}}{\mathrm{d}t}\left(\frac{\partial L}{\partial \dot{\theta}}\right) - \frac{\partial L}{\partial \theta} = 0$$

which is

$$\frac{\mathrm{d}}{\mathrm{d}t}(ma^2\dot{\theta}^2) + mga\sin\theta - ma^2\sin\theta\cos\theta\dot{\phi}^2 = 0$$

This is, on substitution for $\dot{\phi}^2$,

$$\frac{\mathrm{d}}{\mathrm{d}t}(a\dot{\theta}^2) = \frac{u^2\cos\theta(a^2 - h_1^2)}{a^3\sin^3\theta} - g\sin\theta$$

For the particle to rise initially,

$$\frac{\mathrm{d}}{\mathrm{d}t}(a\dot{\theta}^2) > 0 \text{ at } a\cos\theta = h_1$$

that is,

$$u^2h_1(a^2 - h_1^2) > ga^4\sin^4\theta = ga^4\left(1 - \frac{h_1^2}{a^2}\right)^2$$
$$= g(a^2 - h_1^2)^2$$

so that

$$u^2h_1 > g(a^2 - h_1^2)$$

as required.

11.6 A light inelastic string OAB is attached to a fixed point at O, and carries a mass $2m$ at A and a mass m at B. The lengths OA, OB are a, b respectively. The system is free to move in a vertical plane, and performs small oscillations about the position of equilibrium. The inclinations of OA, AB to the vertical are θ, ϕ respectively. Establish the equations of motion:

$$\ddot{\theta} + \tfrac{1}{3}\lambda\ddot{\phi} + n^2\theta = 0$$

and

$$\ddot{\theta} + \lambda\ddot{\phi} + n^2\phi = 0$$

175

where $\lambda = b/a$ and $n^2 = g/a$.

Find the equation to determine the periods of the normal modes. Show that, if $\lambda = \frac{3}{2}$ and if the motion is set up from rest in the equilibrium position by a small horizontal impulse mu applied at $t = 0$ to the mass at B, then the displacement of B at any subsequent time is

$$\frac{u}{9n\sqrt{2}} \left[\sin\left(nt\sqrt{2}\right) + 16\sin\left(nt/\sqrt{2}\right) \right].$$

Solution This question provides an example of how the use of Lagrange's equations can simplify solutions of problems involving small oscillations (see Chapter 10). Figures 11.3(a) and (b) show the two particles and the coordinates, θ and ϕ. The kinetic energy of the system is

$$T = \tfrac{1}{2} 2ma^2\dot{\theta}^2 + \tfrac{1}{2}m(a\dot{\theta} + b\dot{\phi})^2$$

This problem is best solved using the Lagrangian $L = T - V$. To this end, we find the potential V referred to O. Simple trigonometry gives

$$V = -2mga\cos\theta - mg(b\cos\phi + a\cos\theta)$$

or

$$V = -3mga\cos\theta - mgb\cos\phi$$

Hence

$$L = T - V$$
$$= ma^2\dot{\theta}^2 + \tfrac{1}{2}m(a\dot{\theta} + b\dot{\phi})^2 + 3mga\cos\theta + mgb\cos\phi$$

Lagrange's equations are

$$\frac{\mathrm{d}}{\mathrm{d}t}\left(\frac{\partial L}{\partial\dot{\theta}}\right) - \frac{\partial L}{\partial\theta} = 0$$

and

$$\frac{\mathrm{d}}{\mathrm{d}t}\left(\frac{\partial L}{\partial\dot{\phi}}\right) - \frac{\partial L}{\partial\phi} = 0$$

which give the pair of equations

$$2ma^2\ddot{\theta} + m(a\ddot{\theta} + b\ddot{\phi})a + 3mga\sin\theta = 0$$

and

$$m(a\ddot{\theta} + b\ddot{\phi})b + mgb\sin\phi = 0$$

For small angles θ and ϕ, these become

$$3\ddot{\theta} + \frac{b}{a}\ddot{\phi} + \frac{3g}{a}\theta = 0$$

and

$$\ddot{\theta} + \frac{b}{a}\ddot{\phi} + \frac{g}{a}\phi = 0$$

or

$$\ddot{\theta} + \tfrac{1}{3}\lambda\ddot{\phi} + n^2\theta = 0 \qquad\qquad (11.9)$$

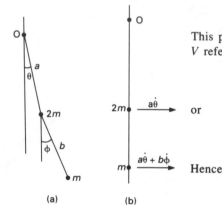

Figure 11.3

(a) (b)

and

$$\ddot{\theta} + \lambda\ddot{\phi} + n^2\phi = 0 \tag{11.10}$$

Equations (11.9) and (11.10) are solved by assuming that

$$\theta = A\sin(pt + \alpha) \quad \text{and} \quad \phi = B\sin(pt + \beta)$$

which lead to the pair of equations

$$-3p^2A - \lambda p^2B + 3n^2A = 0$$

and

$$-p^2A - \lambda p^2B + n^2B = 0$$

from which

$$\begin{vmatrix} -3p^2 + 3n^2 & -\lambda p^2 \\ -p^2 & n^2 - \lambda p^2 \end{vmatrix} = 0$$

Multiplying out gives

$$3n^4 - 3(\lambda + 1)p^2n^2 + 2\lambda p^4 = 0$$

With $\lambda = \tfrac{3}{7}$

$$2n^4 - 5p^2n^2 + 2p^4 = 0$$

or

$$(2n^2 - p^2)(n^2 - 2p^2) = 0$$

Hence the two values of p are $p = n\sqrt{2}, n/\sqrt{2}$. The periods of the normal modes are thus $(\pi/n)\sqrt{2}$ and $(2\pi/n)\sqrt{2}$. Thus

$$\theta = A\sin(nt\sqrt{2} + \alpha) + B\sin(nt/\sqrt{2} + \beta)$$

introducing four arbitrary constants A, α, B, β. Eliminating $\ddot{\phi}$ between Equations (11.9) and (11.10), and substituting for θ and $\ddot{\theta}$, gives

$$\phi = -A\sin(nt\sqrt{2} + \alpha) + 2B\sin(nt/\sqrt{2} + \beta)$$

At $t = 0$, $\theta = \phi = 0$; hence the constants α and β are both zero. Differentiating gives

$$\dot{\theta} = n\sqrt{2}A\,\cos(nt\sqrt{2}) + \frac{nt}{\sqrt{2}}\,B\cos\left(\frac{nt}{\sqrt{2}}\right)$$

and

$$\dot{\phi} = -n\sqrt{2}A\,\cos(nt\sqrt{2}) + \frac{2nt}{\sqrt{2}}\,B\cos\left(\frac{nt}{\sqrt{2}}\right)$$

Initially, B is given an impulse mu; hence, at $t = 0$, $\dot{\theta} = 0$ and $u = b\dot{\phi}$ or

$$\dot{\phi} = \frac{u}{b} = \frac{2u}{3a} \qquad (\lambda = \tfrac{3}{2})$$

Substituting these values into $\dot{\theta}$ and $\dot{\phi}$ at $t = 0$ gives the following two equations for A and B:

$$An\sqrt{2} + \frac{nB}{\sqrt{2}} = 0 \quad \Rightarrow \quad B = -2A$$

and

$$-An\sqrt{2} + \frac{2nB}{\sqrt{2}} = \frac{2u}{3a}$$

Hence

$$n\sqrt{2}(-A - 2A) = \frac{2u}{3a}$$

or

$$A = -\frac{u\sqrt{2}}{9an}, \qquad B = \frac{2u\sqrt{2}}{9an}$$

The displacement of B is

$$a\theta + b\phi = a\theta + \frac{3a}{2}\phi$$

$$= a\left[-\frac{u\sqrt{2}}{9an}\sin(nt\sqrt{2}) + \frac{2u\sqrt{2}}{9an}\sin\left(\frac{nt}{\sqrt{2}}\right) \right]$$

$$+ \frac{3a}{2}\left[\frac{u\sqrt{2}}{9an}\sin(nt\sqrt{2}) + \frac{4u\sqrt{2}}{9an}\sin\left(\frac{nt}{\sqrt{2}}\right) \right]$$

which, on rearrangement, gives

$$\frac{u}{9n\sqrt{2}}\left[\sin(nt\sqrt{2}) + 16\sin\left(\frac{nt}{\sqrt{2}}\right) \right]$$

as required.

11.7 Four equal uniform rods AB, BC, CD, DA, each of length $2a$ and mass m, are freely jointed at their ends so as to form a rhombus. The system is initially at rest on a smooth horizontal table, and a constant force F is applied at the join A in the initial direction of CA. In the subsequent motion the displacement of the centre of this system is x and the angle BAC is θ. Show that the kinetic energy is given by

$$T = 2m(\dot{x}^2 + \tfrac{4}{3}a^2\dot{\theta}^2)$$

and calculate the generalised forces Q_x and Q_θ corresponding to the coordinates x and θ.

Derive the equations of motion of the system and hence, or otherwise, show that when the framework closes up the angular velocity of each rod is

$$[3F(1 - \cos\beta)/4ma]^{1/2}$$

where β is the initial value of θ.

(L.U.)

Solution The four rods are displayed in the general position in Fig. 11.4. The velocity of the centre of mass of each rod is made up of two parts: $\dot{x}$, due to the linear motion of the centre of mass of all four rods (labelled O in Fig. 11.4), and a rotational component, the same for AB and AD, and for BC and CD, but different for each pair. This motion will continue until B and D collide and the rhombus is flat. In order to use Lagrange's equations, we first calculate the kinetic energy. The question asks for generalised forces, so Lagrange's equations in the form

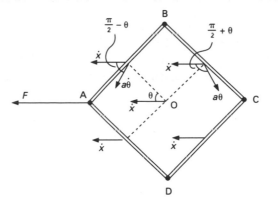

Figure 11.4

$$\frac{\mathrm{d}}{\mathrm{d}t}\left(\frac{\partial T}{\partial \dot{q}_j}\right) - \frac{\partial T}{\partial q_j} = Q_j$$

will be used.

First of all, let us find the total kinetic energy. The velocity of the mid-point of rod AB is the vector addition of $\dot{x}$ in the direction of F ($\overrightarrow{CA}$) and $a\dot{\theta}$ directed at an angle $\pi/2 - \theta$ below this. Similarly, the velocity of the mid-point of rod BC is the vector addition of $\dot{x}$ in the direction of F ($\overrightarrow{CA}$) and $a\dot{\theta}$ directed at an angle $\pi/2 + \theta$ below this. Figure 11.4 shows both of these angles. The total kinetic energy for each rod consists of $\frac{1}{2}m|\mathbf{v}|^2$ (due to the velocity of the centre of mass) and $\frac{1}{2}(\frac{1}{3}ma^2)\dot{\theta}^2$ due to the angular velocity of the rod. Hence the total kinetic energy of all four rods is

$$T = T_{AB} + T_{BC} + T_{CD} + T_{DA} = 2T_{AB} + 2T_{BC}$$

by symmetry. Hence

$$T = 2 \cdot \tfrac{1}{2}m\left[\dot{x}^2 + a^2\dot{\theta}^2 + 2a\dot{\theta}\dot{x}\cos\left(\frac{\pi}{2} - \theta\right)\right] + 2 \cdot \tfrac{1}{2}m\tfrac{1}{3}a^2\dot{\theta}^2$$

$$+ 2 \cdot \tfrac{1}{2}m\left[\dot{x}^2 + a^2\dot{\theta}^2 + 2a\dot{\theta}\dot{x}\cos\left(\frac{\pi}{2} + \theta\right)\right] + 2 \cdot \tfrac{1}{2}m\tfrac{1}{3}a^2\dot{\theta}^2$$

so

$$T = 2m\dot{x}^2 + 2ma^2\dot{\theta}^2 + 2ma\dot{\theta}\dot{x}\sin\theta - 2ma\dot{\theta}\dot{x}\sin\theta + \tfrac{2}{3}ma^2\dot{\theta}^2$$
$$= 2m(\dot{x}^2 + \tfrac{4}{3}a^2\dot{\theta}^2)$$

as required.

If we hold x constant, then A would move with velocity $2a\dot{\theta}\sin\theta$ in the direction $\overrightarrow{CA}$. (This is derived by resolving the velocity due to θ changing, for both AB and AD.) The velocity perpendicular to AC is, of course, zero. Thus the velocity of A is $\dot{x} - 2a\dot{\theta}\sin\theta$.

Hence in time δt, A moves an infinitesimal distance

$$\delta x - 2a\delta\theta\sin\theta$$

Thus, if Q_x is the generalised force associated with x and Q_θ the generalised force associated with θ, then

$$Q_x\delta x + Q_\theta\delta\theta = (\delta x - 2a\sin\theta\delta\theta)F$$

since F is the only force acting. Thus

$$Q_x = F$$

and

$$Q_\theta = -2aF\sin\theta$$

The x equation is

$$\frac{\mathrm{d}}{\mathrm{d}t}\left(\frac{\partial T}{\partial \dot{x}}\right) - \frac{\partial T}{\partial x} = Q_x$$

or

$$4m\ddot{x} = F$$

The θ equation is

$$\frac{\mathrm{d}}{\mathrm{d}t}\left(\frac{\partial T}{\partial \dot{\theta}}\right) - \frac{\partial T}{\partial \theta} = Q_\theta$$

or

$$\frac{16}{3} ma^2\ddot{\theta} = -2aF\sin\theta$$

Multiplying this last equation by $\dot{\theta}$ and integrating with respect to t gives

$$\tfrac{8}{3} ma^2\dot{\theta}^2 = 2aF\cos\theta + K$$

where K is an arbitrary constant. $\dot{\theta} = 0$ when $\theta = \beta$; hence $K = -aF\cos\beta$. Therefore

$$\tfrac{8}{3} ma^2\dot{\theta}^2 = 2aF(\cos\theta - \cos\beta)$$

and when $\theta = 0$

$$\dot{\theta}^2 = \frac{3aF(1 - \cos\beta)}{4ma}$$

as required.

11.8 A circular hoop of mass M and radius a has a light smooth rod AB of length $2a$ fixed to its circumference at the opposite ends A and B of a diameter. A particle P of mass m slides freely on the rod and the system rolls without slipping on a rough horizontal table, so as to lie always in a fixed vertical plane. Calculate the kinetic and potential energy of the system using as generalised coordinates θ, the angle made by AB with the horizontal, and x, the distance of P from the centre O of the hoop, x being positive if P lies in the segment OB of the rod.

Obtain Lagrange's equations and show that if the system is released from rest with $\theta = 0$ and $x = b(0<b<a)$ then initially,

$$\frac{\mathrm{d}^2 x}{\mathrm{d}t^2} = -\frac{abmg}{(2Ma^2 + mb^2)}$$

where g is the gravitational acceleration.

(L.U.)

Solution Figure 11.5 shows the hoop and fixed rod in general position. Notice that, using the coordinates specified in the question, the bottom of the hoop is an instantaneous centre of rotation and the centre of the hoop moves horizontally with speed $a\dot{\theta}$. The kinetic energy of the hoop = KE of centre of mass + KE relative to centre of mass:

$$\tfrac{1}{2}M(a\dot{\theta})^2 + \tfrac{1}{2}(Ma^2)\dot{\theta}^2 = Ma^2\dot{\theta}^2$$

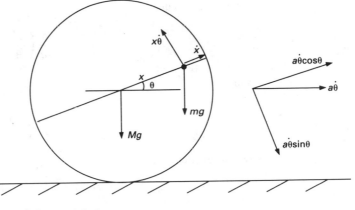

Figure 11.5

The kinetic energy of the particle is

$$\tfrac{1}{2}m[(\dot{x} + a\dot{\theta}\cos\theta)^2 + (x\dot{\theta} - a\dot{\theta}\sin\theta^2)]$$

and the total kinetic energy, T, is given by

$$T = Ma^2\dot{\theta}^2 + \tfrac{1}{2}m(\dot{x}^2 + a^2\dot{\theta}^2 + x^2\dot{\theta}^2 + 2a\dot{x}\dot{\theta}\cos\theta + 2ax\dot{\theta}^2\sin\theta)$$

The potential energy due to the particle, V, is given by

$$V = mgx\sin\theta$$

where the level of the centre of the hoop is the level of zero potential. This answers the first part of the question. Note that we can define a potential here despite there being friction between the hoop and the floor because the hoop *rolls*, and hence the friction does no work.

The Lagrangian, $L = T - V$, is thus given by the expression

$$L = Ma^2\dot{\theta}^2 + \tfrac{1}{2}m(\dot{x}^2 + a^2\dot{\theta}^2 + x^2\dot{\theta}^2 + 2a\dot{x}\dot{\theta}\cos\theta + 2ax\dot{\theta}^2\sin\theta) - mgx\sin\theta$$

Hence

$$\frac{\partial L}{\partial \dot{x}} = \tfrac{1}{2}m(2\dot{x} + 2a\dot{\theta}\cos\theta)$$

and

$$\frac{\mathrm{d}}{\mathrm{d}t}\left(\frac{\partial L}{\partial \dot{x}}\right) = m(\ddot{x} + a\ddot{\theta}\cos\theta - a\dot{\theta}^2\sin\theta)$$

Also

$$\frac{\partial L}{\partial \dot{\theta}} = 2Ma^2\dot{\theta} + \tfrac{1}{2}m(2a^2\dot{\theta} + 2x^2\dot{\theta} + 2a\dot{x}\cos\theta + 4ax\dot{\theta}\sin\theta)$$

and, differentiating this with respect to t,

$$\frac{\mathrm{d}}{\mathrm{d}t}\left(\frac{\partial L}{\partial \dot{\theta}}\right) = 2Ma^2\ddot{\theta} + m(a^2\ddot{\theta} + x^2\ddot{\theta} + 2x\dot{\theta}\dot{x} + \ddot{x}a\cos\theta + \dot{x}\dot{\theta}a\sin\theta + 2ax\ddot{\theta}\sin\theta + 2ax\dot{\theta}^2\cos\theta)$$

Remember when we differentiate with respect to t to use

$$\frac{\mathrm{d}}{\mathrm{d}t}f(\theta) = \dot{\theta}\frac{\mathrm{d}f}{\mathrm{d}\theta}$$

for any function $f(\theta)$.

Lagrange's equations are

$$\frac{d}{dt}\left(\frac{\partial L}{\partial \dot{\theta}}\right) - \frac{\partial L}{\partial \theta} = 0$$

and

$$\frac{d}{dt}\left(\frac{\partial L}{\partial \dot{x}}\right) - \frac{\partial L}{\partial x} = 0$$

which, explicitly, are

$$m(\ddot{x} + a\ddot{\theta}\cos\theta - a\dot{\theta}^2\sin\theta) - mg\sin\theta = 0 \qquad (11.11)$$

and

$$2Ma^2\ddot{\theta} + m(a^2\ddot{\theta} + x^2\ddot{\theta} + 2x\dot{x}\dot{\theta} + a\ddot{x}\cos\theta + ax\dot{\theta}\sin\theta + 2ax\ddot{\theta}\sin\theta + 2ax\dot{\theta}^2\cos\theta) - mgx\cos\theta = 0$$
$$(11.12)$$

This answers the second part of the question.

These two equations are insoluble in any exact form (except for $T + V =$ constant). This is why the question merely requests the insertion of boundary conditions. We are told that, initially, $\theta = 0$, $x = b$, $\dot{\theta} = 0$ and $\dot{x} = 0$. If we label $\ddot{x} = \ddot{x}_0$ and $\ddot{\theta} = \ddot{\theta}_0$ at time $t = 0$, then Equations (11.11) and (11.12) become

$$\ddot{x}_0 + a\ddot{\theta}_0 = 0 \qquad (11.13)$$

and

$$2Ma^2\ddot{\theta}_0 + m(a^2\ddot{\theta}_0 + b^2\ddot{\theta}_0 + a\ddot{x}_0) - mgb = 0 \qquad (11.14)$$

Substituting for $\ddot{\theta}_0$ from Equation (11.13) into Equation (11.14) gives

$$-2Ma\ddot{x}_0 + m(-a\ddot{x}_0 - \frac{b^2}{a}\ddot{x}_0 + a\ddot{x}_0) - mgb = 0$$

whence

$$\ddot{x}_0\left(2Ma + m\frac{b^2}{a}\right) = -mgb$$

or

$$\ddot{x}_0 = -\frac{mgab}{2Ma^2 + mb^2}$$

Hence

$$\frac{d^2x}{dt^2} = -\frac{abmg}{2Ma^2 + mb^2}$$

initially, as required.

11.9 Show that the periods, $2\pi/\omega$, of normal modes of small oscillations of a holonomic conservative system of n coordinates about a position of stable equilibrium are given by an equation of the form

$$|\mathbf{V} + \lambda\mathbf{T}| = 0$$

where $\lambda = -\omega^2$, and $\mathbf{V}$ and $\mathbf{T}$ are real symmetric $n \times n$ matrices with constant elements. Show also that with the associated quadratic forms $\mathbf{q}^{\mathsf{T}}\mathbf{V}\mathbf{q}$ and $\mathbf{q}^{\mathsf{T}}\mathbf{T}\mathbf{q}$ both positive definite the roots λ are real and negative.

Solution   This question assumes that the reader has some knowledge of the algebra of quadratic forms. If you do not, then our advice is to pass over this example. However, the results here are general and underlie the principles of how a dynamical system oscillates about its equilibrium positions.

The kinetic energy of a dynamical system having generalised coordinates $(q_1, q_2, \ldots, q_n)$ takes the form

$$T_* = \sum_{r=1}^{n} \sum_{s=1}^{n} a_{rs} \dot{q}_r \dot{q}_s$$

The potential energy $\mathbf{V}_* = \mathbf{V}_*(q_1, q_2, \ldots, q_n)$. We use Taylor's theorem to expand $\mathbf{V}_*$ about an equilibrium position $q_1 = (q_1)_0, q_2 = (q_2)_0, \ldots, q_n = (q_n)_0$. This gives

$$\mathbf{V}_* = \mathbf{V}_0 + \sum_{r=1}^{n} q_r \left(\frac{\partial \mathbf{V}}{\partial q_r} \right)_0 + \sum_{r=1}^{n} \sum_{s=1}^{n} q_r q_s \left(\frac{\partial^2 \mathbf{V}}{\partial q_r \partial q_s} \right)_0 + \cdots$$

where the ignored terms involve products of three of the q_is ($i = 1, 2, \ldots, n$). Since the subscript zero denotes an equilibrium position,

$$\left(\frac{\partial \mathbf{V}}{\partial q_i} \right)_0 = 0 \qquad \text{for } i = 1, 2, \ldots, n$$

Hence

$$\mathbf{V}_* = \mathbf{V}_0 + \sum_{r=1}^{n} \sum_{s=1}^{n} q_r q_s \left(\frac{\partial^2 \mathbf{V}}{\partial q_r \partial q_s} \right)_0$$

Lagrange's equation for coordinate q_r is

$$\frac{\mathrm{d}}{\mathrm{d}t} \left(\frac{\partial \mathbf{T}_*}{\partial \dot{q}_r} \right) - \frac{\partial \mathbf{T}_*}{\partial q_r} = - \frac{\partial \mathbf{V}_*}{\partial q_r}$$

Now

$$\frac{\partial \mathbf{T}_*}{\partial \dot{q}_r} = \sum_{s=1}^{n} a_{rs} \dot{q}_s, \qquad \frac{\partial \mathbf{T}_*}{\partial q_r} = 0$$

for all r, and

$$\frac{\partial \mathbf{V}_*}{\partial q_r} = \sum_{s=1}^{n} q_s \left(\frac{\partial^2 \mathbf{V}}{\partial q_r \partial q_s} \right) = \sum_{s=1}^{n} b_{rs} q_s$$

Hence we obtain the linear equation

$$\sum_{s=1}^{n} a_{rs} \ddot{q}_s = - \sum_{s=1}^{n} b_{rs} q_s, \qquad s = 1, 2, \ldots, n$$

or, writing the n Lagrange's equations in matrix form:

$$\mathbf{A}\ddot{\mathbf{q}} + \mathbf{B}\mathbf{q} = \mathbf{0}$$

Of course it is only because we are close to an equilibrium position that the matrices $\mathbf{A}$ and $\mathbf{B}$ contain constant elements. This is a consequence of being able to linearise.

Now, $\ddot{q}_r = -\omega^2 q_r$ $(r = 1, 2, \ldots, n)$, where $2\pi/\omega$ is the period of oscillation about the equilibrium position. Thus

$$(\mathbf{V} + \lambda \mathbf{T})\mathbf{q} = \mathbf{0}$$

writing $\mathbf{B} = \mathbf{V}$, $\mathbf{A} = \mathbf{T}$ and $\omega^2 = -\lambda$.

A 'well-known' theorem in linear algebra states that the matrix $\mathbf{T}$, which is positive definite since it is derived from the kinetic energy, can be diagonalised via a linear transformation. In fact, under this transformation, labelled ϕ,

$$\mathbf{T} \overset{\phi}{\to} \mathbf{I}_n$$

and

$$\mathbf{V} \overset{\phi}{\to} \operatorname{diag}(c_1, c_2, \ldots, c_n)$$

so the n equations

$$(\mathbf{V} + \lambda\mathbf{T})\mathbf{q} = \mathbf{0}$$

become

$$(\operatorname{diag}(c_1, c_2, \ldots, c_n) + \lambda\mathbf{I}_n)\mathbf{q} = \mathbf{0}$$

from which

$$c_r + \lambda = 0, \qquad r = 1, 2, \ldots, n$$

Hence $c_r = \omega^2$. As $\mathbf{V}$ is positive definite, $c_r > 0$ for all r, so

$$\omega = \pm c_r^{1/2}$$

Therefore ω is real and ω^2 is positive for all roots. This is equivalent to ensuring that the quadratic forms $\mathbf{q}^T\mathbf{V}\mathbf{q}$ and $\mathbf{q}^T\mathbf{T}\mathbf{q}$ are positive definite (superscript T denotes transpose). To learn more about the underlying algebra, see for example, Anton and Rorres (1987).

11.10 The kinetic energy T and potential energy V of a conservative holonomic dynamic system with one degree of freedom have the forms

$$T = \alpha(q)\dot{q}^2 + \beta(q)\dot{q} + \gamma(q), \qquad V = V(q)$$

Which of the conditions sufficient for the existence of an energy integral does the system fail to satisfy?

Use Lagrange's equation to express $\ddot{q}$ in terms of q and $\dot{q}$.

If

$$I = f(q)\dot{q}^2 + g(q)\dot{q} + h(q)$$

is a constant of the motion, use the equation $\mathrm{d}I/\mathrm{d}t = 0$ to obtain a second expression for $\ddot{q}$. Hence obtain a cubic expression in $\dot{q}$ which is identically zero.

Show that if $V - \gamma \neq$ constant then

$$f = c\alpha, \qquad g = 0, \qquad h = c(V - \gamma) + k$$

where c and k are constants.

(L.U.)

Solution In order for $T + V =$ constant, which is the energy integral implied in the question, not only do T and V have to exist, but $L = T - V$ must be a homogeneous quadratic function $\dot{q}$. What this caters for are circumstances where energy may be fed into a system by design, so a potential still exists but energy is not conserved (Exercise 11.4 is such a case).

Lagrange's equation is

$$\frac{\mathrm{d}}{\mathrm{d}t}\left(\frac{\partial L}{\partial \dot{q}}\right) - \frac{\partial L}{\partial q} = 0$$

where

$$L = \alpha \dot{q}^2 + \beta \dot{q} + \gamma - V$$

Hence

$$\frac{\mathrm{d}}{\mathrm{d}t}(2\alpha\dot{q} + \beta) - \alpha'\dot{q}^2 - \beta'\dot{q} - \gamma' + V' = 0 \tag{11.15}$$

where the dash denotes differentiation with respect to q.

In general,

$$\frac{\mathrm{d}}{\mathrm{d}t}(F(q)\dot{q}) = F'\dot{q}^2 + F\ddot{q}$$

using the rules of calculus; hence Equation (11.15) implies

$$2\alpha\ddot{q} + \alpha'\dot{q}^2 - \gamma' + V' = 0 \tag{11.16}$$

We are given that $I = f\dot{q}^2 + g\dot{q} + h = $ constant. Differentiating this with respect to t gives

$$\frac{\mathrm{d}I}{\mathrm{d}t} = f'\dot{q}^3 + 2f\ddot{q}\dot{q} + g'\dot{q}^2 + g\ddot{q} + h'\dot{q} = 0$$

Substituting for $\ddot{q}$ from Equation (11.16)

$$\alpha f'\dot{q}^3 + fq(\gamma' - V' - \alpha'\dot{q}^2) + \alpha g'\dot{q}^2 + \tfrac{1}{2}g(\gamma' - V' - \alpha'\dot{q}^2) + \alpha h'\dot{q} = 0 \tag{11.17}$$

Equation (11.17) must be valid for all $\dot{q}$; hence it is an identity and we can equate coefficients of powers of $\dot{q}$ to zero. Doing this gives the four equations:

$\dot{q}^3$: $\qquad\qquad \alpha f' - f\alpha' = 0 \qquad$ (from which $f = c\alpha$ on integration)

$\dot{q}^2$: $\qquad\qquad \alpha g' - \tfrac{1}{2}g\alpha' = 0$

$\dot{q}$: $\qquad F(\gamma' - V') + \alpha h' = 0 \tag{11.18}$

$\dot{q}^0$: $\qquad\qquad \tfrac{1}{2}g(\gamma' - V') = 0 \tag{11.19}$

Equation (11.19) gives $g = 0$, since $\gamma' - V' \neq 0$ (condition in question). Finally, substituting $f = c\alpha$ into Equation (11.18) leads to

$$c(\gamma' - V') + h' = 0$$

Integrating this with respect to q gives

$$h = c(V - \gamma) + k$$

as required.

11.3 Exercises

11.1 Show that if L is not a function of t explicitly, and if T is a homogeneous quadratic function, then $T + V = $ constant.

11.2 Obtain Lagrange's equations for the 10 systems depicted in Fig. 11.6(a)–(j).

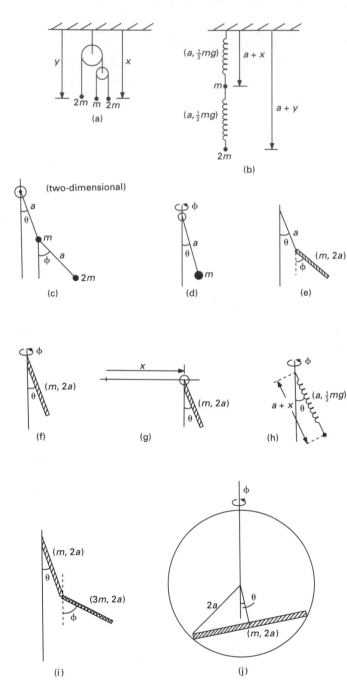

Figure 11.6

11.3 A uniform rod of mass $3m$ and length $2l$ has its mid-point fixed and a particle of mass m attached at one extremity. The rod, when in a horizontal position, is set rotating about a vertical axis through its centre with angular velocity $(2ng/l)^{1/2}$. Show

that the heavy end of the rod will fall until the inclination of the rod to the vertical is

$$\cos^{-1}[(n^2 + 1)^{1/2} - n] \qquad \text{(L.U.)}$$

11.4 The position vector of each point in a certain dynamical system is a function of a single coordinate q and of time t. Show that the kinetic energy of the system is

$$T = \alpha\dot{q}^2 + \beta\dot{q} + \gamma$$

where α, β and γ are, in general, functions of q and t.

If the work done in a small variation of q can be derived from a potential function $V(q)$ and if V, α, β and γ do not involve t explicitly, deduce from Lagrange's equation that

$$\alpha\dot{q}^2 - \gamma + V = \text{constant}$$

throughout the motion.

A bead slides on a wire in the form of a circle of radius a. The circular wire is made to rotate about a vertical diameter with constant angular velocity ω. Find the kinetic energy of the bead when the radius to the bead makes an angle θ with the downward vertical. Deduce that, if $\dot{\theta} = 0$ when $\theta = \frac{1}{2}\pi$, then subsequently

$$a\dot{\theta}^2 = (2g - a\omega^2\cos\theta)\cos\theta \qquad \text{(L.U.)}$$

(See fact sheet for a hint!)

11.5 A wire is bent into a smooth plane curve which has a single minimum value, and the curve is symmetric with respect to a normal drawn through that minimum. The wire is held with its axis of symmetry vertical, and a bead of mass m can slide without friction on the wire. Write down expressions for the potential energy and kinetic energy of the system in cylindrical polar coordinates, if the wire is set spinning about its axis of symmetry. Hence find Lagrange's equations of motion. Show that a steady motion is possible with the bead a distance a from the axis of symmetry, if

$$a\omega^2 = gf'(a)$$

where $f(r)$ is the height of the bead above the minimum when it is at distance r from the axis. Show that this motion is stable if

$$(ma^2 + I)gf''(a) + (3ma^2 - I)\omega^2 > 0$$

where I is the moment of inertia of the wire about its axis of symmetry. (L.U.)

11.6 A uniform rod OA, of mass $3m$ and length $2a$, swings about a smooth horizontal axis at O, and a light elastic string AB of natural length a and modulus of elasticity $mg/2$ is fastened to its lower end A. A particle of mass m is attached to the other end B of the string. Show that, for small oscillations in a vertical plane

$$8\ddot{\theta} + 6\ddot{\phi} = -5n^2\theta$$

$$2\ddot{\theta} + 3\ddot{\phi} = -n^2\phi$$

and

$$\ddot{x} = -\tfrac{1}{2}n^2x$$

where θ and ϕ are the angles made with the vertical by OA and

AB respectively. $3a + x$ is the length of the string at time t, and $n^2 = g/a$.

Find the periods of the normal modes of the system. (L.U.)

11.7 The balance wheel of a watch oscillates under the action of a spring, with a period which is $2\pi/p$ if the watch is held fixed. Show that, if the watch hangs on a nail, the motion in the vertical plane through the wheel may be described approximately by kinetic and potential energy functions of the forms

$$2T = (A - B)\dot{\theta}^2 + B(\dot{\theta} + \dot{\phi})^2$$

and

$$2V = Aq^2\theta^2 + Bp^2\phi^2$$

where A is the moment of inertia of the watch (including the balance wheel) about the nail, B is the moment of inertia of the balance wheel about its axis, and $q^2 = Mgh/A$ where M is the total mass of the watch, and h is the distance from its centre of mass to the nail.

Taking $A/B = 10^4$, $2\pi/p = \frac{2}{5}$ s and $2\pi/q = \frac{1}{2}$ s, show that, if the watch runs true when fixed, it will be in error by about 12 s a day when hanging. Does it gain or lose when hanging? (L.U.)

11.8 In Ancient Egypt the slaves are at work making a pyramid. At one stage, a wedge-shaped piece of stone of mass M is being hauled up a smooth incline. The slope of the incline and the angle of the wedge are both α, so that the top face of the wedge is horizontal. On this horizontal face lies a cylindrical stone pillar, mass m, with its generator perpendicular to the line of the pull (see Fig. 11.7). Suppose that the whole is initially supported in equilibrium, but then the force up the slope is increased at a constant rate of P per unit time. If the pillar (assumed solid and homogeneous, as is the wedge) is initially a distance b from the corner of the wedge, show that it will roll off at time t, where

$$2Pt^3\cos\alpha = 3b[3(M + m) + m\cos^2\alpha]$$

The contact between the pillar and wedge is rough, so no slipping occurs.

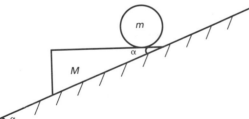

Figure 11.7

11.4 Outline Solutions to Exercises

11.1 $L = L(q_1, \ldots, q_n, \dot{q}_1, \ldots, \dot{q}_n)$

$$\Rightarrow \frac{\mathrm{d}L}{\mathrm{d}t} = \sum_{k=1}^{n}\left(\frac{\partial L}{\partial q_k}\dot{q}_k + \frac{\partial L}{\partial \dot{q}_k}\ddot{q}_k\right) \quad \text{(chain rule)}$$

$$= \sum_{k=1}^{n}\left[\frac{\mathrm{d}}{\mathrm{d}t}\left(\frac{\partial L}{\partial \dot{q}_k}\right)\dot{q}_k + \frac{\partial L}{\partial \dot{q}_k}\ddot{q}_k\right] \quad \text{by Lagrange's equations}$$

$$= \sum_{k=1}^{n}\frac{\mathrm{d}}{\mathrm{d}t}\left(\dot{q}_k\frac{\partial L}{\partial \dot{q}_k}\right) = \frac{\mathrm{d}}{\mathrm{d}t}\left[\sum_{k=1}^{n}\left(\dot{q}_k\frac{\partial L}{\partial \dot{q}_k}\right)\right]$$

$$\therefore \quad -L + \sum_{k=1}^{n}\dot{q}_k\frac{\partial L}{\partial \dot{q}_k} = \text{constant} = H$$

Writing $L = T - V$ implies

$$\sum_{k=1}^{n}\dot{q}_k\frac{\partial T}{\partial \dot{q}_k} - T + V = H$$

Recall Euler's theorem for homogeneous functions:

$$x_1\frac{\partial F}{\partial x_1} + x_2\frac{\partial F}{\partial x_2} + \ldots + x_n\frac{\partial F}{\partial x_n} = mF$$

where m is the *degree* of the function F. In this case, $m = 2$,

$$\Rightarrow \sum_{k=1}^{n}\dot{q}_k\frac{\partial T}{\partial \dot{q}_k} = 2T$$

hence the result. (H is called the Hamiltonian. More is made of all this in quantum mechanics.)

11.2 (a) If k is the depth of the large pulley below the support, and a and b are the lengths of the strings, then the distances below the support of the three masses are

$$y, \quad 2a + b - 4k - 2y - x, \quad x$$

giving

$$V - K - xmg$$

and

$$T = 3m\dot{y}^2 + \tfrac{3}{2}m\dot{x}^2 + 2m\dot{x}\dot{y}$$

(with $L = T - V$). Lagrange's equations are thus

$$\left.\begin{array}{ll} x: & 3\ddot{x} + 2\ddot{y} = g \\ y: & \ddot{x} + 3\ddot{y} = 0 \end{array}\right\} \text{ so } \ddot{x} = \tfrac{3}{7}g, \ddot{y} = -\tfrac{1}{7}g.$$

(b) $V = -m(a + x)g - 2m(a + y)g + \tfrac{1}{4}mg\dfrac{x^2}{a} + \tfrac{1}{4}mg\dfrac{y^2}{a}$

$T = \tfrac{3}{2}m\dot{x}^2 + \tfrac{1}{2}m\dot{y}^2 + 2m\dot{x}\dot{y}$

$L = T - V$

Lagrange's equations are

$$2\ddot{y} + 3\ddot{x} = g - \frac{gx}{2a}$$

and

$$\ddot{y} + 2\ddot{x} = 2g - \frac{gy}{a}$$

(c) $V = -2mga(\tfrac{3}{2}\cos\theta + \cos\phi)$

$T = \tfrac{3}{2}m(a\dot{\theta})^2 + m(a\dot{\phi})^2 + 2ma^2\dot{\theta}\dot{\phi}\cos(\phi - \theta)$

187

(The velocity of the particle of mass $2m$ is the vector combination of $\mathbf{e}_1 a\dot\theta$ and $\mathbf{e}_2 a\dot\phi$, where the angle between $\mathbf{e}_1$ and $\mathbf{e}_2$ is $\phi - \theta$.)

Lagrange's equations are

$$\frac{d}{dt}[3a\dot\theta + 2a\dot\phi\cos(\phi - \theta)] - 2a\dot\phi\dot\theta\sin(\phi - \theta) = -3g\sin\theta$$

and

$$\frac{d}{dt}[a\dot\phi + 2a\dot\theta\cos(\phi - \theta)] - 2a\dot\phi\dot\theta\sin(\phi - \theta) = -2g\sin\phi$$

(d) $V = -mag\cos\theta$

$T = \tfrac{1}{2}ma^2(\dot\theta^2 + \dot\phi^2\sin^2\theta)$

Lagrange's equations are

$$a\ddot\theta - a\dot\phi^2\sin\theta\cos\theta = -g\sin\theta$$

and

$$\frac{d}{dt}(a^2\sin^2\theta\dot\phi) = 0$$

(conservation of angular momentum).

(e) (Similar geometry to (c)).

$V = -mga(\cos\theta + \cos\phi)$

$T = \tfrac{1}{2}m[(a\dot\theta)^2 + (a\dot\phi)^2 + 2a^2\dot\phi\dot\theta\cos(\phi - \theta)] + \tfrac{1}{2}\cdot\tfrac{1}{3}ma^2\dot\phi^2$

$\quad = \tfrac{2}{3}ma^2\dot\phi^2 + \tfrac{1}{2}ma^2\dot\theta^2 + ma^2\dot\theta\dot\phi\cos(\phi - \theta)$

Lagrange's equations are

$$\frac{d}{dt}[a\dot\theta + a\dot\phi\cos(\phi - \theta)] - a\dot\theta\dot\phi\sin(\phi - \theta) = -g\sin\theta$$

and

$$\frac{d}{dt}[\tfrac{4}{3}a\dot\phi + a\dot\theta\cos(\phi - \theta)] + a\dot\theta\dot\phi(\phi - \theta) = -g\sin\phi$$

(f) $V = -mag\cos\theta$

$T = \tfrac{2}{3}ma^2(\dot\theta^2 + \dot\phi^2\sin^2\theta)$

lead to Lagrange's equations:

$$\tfrac{4}{3}a\ddot\theta - \tfrac{4}{3}a\dot\phi^2\sin\theta\cos\theta = -g\sin\theta$$

and

$$\frac{d}{dt}(\tfrac{4}{3}a^2\sin^2\theta\dot\phi) = 0$$

(conservation of angular momentum).

(g) $V = -mag\cos\theta$

$T = \tfrac{2}{3}ma^2\dot\theta^2 + \tfrac{1}{2}m\dot{x}^2 + ma\dot\theta\dot{x}\cos\theta$

Lagrange's equations are

$$\frac{d}{dt}(\tfrac{4}{3}a\dot\theta + \dot{x}\cos\theta) + \dot{x}\dot\theta\sin\theta = g\sin\theta$$

and

$$\frac{d}{dt}(\dot{x} + a\dot\theta\cos\theta) = 0$$

(h) $V = -mg(a + x)\cos\theta + \dfrac{mgx^2}{4a}$

$T = \tfrac{1}{2}m(a^2\dot\theta^2 + a^2\sin^2\phi\dot\phi^2 + \dot{x}^2)$

Lagrange's equations are

$$a^2 - a^2\dot\phi^2\cos\theta\sin\theta = -g(a + x)\sin\theta$$

$$\frac{d}{dt}(a^2\sin^2\theta\dot\phi) = 0$$

and

$$\ddot{x} = g\cos\theta - \frac{gx}{2a}$$

(i) $V = -7mga\cos\theta - 3mga\cos\phi$

$T = \tfrac{1}{2}ma^2\dot\phi^2 + \tfrac{2}{3}ma^2\dot\theta^2 + \tfrac{3}{2}m[a^2\dot\phi^2 + 4a^2\dot\theta^2 + 4a^2\dot\theta\dot\phi\cos(\phi - \theta)]$

$\quad = 2ma^2\dot\phi^2 + \tfrac{20}{3}ma^2\dot\theta^2 + 6ma^2\dot\theta\dot\phi\cos(\phi - \theta)$

Lagrange's equations are

$$\frac{d}{dt}[\tfrac{40}{3}a\dot\theta + 6a\dot\phi\cos(\phi - \theta)] - 6a\dot\theta\dot\phi\sin(\phi - \theta) + 7g\sin\theta = 0$$

and

$$\frac{d}{dt}[4a\dot\theta + 6a\dot\theta\cos(\phi - \theta)] + 6a\dot\theta\dot\phi\sin(\phi - \theta) + 3g\sin\phi = 0$$

(j) $V = -mga\sqrt{3}\cos\theta$

$T = \tfrac{3}{2}ma^2\dot\theta^2 + 2ma^2\dot\phi^2\sin^2\theta$

Lagrange's equations are

$$3a\ddot\theta - 4a\dot\phi^2\cos\theta\sin\theta = -g\sqrt{3}\sin\theta$$

and

$$\frac{d}{dt}(4a^2\sin^2\theta\dot\phi) = 0$$

11.3 Figure 11.8 shows the rod in the general position.

$$V = -mgl\cos\theta$$

$$T = ml^2\dot\theta^2 + ml^2\sin^2\theta\dot\phi^2$$

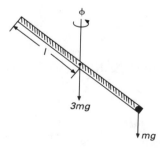

Figure 11.8

so

$$L = l^2\dot{\theta}^2 + l^2\sin^2\theta\dot{\phi}^2 + gl\cos\theta$$

Lagrange's equations are

$$2l^2\ddot{\theta} - 2l^2\sin\theta\cos\theta\dot{\phi}^2 + gl\sin\theta = 0$$

and

$$\frac{d}{dt}(\sin^2\theta\dot{\phi}) = 0$$

so

$$\dot{\phi}^2 = \frac{2ng}{l\sin^2\theta}$$

(using initial conditions). In fact, this is the energy equation. $\dot{\theta} = 0$ when $\cos\theta(\cos^2\theta + 2n\cos\theta - 1) = 0$, so $\theta = \pi/2$ (initial condition) or $\cos\theta = -n + (n^2 + 1)^{1/2}$. Hence

$$\theta = \cos^{-1}[(n^2 + 1)^{1/2} - n]$$

as required.

11.4   Since

$$\dot{\mathbf{r}} = \dot{q}\frac{\partial\mathbf{r}}{\partial q} + \frac{\partial\mathbf{r}}{\partial t}$$

and $T = \frac{1}{2}m|\dot{\mathbf{r}}|^2$, it follows that T is a quadratic (scalar) function of $\dot{q} = \alpha\dot{q}^2 + \beta\dot{q} + \gamma$. $L = \alpha\dot{q}^2 + \beta\dot{q} + \gamma - V$ is a function of q and $\dot{q}$ only.

Consider

$$\begin{aligned}
\frac{d}{dt}\left(L - \dot{q}\frac{\partial L}{\partial\dot{q}}\right) &= \frac{dL}{dt} - \frac{d}{dt}\left(\dot{q}\frac{\partial L}{\partial\dot{q}}\right)\\
&= \dot{q}\frac{\partial L}{\partial q} + \ddot{q}\frac{\partial L}{\partial\dot{q}} - \ddot{q}\frac{\partial L}{\partial\dot{q}} - \dot{q}\frac{d}{dt}\left(\frac{\partial L}{\partial\dot{q}}\right)\\
&= \dot{q}\left[\frac{\partial L}{\partial q} - \frac{d}{dt}\left(\frac{\partial L}{\partial\dot{q}}\right)\right] = 0
\end{aligned}$$

by Lagrange's equation. Now,

$$L - \dot{q}\frac{\partial L}{\partial\dot{q}} = -\alpha\dot{q}^2 + \gamma - V$$

so that

$$\alpha\dot{q}^2 - \gamma + V = \text{constant} \qquad \textbf{(11.19)}$$

Writing

$$T = \tfrac{1}{2}ma^2\dot{\theta}^2 + \tfrac{1}{2}ma^2\omega^2\sin^2\theta$$

and

$$V = -mga\cos\theta$$

using Equation (11.19) with $\alpha = \frac{1}{2}ma^2$, $q = \theta$, $\gamma = \frac{1}{2}ma^2\omega^2\sin^2\theta$ gives

$$\tfrac{1}{2}a\dot{\theta}^2 - \tfrac{1}{2}a\omega^2\sin^2\theta - g\cos\theta = k$$

$\theta = \pi/2$, $\dot{\theta} = 0$ implies $k = -\frac{1}{2}a\omega^2$, which gives the result.

11.5   The kinetic energy, $T = \frac{1}{2}I\dot{\theta}^2 + \frac{1}{2}mr^2\dot{\theta}^2 + \frac{1}{2}m\dot{s}^2$ where $\dot{s}$ is the speed of the bead tangential in the plane of the wire, and r, θ (and z) are cylindrical polar coordinates, $\dot{r} = \dot{s}\cos\lambda$ where $f'(r) = \tan\lambda$ (λ is the angle the tangent to the wire makes with the r-axis). Hence

$$\dot{s}^2 = \dot{r}^2\left(1 + \frac{1}{(f')^2}\right)$$

$$T = \tfrac{1}{2}(I + mr^2)\dot{\theta}^2 + \tfrac{1}{2}mr^2\left(1 + \frac{1}{(f')^2}\right)$$

$$V = mgf(r)$$

and

$$L = T - V$$

giving the two Lagrange's equations

$$\ddot{r}\left(1 + \frac{1}{(f')^2}\right) - \frac{2m\dot{r}^2f''}{(f')^3} - mr\dot{\theta}^2 + mgf'(r) + \frac{mr^2f''}{(f')^3} = 0$$

$$\textbf{(11.20)}$$

and

$$\frac{d}{dt}[(I + mr^2)\dot{\theta}] = 0 \qquad \textbf{(11.21)}$$

From Equation (11.20), $\dot{r} = \ddot{r} = 0$ is allowable if $r\dot{\theta}^2 = gf'(r)$ or $a\omega^2 = gf'(r)$ as required ($\theta = \omega$, $r = a$).

Near a, write $r = a + \varepsilon$, $f(r) = f(a) + \varepsilon f'(a) + \frac{1}{2}\varepsilon^2 f''(a)$, where $gf'(a) = a\omega^2$. Equation (11.21) gives

$$r\dot{\theta}^2 \approx a\omega^2 + \varepsilon\omega^2\left(\frac{I - 3ma^2}{I + ma^2}\right)$$

after expansion. Equation (11.20) gives

$$\ddot{\varepsilon}\left(\frac{1 + (a\omega^2/g)^2}{(a\omega^2/g)^2}\right) + \varepsilon\left[gf'' - \omega^2\left(\frac{I - 3ma^2}{I + ma^2}\right)\right] = 0$$

from which the stability condition

$$gf'' - \omega^2\left(\frac{I - 3ma^2}{I + ma^2}\right) > 0$$

follows.

(Note: Unlike the previous exercise, energy is conserved. In Exercise 11.4 the wire is *made* to rotate with constant $\dot{\theta}$, whereas here the wire is *free* to rotate.)

11.6   Figure 11.9 shows the situation. At equilibrium, $\theta = \phi = 0$, so

$$T = mg = \frac{\lambda x}{a} = \frac{mgx}{2a}$$

Hence $x = 2a$ and the length of AB is $3a$. The kinetic energy, T, is

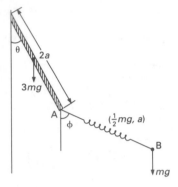

Figure 11.9

$$T = \tfrac{3}{2}m\tfrac{4}{3}a^2\dot\theta^2 + \tfrac{1}{2}m[\dot x^2 + (2a\dot\theta + 3a\dot\phi)^2]$$

The potential energy, V, is

$$V = -3mga\cos\theta - mg[(3a + x)\cos\phi + 2a\cos\theta] + \frac{mg}{2a}(x + 2a)^2$$

where the last term is the stored energy of the stretched string. Forming $L = T - V$ and using Lagrange's equations gives

θ: $\qquad 8\ddot\theta + 6\ddot\phi + 5n^2\theta = 0$

ϕ: $\qquad 2\ddot\theta + 3\ddot\phi + n^2\phi = 0$

x: $\qquad\qquad \ddot x + \tfrac{1}{2}n^2 x = 0$

as required. Solving the first two by writing $\dot\theta = -\omega^2\theta$, $\dot\phi = -\omega^2\phi$ (normal modes) gives

$$\begin{vmatrix} 5n^2 - 8\omega^2 & -6\omega^2 \\ -2\omega^2 & n^2 - 3\omega^2 \end{vmatrix} = 0$$

from which

$$\omega^2 = \frac{5n^2}{3}, \frac{n^2}{4}$$

leading to the periods of normal modes

$$\frac{2\pi}{n}\sqrt{\frac{3}{5}}, \frac{4\pi}{n}$$

11.7 With the definitions given, $\tfrac{1}{2}(A - B)\dot\theta^2$ is the KE of the watch (without the balance wheel) and $\tfrac{1}{2}B(\dot\theta + \dot\phi)^2$ is the KE of the balance wheel. Hence $2T = (A - B)\dot\theta^2 + B(\dot\theta + \dot\phi)^2$

The PE of the whole watch is $Mgh(1 - \cos\theta) \approx \tfrac{1}{2}Mgh\theta^2$. Using $q^2 = Mgh/A$, this is $\tfrac{1}{2}Aq^2\theta^2$.

There is also stored PE in the balance wheel:

$$B\ddot\phi = \text{torque} = \text{restoring couple}$$

If λ is the stiffness of the watch spring, tension $= T = \lambda a\phi$. Hence the restoring couple $= aT = \lambda a^2\phi$. Thus $B\ddot\phi = -\lambda a^2\phi$ (torque = rate of change of angular momentum).

But period $= 2\pi/p$, so $\lambda a^2/B = p^2$ and energy $= \tfrac{1}{2}\theta a^2\phi^2 = \tfrac{1}{2}p^2B\phi^2$, so total PE $= \tfrac{1}{2}Aq^2\theta^2 + \tfrac{1}{2}Bp^2\phi^2$, as required.

Lagrange's equations are

θ: $\qquad A\ddot\theta + B\ddot\phi + Aq^2\theta = 0$

ϕ: $\qquad\qquad \ddot\theta + \ddot\phi + p^2\phi = 0$

Writing $\ddot\theta = -\omega^2\theta$ and $\ddot\phi = -\omega^2\phi$ (normal modes) and solving

$$10^{-4}\omega^4 - (q^2 - \omega^2)(p^2 - \omega^2) = 0$$

gives

$$\omega^2 = \frac{(p^2 - q^2) \pm [(p^2 - q^2) + 4 \times 10^{-4}p^2q^2]^{1/2}}{2(1 - 10^{-4})}$$

With $p = 5\pi$, $q = 4\pi$ we obtain $\omega = 5.000\,69\pi$, 3.9996π so the period of the balance is $2/5.000\,69$ s, which is shorter than $\tfrac{2}{5}$ s. In 24 h, the watch will record

$$\frac{5.000\,69 \times 24}{5} = 24.0033 \text{ h}$$

i.e. fast by 12 s as required. The watch *gains*.

11.8 Let Fig. 11.10 define the coordinates. For equilibrium,

$$F = (M + m)g\sin\alpha \text{ at } t = 0$$

hence

$$F = (M + m)g\sin\alpha + Pt$$

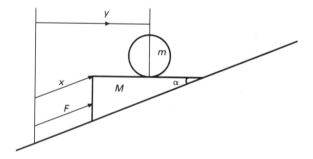

Figure 11.10

The kinetic energy is

$$T = \tfrac{1}{2}M\dot x^2 + \tfrac{1}{2}m(\dot x^2 + \dot y^2 + 2\dot x\dot y\cos\alpha) + \tfrac{1}{4}m(\dot x\cos\alpha - \dot y)^2$$

since the rotation rate of the cylinder is $(\dot x\cos\alpha - \dot y)$ divided by its radius. The generalised forces in the x- and y-directions are Q_x and Q_y where

$$Q_x = -(M + m)g\sin\alpha + F$$

$$Q_y = 0$$

and

$$\delta W = Q_x\delta x + Q_y\delta y$$

Lagrange's equations

$$\frac{\mathrm{d}}{\mathrm{d}t}\left(\frac{\partial T}{\partial \dot x}\right) - \frac{\partial T}{\partial x} = Q_x$$

and

190

$$\frac{\mathrm{d}}{\mathrm{d}t}\left(\frac{\partial T}{\partial \dot{y}}\right) - \frac{\partial T}{\partial y} = 0$$

lead to

$$(M + m + \tfrac{1}{2}m\cos^2\alpha)\ddot{x} + \tfrac{1}{2}m\ddot{y}\cos\alpha = Pt \qquad \textbf{(11.22)}$$

and

$$\tfrac{3}{2}m\ddot{y} + \tfrac{1}{2}m\ddot{x}\cos\alpha = 0$$

Integrating the second gives

$$y = b - \tfrac{1}{3}x\cos\alpha \qquad \textbf{(11.23)}$$

(taking $x = 0$ at $t = 0$; hence Equation (11.22) integrated twice gives

$$(M + m + \tfrac{1}{3}m\cos^2\alpha)x = \tfrac{1}{6}Pt^3$$

When $y = x\cos\alpha$ the cylinder falls; hence $x = 3b/4\cos\alpha$ (from Equation (11.23)). When this happens, t obeys $3[3(M + m) + m\cos^2\alpha]b = 2Pt^3\cos\alpha$, as required.

Topic Guide

Phase plane diagrams
Equilibrium
Trajectories
Van der Pol Oscillator
Chaotic Attractor

12 Non-linear Dynamics

12.1 Fact Sheet

One-dimensional Motion

One-dimensional motion of a particle is written in terms of one generalised coordinate q, its derivative $\dot{q}$ and time t. It is usually described by the equation

$$\ddot{q}_1 = f(q_1, \dot{q}_1, t)$$

If t does not appear explicitly, the system is said to be **autonomous**, in which case

$$\ddot{q}_1 = f(q_1, \dot{q}_1)$$

Equilibrium occurs when both $\ddot{q}$ and $\dot{q}$ vanish. The system is **conservative** if, further, it can be written

$$\ddot{q}_1 = f(q_1)$$

so that

$$\dot{q}_1 = q_2 \text{ and } \dot{q}_2 = f(q_1)$$

or

$$\frac{\mathrm{d}q_2}{\mathrm{d}q_1} = \frac{f(q_1)}{q_2}$$

This differential equation is solved, and the solution $\phi(q_1, q_2) =$ constant is plotted as a series of contours on the q_1, q_2 plane, called the **phase plane**. A number of features may appear on the phase plane. An isolated point can be a focus for the solution curves: such points are called **equilibrium points**. These points can represent stable equilibrium (if the solution curves all spiral in) or unstable equilibrium (otherwise). Sometimes there is a closed curve, which represents an oscillation, that acts as an attractor for phase plane curves. This closed curve is called a **limit cycle**, and most commonly, but certainly not exclusively, occurs in forced oscillation.

In three and more dimensions, more complicated equilibrium cycles are possible.

Chaotic Dynamics

For certain equations, of the type $\ddot{q} = f(\dot{q}, q, t)$, there is a sensitivity to initial conditions that renders phase plane plots of little use. In these circumstances, only solutions at $t =$ integer multiples of the fundamental period (perhaps the forcing period) are plotted as dots. The resulting diagram is called the **Poincaré map**, and attractors for the dots are called **chaotic** (or strange) **attractors**.

A detailed treatment of Poincaré maps and chaotic attractors is outside the scope of this text but may be found in modern books on non-linear dynamics (see, for example, Thompson and Stewart (1986)).

12.2 Worked Examples

12.1 A particle is travelling vertically with resistance proportional to the square of the speed. Interpret the two phase plane diagrams, one for ascending and one for descending.

Solution If we take the ground as $x = 0$, with x pointing upwards, the equation of motion for an ascending particle is

$$m\frac{d^2x}{dt^2} = -mg - mkv^2$$

or

$$\dot{v} = -g - kv^2$$
$$\dot{x} = v$$

This is a conservative system, since, by dividing these two equations, we obtain

$$\frac{dv}{dx} = \frac{-g - kv^2}{v}$$

(This is the same equation as would be obtained by using acceleration $= v\,dv/dx$, of course.) Integrating this equation leads to

$$g + kv^2 = Ae^{-2kx} \tag{12.1}$$

where A is an arbitrary constant.
   If the particle is falling, then

$$\dot{v} = -g + kv^2$$
$$\dot{x} = v$$

whence

$$\frac{dv}{dx} = \frac{-g + kv^2}{v}$$

with solution

$$kv^2 - g = Be^{2kx}$$

where B is a second arbitrary constant.
   Now, at the topmost point of the trajectory, $v = 0$ and $x = x_1$ (say). Since the paths coincide there, we have

$$B = -Ae^{-4kx_1}$$

Thus

$$kv^2 = g - Ae^{2k(x - 2x_1)}$$

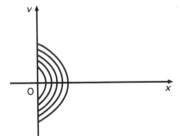

Figure 12.1

and the phase plot is given in Fig. 12.1. The launch velocity determines precisely the path. The origin is the only fixed point, and it is stable.

12.2 Investigate, via the phase plane, the motion of a simple pendulum.

Solution The equation of motion is most easily derived using conservation of energy. A glance at Fig. 12.2 shows that, if the pendulum bob has mass m and the pendulum string is of length a, the energy equation is

$$mga(1 - \cos\theta) + \tfrac{1}{2}ma^2\dot\theta^2 = \text{constant}$$

Differentiating gives

$$a\ddot\theta + g\sin\theta = 0$$

In order to plot the phase plane, we write

$$\omega = \dot\theta$$

and

$$a\dot\omega = -g\sin\theta$$

so that

$$a\frac{d\omega}{d\theta} = -g\frac{\sin\theta}{\omega}$$

This integrates to give

$$\tfrac{1}{2}a\omega^2 = g\cos\theta + A$$

(which returns us, of course, to the energy equation).

If A is very large, then ω is, in turn, very large. It is also approximately constant:

$$(\omega^2 \approx 2A/a)$$

If $A = g$, then $\omega = 0$ only when $\theta = \pi$. This corresponds to the pendulum pointing up. If $A < g$, then the value of θ is restricted to lie between two values $\pm \cos^{-1}(A/g)$ and the path is closed. Indeed, for small enough θ

$$\tfrac{1}{2}a\omega^2 \approx g\left(1 - \frac{\theta^2}{2!}\right) + A$$

and the path is approximately elliptical. Figure 12.3 shows the phase plane. The motion is periodic in θ, and the picture between $-\pi$ and π is repeated *ad infinitum*. The point $\theta = 0$, $\omega = 0$ is a point of stable equilibrium. The points $\theta = \pm\pi$, $\omega = 0$ are points of unstable equilibrium. If ω exceeds $2(g/a)^{1/2}$ (with $A = g$) then it never crosses the θ-axis; the value $\omega = 2(g/a)^{1/2}$ is known as a **separatrix**.

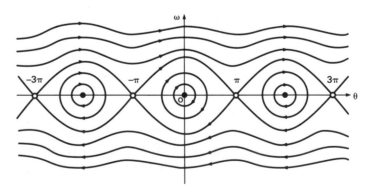

Figure 12.3

12.3 Use the energy equation to derive conditions on the potential function that determine whether on not equilibrium conditions are stable or unstable. Draw the phase plane diagrams close to these equilibrium positions in each case.

Solution   The energy equation takes the standard form

$$\tfrac{1}{2}mv^2 + mf(x) = \text{constant}$$

or

$$\tfrac{1}{2}v^2 + f(x) = A$$

Now, suppose that $x = 0$ is a level of zero potential so that $f(0) = 0$. Suppose further that $x = 0$ is a position of equilibrium. This gives rise to three cases:

$$f'' > 0 \quad (\text{minimum})$$

$$f'' < 0 \quad (\text{maximum})$$

$$f'' = 0 \quad (\text{inflection})$$

The Maclaurin expansion for $f(x)$ has leading term

$$f(x) = \tfrac{1}{2}f''(0)x^2$$

Hence the energy equation close to $x = 0$ is approximately

$$\tfrac{1}{2}v^2 + \tfrac{1}{2}f''(0)x^2 = A \qquad\qquad\qquad \textbf{(12.2)}$$

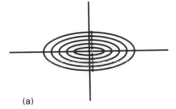

(a)

We examine the three cases and sketch the phase plane diagrams (phase portraits) in each case.
  (a) $f''(0) > 0$
  In this case, Equation (12.2) is an ellipse with phase portrait as in Fig. 12.4(a). This represents stable equilibrium, since the potential energy is a minimum.
  (b) $f''(0) < 0$
  In this case, Equation (12.2) is a hyperbola with phase portrait as in Fig. 12.4(b). This represents unstable equilibrium, since the potential energy is a maximum.
  (c) $f''(0) = 0$
  In this last case, the energy equation needs to be examined from first principles. If $f'''(0)$ is non-zero, the energy equation is

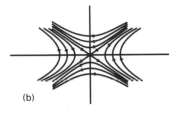

(b)

$$v^2 + f'''(0)x^3 = 2A$$

One example of the phase portrait is shown in Fig. 12.4(c). In all cases, the position is unstable equilibrium if $f'''(0) \neq 0$. (Further cases need to be examined from first principles).
  In summary: $f''(0) > 0$ is the condition for an equilibrium position at $x = 0$ to be stable; $f''(0) < 0$ for $x = 0$ to be unstable; and if $f''(0) = 0$ the case needs to be examined from first principles.

12.4   Investigate the damped system

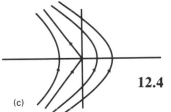

(c)

Figure 12.4

$$\ddot{x} + 2\alpha\omega\dot{x} + \omega^2 x = 0$$

where α is the damping factor and ω the natural frequency, drawing the phase portraits where appropriate. Distinguish between the three cases of underdamped, overdamped and critically damped motion.

Solution   When damping is present, energy is no longer conserved. It is still possible to set up the equations in terms of $v \,(= \dot{x})$ and x as follows:

$$\dot{v} = -2\alpha\omega v - \omega^2 x$$

$$\dot{x} = v$$

and to solve. However, this solution method is by no means the best to adopt here. Instead, we solve in terms of time (see Example 6.2).
  Let $x = e^{\lambda t}$ to obtain the auxiliary equation

$$\lambda^2 + 2\alpha\omega\lambda + \omega^2 = 0$$

giving

$$\lambda = \omega[-\alpha \pm (\alpha^2 - 1)^{1/2}]$$

Obviously there are three cases to consider here, corresponding to real distinct, coincident and complex roots for λ.

Case 1: $\alpha < 1$ (complex conjugate roots). In this case, the solution for x can be written

$$x = A_1 e^{-\alpha\omega t}\sin(kt + \phi)$$

where $k^2 = 1 - \alpha^2$ and A_1 and ϕ are arbitrary constants. Differentiating with respect to t gives

$$v = A_1 e^{-\alpha\omega t}[-\alpha\omega\sin(kt + \phi) + k\cos(kt + \phi)]$$

We can plot v against x by using time t as a parameter. As $t \to \infty$, $x \to 0$ and $v \to 0$ no matter what the values of A_1 and ϕ are. The origin is thus a stable equilibrium point. The smaller α, the more times the trajectory spirals around the origin for a particular incremental shift towards it. Figure 12.5(a) shows the phase portrait in the vicinity of the origin in this particular case.

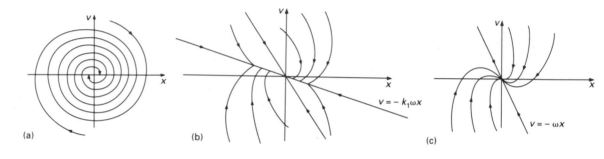

Figure 12.5   (a)   (b)   (c)

Case 2: $\alpha > 1$ (distinct real roots). In this case the system is overdamped and x is given by

$$x = A_2 e^{-k_1\omega t} + B_2 e^{-k_2\omega t}$$

where $k_1 = \alpha - (\alpha^2 - 1)^{1/2}$ and $k_2 = \alpha + (\alpha^2 - 1)^{1/2}$ and, of course A_2 and B_2 are arbitrary constants.

Now, no matter how close α is to 1, there comes a time t when the first term will dominate the equation for x, because $k_1\omega t$ is much smaller than $k_2\omega t$. Similarly, the velocity v, where

$$v = -k_1 A_2 \omega e^{-k_1\omega t} - k_2 B_2 \omega e^{-k_2\omega t}$$

will also be dominated by the first term. When this happens, approximately

$$v \approx -k_1\omega x$$

which is a straight line in phase space. After this time therefore, the trajectory roughly follows this line to the origin. There is no winding around the origin in this case. Figure 12.5(b) displays the trajectories under strong damping.

Case 3: $\alpha = 1$ (coincident roots). In this case (critical damping), the solution is

$$x = (At + B)e^{-\omega t}$$

and, differentiating,

$$v = Ae^{-\omega t} - \omega x$$

The trajectory shown in Fig. 12.5(c) is similar to Fig. 12.5(b), but the asymptote is the 'natural' one of $v = -\omega x$. It can be shown that, in some sense, the trajectory paths have a minimal length in this case.

12.5 Using the results of the previous example, deduce the trajectory of the forced oscillation

$$\ddot{x} - 2\alpha\omega\dot{x} + \omega^2 x = A_0 \sin\sigma t$$

where $\omega \neq \sigma$. Briefly discuss the case $\omega = \sigma$.

Solution The solution to the homogeneous problem is given in the previous example. To this we must add the particular solution. A variety of techniques are available to do this; the simplest is to substitute $x = \alpha\sin\sigma t + \beta\cos\sigma t$ and equate coefficients of $\sin\sigma t$ and $\cos\sigma t$ to find α and β. The most constructive is to write $\sin\sigma t$ as $\mathrm{Re}(-ie^{i\sigma t})$ and assume $x = \mathrm{Re}(ze^{i\sigma t})$, called the method of phasors by electrical engineers. This method gives

$$z = \frac{i(\omega^2 - \sigma^2) - 2\omega\sigma}{(\omega^2 - \sigma^2)^2 + 4\omega^2\alpha^2}$$

so that

$$x = \frac{A_0\cos(\sigma t + \phi)}{(\omega^2 - \sigma^2)^2 + 4\omega^2\alpha^2} \qquad (12.3)$$

where

$$\tan\phi = -\frac{2\omega\alpha}{(\omega^2 - \sigma^2)} \qquad \left(\frac{\pi}{2} < \phi < \pi\right)$$

(see Example 6.2). Expression (12.3) is called the steady state solution, and the (decaying) complimentary function is called the 'transient'. Expression (12.3) is thus added (in turn) to the three answers of the previous example to give three new answers.

For all cases, as $t \to \infty$ the trajectory behaves like

$$x \approx \frac{A_0}{(\omega^2 - \sigma^2)^2 + 4\omega^2\alpha^2} \sin(\sigma t + \phi)$$

$$v \approx \frac{\sigma A_0}{(\omega^2 - \sigma^2)^2 + 4\omega^2\alpha^2} \cos(\sigma t + \phi)$$

so that the solutions decay asymptotically to the ellipse

$$x^2 + \frac{v^2}{\sigma^2} = 1$$

Figure 12.6 shows some of these trajectories.

The case $\sigma = \omega$ is resonance. With $\alpha \neq 0$, this is not singular, but the steady state response is close to maximal. If $\alpha = 0$, then the solution is infinite when $\sigma = \omega$ (i.e. x and $v \to \infty$ as $t \to \infty$ in the phase plane).

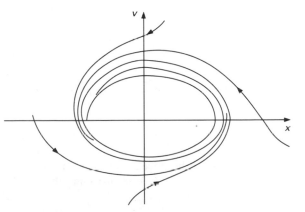

Figure 12.6

197

12.6 Interpret the non-linear, forced, damped pendulum

$$\ddot{q}_1 + 2\alpha\omega\dot{q}_1 + \omega^2 \sin q_1 = g\cos\sigma t$$

in terms of three variables. Show how this formulation shows that the system is conservative if there is no damping.

Solution Writing $q_2 = \dot{q}_1$ and $q_3 = \sigma t$, the equation given in the question can be rewritten as follows

$$\dot{q}_1 = q_2$$

$$\dot{q}_2 = -2\alpha\omega q_2 - \omega^2 \sin q_1 + g\cos q_3$$

and

$$\dot{q}_3 = \sigma$$

We define the three-dimensional space $(q_1, q_2, q_3) = \mathbf{q}$ as **phase space**. This means that the vector $\dot{\mathbf{q}} = (\dot{q}_1, \dot{q}_2, \dot{q}_3)$ represents the velocity in phase space. If S is a closed surface in phase space, then the integral $\int_s \dot{\mathbf{q}}\cdot d\mathbf{S}$ represents the flux out of the surface S. We now use the Gauss flux theorem (sometimes called the divergence theorem) so that

$$\int_s \dot{\mathbf{q}}\cdot d\mathbf{S} = \int_V \nabla\cdot\dot{\mathbf{q}}\, dV$$

where V is the volume enclosed by the surface S in phase space. The divergence operator $\nabla\cdot$ is defined by

$$\nabla\cdot\mathbf{F} = \frac{\partial F_1}{\partial q_1} + \frac{\partial F_2}{\partial q_2} + \frac{\partial F_3}{\partial q_3}$$

Hence we see that

$$\nabla\cdot\dot{\mathbf{q}} = \frac{\partial \dot{q}_1}{\partial q_1} + \frac{\partial \dot{q}_2}{\partial q_2} + \frac{\partial \dot{q}_3}{\partial q_3} = 0 - 2\alpha\omega + 0 = -2\alpha\omega$$

If $\alpha = 0$, corresponding to zero damping, then $\nabla\cdot\dot{\mathbf{q}} = 0$. This means that there is no flux out of the (arbitrary) surface S. The logical interpretation of this, remembering that we are in phase space, is that there is no loss or leakage, so that the system is conservative.

12.7 Investigate the nature of the equilibrium points of the non-linear damped oscillator

$$\ddot{x} + \dot{x} + x^2 - \mu = 0$$

Solution There are always a number of choices for y from a single equation for x. The most informative for our purposes is

$$\dot{x} = y$$

$$\dot{y} = \mu - x^2 - y$$

In order to plot the phase plane portrait, the equation

$$\frac{dy}{dx} = \frac{\mu - x^2 - y}{y}$$

needs to be solved. Although it is possible to do this analytically to obtain a closed form solution, this solution is so cumbersome that it is not useful. Instead, we first of all find the equilibrium points. Since

$$y\frac{dy}{dx} = \mu - x^2 - y$$

and $\dot{x} = y$, we have equilibrium ($\ddot{x} = 0$) if

$$x^2 = \mu$$

or

$$x = \pm \mu^{1/2}$$

The equation of motion is

$$\ddot{x} + \dot{x} + x^2 - \mu = 0$$

and we examine the stability of this at the two points $\dot{x} = 0$, $x = \mu^{1/2}$ and $\dot{x} = 0$, $x = -\mu^{1/2}$.

At $\dot{x} = 0$, $x = \mu^{1/2}$, let us put $x = \mu^{1/2} + \varepsilon$, with ε small enough for ε^2 to be ignored. Hence

$$x^2 = (\mu^{1/2} + \varepsilon)^2 \approx \mu + 2\varepsilon\mu^{1/2}$$

Therefore, close to this point the equation is approximately $\ddot{\varepsilon} + 2\varepsilon\mu^{1/2} = 0$, which has oscillatory solutions, hence implying that the point is a point of stable equilibrium (for positive μ).

At $\dot{x} = 0$, $x = -\mu^{1/2}$, this time $\dot{x} = 0$ and $x = -\mu^{1/2} + \varepsilon$, and

$$x^2 = (-\mu^{1/2} + \varepsilon)^2 \approx \mu - 2\varepsilon\mu^{1/2}$$

Hence

$$\ddot{\varepsilon} - 2\varepsilon\mu^{1/2} = 0$$

and this point is a point of unstable equilibrium.

If $x > 0$ the equilibrium point is stable since $x^2 > 0$ too. On the other hand, if $x < 0$ this is unstable. If $\mu < 0$, there are no points of equilibrium.

Figures 12.7(a), (b) and (c) are the phase plane portraits for $\mu = 0.5$, 0 and -0.5 respectively. Figure 12.7(a) clearly shows the two equilibrium points at $(-0.7,0)$ (unstable) and $(0.7,0)$ (stable), and Fig. 12.7(b) shows that the origin is an unstable point for negative x, but is stable for positive x. Finally, the third phase portrait contains no points of equilibrium.

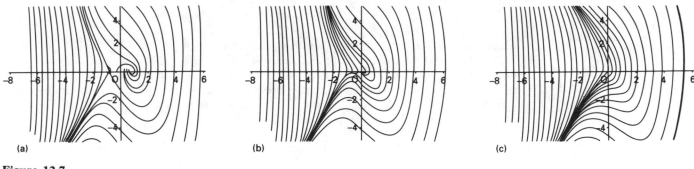

(a)　　　　　　　　　　　(b)　　　　　　　　　　　(c)

Figure 12.7

12.8 The periodically forced van der Pol oscillator is governed by the equation

$$\ddot{x} + \alpha(x^2 - 1)\dot{x} + \omega^2 x = A\sin\omega_0 t$$

(a) With $A = 0$, $\omega = 1$ and $\alpha = 0.5$, sketch the phase portrait and discuss the concept of a *limit cycle*.

(b) Keeping ω and α the same, use $A \neq 0$ to introduce the ideas of a *Poincaré map* and a *chaotic attractor*.

Solution   (a) Since the equation of motion is now

$$\ddot{x} + 0.5(x^2 - 1)\dot{x} + x = 0$$

we may write $\dot{x} = y$ so that

$$\dot{y} = -0.5(x^2 - 1)y - x$$

Dividing these equations gives the first-order equation

$$\frac{dy}{dx} = \frac{0.5(1 - x^2)y - x}{y} \tag{12.4}$$

The solution of this differential equation for various initial conditions can be drawn (see Fig. 12.8) using proprietary software.

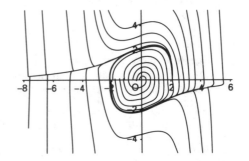

Figure 12.8

An obvious feature of the phase portrait is the *limit cycle*. If the start conditions are (roughly) outside a circle of radius 2, that is $\dot{x}^2 + x^2 \geq 4$, then the solution curve of the differential Equation (12.4) moves towards the curve from the outside. If, on the other hand, the start conditions correspond to a point on the phase portrait close to the origin, the solution curve of the differential equation spirals outward towards the same curve from the inside. The oscillations on some of the lines are due to imperfections in the software (no criticism implied here – van der Pol's equation is notoriously tricky to solve, even numerically).

Before the advent of easily available computers of high enough power, the use of Taylor's series was employed to show that there is a limit cycle of the equation

$$\ddot{x} + \alpha(x^2 - 1)\dot{x} + x = 0$$

which is close to $\dot{x}^2 + x^2 = 4$ for small but non-zero α.

The older texts McClusky (1959) and Andronow and Chaikin (1949) contain analytical treatments. We display the limit cycles for this equation with $\alpha = 0.01$ (Fig. 12.9) and $\alpha = 10$ (Fig. 12.10). For $\alpha = 0.01$ it is virtually circular; for $\alpha = 10$ it is virtually a parallelogram.

(b) If there is a forcing term, it is still possible to analyse the response (in a descriptive sense) in terms of phase portraits. The equation is now

$$\ddot{x} + \alpha(x^2 - 1)\dot{x} + x = A\sin\omega_0 t \tag{12.5}$$

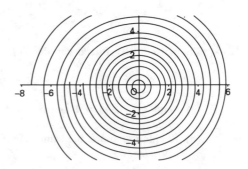

Figure 12.9

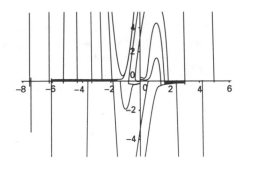

Figure 12.10

Writing

$$\dot{x} = y$$

and

$$\dot{y} = -\alpha(x^2 - 1)y + A\sin\omega_0 t$$

we see that, at times π/ω_0, $\dot{x}$ and $\dot{y}$ have the same values as they have in the unforced situation. At other times, $\dot{y}$ has an additional displacement. Of course, this displacement is periodic, of period $2\pi/\omega_0$. Hence a more useful pictorial representation is to plot the phase portrait at times $t = 0$, $2\pi/(k\omega_0)$, $k = 0,1,2,\ldots$ this portrait thus consists of dots and is termed the *Poincaré map* of the equation and is a map of 'returns'.

For Equation (12.5) we can easily deduce the Poincaré map, for it will be the same as the solution of Equation (12.4), except that only x and y ($=\dot{x}$) which correspond to times which are an integer multiple of $2\pi/\omega_0$ will be permitted. Hence we expect a 'dotted' version of Fig. 12.8. The limit cycle in these circumstances could possibly be a chaotic or strange attractor but this is not essential. For different choices, for example $t = \pi/(6\omega_0) + 2\pi n/\omega_0$, where n is an integer, the Poincaré map will be the dotted version of the phase portrait of

$$\frac{dy}{dx} = \frac{0.5(1 - x^2)y + 0.5A - x}{y}$$

This is not chaotic.

12.9 Plot the Poincaré map of the solution to the forced, damped, non-linear van der Pol oscillator whose equation is

$$\ddot{x} + 0.4\dot{x} - x + x^3 = 0.4\sin t$$

Solution First of all, we note that this problem cannot be done without the aid of a computer. Writing $y = \dot{x}$ we deduce that

$$\frac{dy}{dx} = 0.4\sin t - 0.4y + x - x^3 \tag{12.6}$$

which, of course, varies explicitly with t. We cannot therefore plot the phase plane. Instead, we select a sequence of times for which the Equation (12.6) is unchanged. An obvious choice is the sequence

$$t = \{\pi k, \; k = 0,1,\ldots\}$$

Equation (12.6) at these times is

$$\frac{dy}{dx} = -0.4y + x - x^3 \tag{12.7}$$

Of course, the solution of this equation is only valid at discrete times (integer multiples of π). We thus can only plot the points $(k\pi, y(k\pi))$, and this has been done in Fig. 12.11 for $k = 1, 2, \ldots,$ 1000. One feature of this figure is clear: the convergence, in some fuzzy sense, of the solution points to a rather decorative curve. This curve is called a chaotic or strange attractor. If a mechanical device responds to a force with a displacement which can be represented by this x, then it will be seen to look periodic, perhaps, but will never quite 'settle down'. Several executive toys work on this principle.

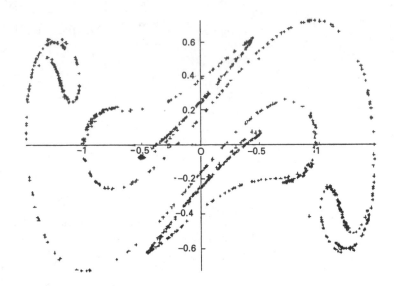

Figure 12.11

12.3 Exercises

12.1 The energy equation for a dynamical system is

$$a(1 + 3\sin^2\theta)\dot{\theta}^2 - 6g\cos\theta(1 - \cos\theta) = \text{constant}$$

Find the equilibrium positions and determine the period of small oscillations about the stable one.

12.2 A particle is travelling vertically, subject to a resistance proportional to velocity. Plot the phase plane diagram corresponding to launch and return to ground level.

12.3 A rower rows a boat across a river of width h occupying the strip $0 \leq x \leq h$ in the x–y plane, always rowing towards a fixed point on one bank. The boat moves at a constant speed u relative to the water. The river flows at a constant speed U. Determine $\dot{x}$ and $\dot{y}$ if the fixed point is taken as the origin. Find an expression connecting y and x, and interpret what happens when $u < U$.

12.4 This question concerns Duffing's equation:

$$\ddot{x} + k\dot{x} + \alpha x + \beta x^3 = A\cos\omega t$$

which arises from forced, damped oscillation of a non-linear spring (force proportional to $-\alpha x - \beta x^3$). Calculate the phase curves for zero damping, plotting them for the two cases (a) $\alpha = 1$, $\beta = 0.1$ and (b) $\alpha = 1$, $\beta = 5$. Hence deduce the phase curves for non-zero ($k = 1$) damping.

12.5 A particle slides on a wire which is shaped as a parabola, and the whole spins about its axis of symmetry, which is held vertical. The distance x from the axis of rotation satisfies the equation

$$(1 + x^2)\ddot{x} + (g - \omega^2 + \dot{x}^2)x = 0$$

Analyse what happens to the bead by drawing the phase plane.

12.6 A mass m is attached to the mid-point of an elastic string of length $2a$ and stiffness λ. Ignoring gravity, and taking the tension as zero in equilibrium, obtain the equation of motion and sketch the phase paths.

12.7 A single degree of freedom system has kinetic energy T and potential energy V given by

$$T = \alpha(x) + \dot{x}\beta(x) + \dot{x}^2\gamma(x)$$

$$V = V(x)$$

Use Lagrange's equation to obtain the equation of motion of the system. Show that the equilibrium points of the system are stationary point of $\alpha(x) - V(x)$ and determine the phase paths of the system.

12.8 Construct the phase diagram for the coupled dynamical system

$$\dot{x} = x - y$$

$$\dot{y} = 1 - xy$$

using the following routine:

(a) Find the equilibrium points.
(b) Analyse the nature of these points.

If you have access to software for plotting portraits, check your solution.

12.9 (Only those students with access to software that can solve differential equations and produce Poincaré maps can solve this exercise.)

A mechanical system is governed by the following forced Duffing equation

$$\ddot{x} + 0.4\dot{x} - x + x^3 = 0.4\sin t$$

Plot the phase plane for the unforced equation and compare it with the phase portrait of the unforced and undamped equation

$$\ddot{x} - x + x^3 = 0$$

Finally, compare both with the Poincaré map of the original forced and damped equation.

12.10 (Software is required for this exercise.)

Sketch the Poincaré map for the sinusoidally forced Duffing equation

$$\ddot{x} + 0.05\dot{x} + 0.2x + x^3 = 7.5\sin t$$

What evidence is there that this is a strange attractor?

12.4 Outline Solutions to Exercises

12.1 $a(1 + 3\sin^2\theta)\dot{\theta}^2 - 6g\cos\theta(1 - \cos\theta) = K$. Differentiating gives

$$2a(1 + 3\sin^2\theta)\ddot{\theta} + 6a\sin\theta\dot{\theta}^2 + 6g\sin\theta(1 - 2\cos\theta) = 0 \text{ (12.8)}$$

For equilibrium,

$$\sin\theta(1 - 2\cos\theta) = 0$$

i.e. $\theta = 0, \pi/3, \pi$. $\theta = 0$ is unstable, as is $\theta = \pi$. Near $\theta = \pi/3$,

$$\cos\theta \approx \tfrac{1}{2} - \frac{\varepsilon\sqrt{3}}{2}$$

$$\sin\theta \approx \frac{\varepsilon\sqrt{3}}{2} + \frac{1}{2}\varepsilon$$

Thus

$$2\dot{a}(1 + 3\sin^2\theta) \approx \tfrac{13}{2}a$$

and

$$6g\sin\theta(1 - 2\cos\theta) \approx 9g\varepsilon$$

Thus Equation (12.8) is approximately

$$\tfrac{13}{2}a\ddot{\varepsilon} + 9g\varepsilon = 0$$

which represents an oscillation of period $2\pi(13a/18g)^{1/2}$. Software can be used to draw the phase plane plot of Equation (12.8).

12.2 For ascending motion

$$m\frac{dv}{dt} = -mg - mkv$$

where $v = dx/dt$.

Hence

$$\frac{dv}{dx} = \frac{-g - kv}{v}$$

so that

$$x = -\frac{v - u}{k} - \frac{g}{k}\ln\left(\frac{kv + g}{ku + g}\right)$$

For descending motion

$$\frac{dv}{dx} = \frac{-g + kv}{v}$$

so that

$$x = \frac{v - u}{k} - \frac{g}{k}\ln\left(\frac{kv - g}{ku - g}\right)$$

The phase plane is shown in Fig. 12.12.

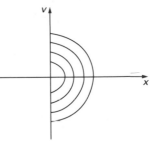

Figure 12.12

12.3 The velocity of the boat is, in polar coordinates (r, θ)

$$\mathbf{v} = -u\hat{\mathbf{r}} - U\hat{\mathbf{j}} \text{ (taking } U \text{ along } -\hat{\mathbf{j}})$$

Converting to Cartesian coordinates:

$$\dot{x} = \frac{-ux}{(x^2 + y^2)^{1/2}}$$

$$\dot{y} = -U - \frac{uy}{(x^2 + y^2)^{1/2}}$$

Dividing these equations and solving the resulting homogeneous ordinary differential equation (write $xp = y$, when the equation becomes separable – or use software!) gives

$$y + (1 + y^2)^{1/2} = Cx^{(u-U)/u}$$

when $u < U$, the phase plane shows that $(0,0)$ is never reached.

12.4 With no damping, it is easy to deduce that

$$y^2 + \alpha x^2 = c - \tfrac{1}{2}\beta x^5$$

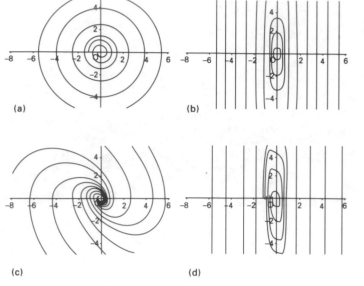

(a)   (b)

(c)   (d)

Figure 12.13

these lead to Fig. 12.13(a) and (b) for $\alpha = 1$ and $\beta = 0.01$ and 5, respectively. With non-zero damping, the centre $(0,0)$ becomes a stable node, as shown in Fig. 12.13(c) and (d).

12.5 The phase portraits depicted in Fig. 12.14 arise from

$$y' = -\frac{x(g - \omega^2 + y^2)}{y(1 + x^2)} \qquad (y = \dot{x})$$

If $\omega^2 > g$, then $y^2 = \omega^2 - g$ leads to constant speed. All other initial speeds lead to $x \to \infty$ and $\dot{x}^2 \to \omega^2 - g$ (see Fig. 12.14(a)).

If $\omega^2 = g$, then $\dot{x} \to 0$ for every initial condition, as depicted in Fig. 12.14(b).

If $\omega^2 < g$, then the bead performs oscillations about $(0,0)$, as shown in Fig. 12.14(c).

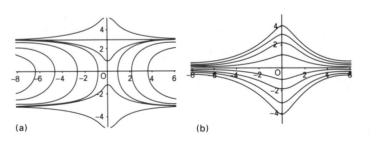

(a)   (b)

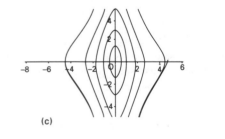

(c)

Figure 12.14

12.6 Figure 12.15 shows the setup. Since there is no tension at

equilibrium, natural length of string $= a$. Let θ be the angle between the string and the x-direction; also suppose that $2y$ is the length of the stretched string. Hence

$$m\ddot{x} = -2T\cos\theta$$

$$T = \lambda(y - a)/y$$

Also,

$$y^2 = x^2 + a^2$$

$$\cos\theta = x/y$$

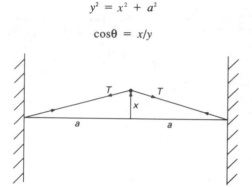

Figure 12.15

Hence

$$am\ddot{x}(x^2 + a^2)^{1/2} = -2\lambda x[(x^2 + a^2)^{1/2} - a]$$

is the required equation. The phase plane is shown in Fig. 12.16, and clearly each path is closed and symmetric about the origin. The motion is not simple harmonic, so the paths are not circular. The larger the amplitude, the closer the motion is to SHM.

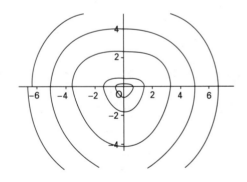

Figure 12.16

12.7 Using Lagrange's equation in the form

$$\frac{\mathrm{d}}{\mathrm{d}t}\left(\frac{\partial T}{\partial \dot{x}}\right) - \frac{\partial T}{\partial x} = -\frac{\partial V}{\partial x}$$

it follows immediately that $\mathrm{d}/\mathrm{d}x \, (\alpha - V)$ is zero if $\dot{x} = \ddot{x} = 0$. Lagrange's equation implies that

$$\frac{\partial}{\partial x}(\gamma\dot{x}^2 - \alpha + V) = 0$$

whence $\gamma\dot{x}^2 - \alpha + V = \text{constant}$ (see Exercise 11.4). These are the phase paths of the system.

12.8 Equilibrium points are $x = y = 1$, $x = y = -1$. Near $(1,1)$, write $x = 1 + p$, $y = 1 + q$ and linearise to give

$$\dot{p} = p - q$$

and

$$\dot{q} = -p - q$$

which gives the vector equation

$$\dot{\mathbf{v}} = \mathbf{A}\mathbf{v}$$

$$A = \begin{bmatrix} 1 & -1 \\ -1 & -1 \end{bmatrix}, \qquad \mathbf{v} = \begin{pmatrix} p \\ q \end{pmatrix}$$

The eigenvalues of A are $\pm\sqrt{2}$ which gives unstable equilibrium. Moreover, the lines with gradients $1 \pm \sqrt{2}$ give the orientation of the saddle point: $1 + \sqrt{2}$ is a convergent direction and $1 - \sqrt{2}$ a divergent direction.

Near $(-1,-1)$ similar analysis reveals eigenvalues $1 \pm i$, and hence also unstable equilibrium, but this time the phase lines spiral outwards. The phase plot is as in Fig. 12.17.

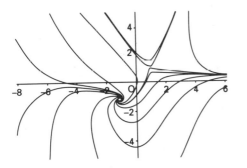

Figure 12.17

12.9 Writing $y = \dot{x}$, $\ddot{x} = x + x^3 = 0$ integrates to

$$y^2 - x^2 + \tfrac{1}{2}x^4 = \text{constant} \qquad \textbf{(12.9)}$$

with equilibrium points $x = \pm 1$. Using linearisation ($x = \pm 1 + \varepsilon$), both equilibrium points are stable.

The curves described by Equation (12.9) are rather like peanuts centred at $x = 1$ and $x = -1$. Including damping leads to a spiralling in of the phase portrait, as depicted in Fig. 12.18. The

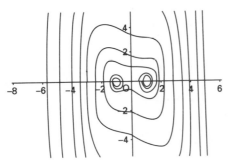

Figure 12.18

forced equation has a Poincaré map, as shown in Fig. 12.19. Despite the appearance, this is not a chaotic attractor, since the lines of the Poincaré map are along well-defined paths, not fuzzy paths.

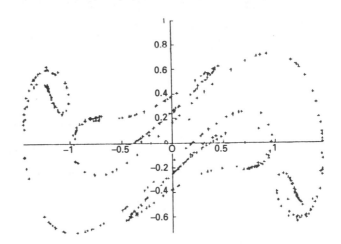

Figure 12.19

12.10 The Poincaré map for this equation is shown in Fig. 12.20. The fuzzy nature of the diagram is positive evidence that we have a chaotic or strange attractor here. Physically, this means that, as the sinusoidal oscillation continues to be applied, the resulting displacement and velocity never settles down. This is a feature of several 'executive toys', e.g. two magnets on a plane board with a steel pendulum in the form of a stiff wire, freely pivoted, on the end of which is an iron ball, mounted so as to be equidistant from the magnets.

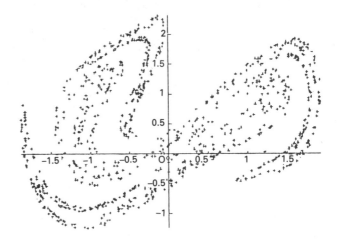

Figure 12.20

Appendix A: Vector Calculus

In this appendix, we shall give some standard results of vector calculus. Vectors are quantities with both magnitude and direction and are either denoted by bold characters **a**, or by large letters with an overhead arrow, $\overrightarrow{AB}$. The latter notation is less used today, being reserved for problems of a geometrical nature. Vectors obey all the usual rules of algebra, so if **a**, **b** and **c** are three vectors, the following are true:

$$\mathbf{a} + \mathbf{b} = \mathbf{b} + \mathbf{a}$$

$$(\mathbf{a} + \mathbf{b}) + \mathbf{c} = \mathbf{a} + (\mathbf{b} + \mathbf{c})$$

$$\mathbf{a} + \mathbf{0} = \mathbf{a}$$

$$\mathbf{a} + (-\mathbf{a}) = \mathbf{0}$$

There are two ways of multiplying vectors: the scalar product **a·b**, which leads to a scalar quantity, and the vector product $\mathbf{a} \times \mathbf{b}$ (or $\mathbf{a} \wedge \mathbf{b}$ in some books) which leads to a vector quantity. If θ is the angle between the two vectors **a** and **b**, then

$$\mathbf{a} \cdot \mathbf{b} = |\mathbf{a}|\,|\mathbf{b}|\,\cos\theta$$

and

$$\mathbf{a} \times \mathbf{b} = |\mathbf{a}|\,|\mathbf{b}|\,\sin\theta\;\hat{\mathbf{e}}$$

where $\hat{\mathbf{e}}$ is a unit vector perpendicular to the plane of **a** and **b** such that **a**, **b** and $\hat{\mathbf{e}}$ form a right-handed system. If **a** and **b** are written in component form

$$\mathbf{a} = a_1\hat{\mathbf{i}} + a_2\hat{\mathbf{j}} + a_3\hat{\mathbf{k}} = (a_1, a_2, a_3)$$
$$\mathbf{b} = b_1\hat{\mathbf{i}} + b_2\hat{\mathbf{j}} + b_3\hat{\mathbf{k}} = (b_1, b_2, b_3)$$

then

$$\mathbf{a} \cdot \mathbf{b} = a_1 b_1 + a_2 b_2 + a_3 b_3$$

and

$$\mathbf{a} \times \mathbf{b} = \begin{vmatrix} \hat{\mathbf{i}} & \hat{\mathbf{j}} & \hat{\mathbf{k}} \\ a_1 & a_2 & a_3 \\ b_1 & b_2 & b_3 \end{vmatrix}$$

$$= \hat{\mathbf{i}}(a_2 b_3 - a_3 b_2) + \hat{\mathbf{j}}(a_3 b_1 - a_1 b_3) + \hat{\mathbf{k}}(a_1 b_2 - a_2 b_1)$$

Two other products involve three vectors, **a**, **b** and **c**. They are the scalar triple product and the vector triple product. The scalar triple product is defined by

$$\mathbf{a} \times \mathbf{b} \cdot \mathbf{c} = \begin{vmatrix} a_1 & a_2 & a_3 \\ b_1 & b_2 & b_3 \\ c_1 & c_2 & c_3 \end{vmatrix}$$

where $\mathbf{c} = c_1\hat{\mathbf{i}} + c_2\hat{\mathbf{j}} + c_3\hat{\mathbf{k}} = (c_1, c_2, c_3)$ and no parentheses are necessary since $\mathbf{a} \times \mathbf{b}$ must be performed first. From the properties of determinants, all the following are the same:

$$\mathbf{a} \times \mathbf{b} \cdot \mathbf{c},\; \mathbf{a} \cdot \mathbf{b} \times \mathbf{c},\; \mathbf{c} \times \mathbf{a} \cdot \mathbf{b},\; \mathbf{c} \cdot \mathbf{a} \times \mathbf{b}$$

The vector triple product *does* need parentheses. A useful identity is:

$$\mathbf{a} \times (\mathbf{b} \times \mathbf{c}) = (\mathbf{a} \cdot \mathbf{c})\mathbf{b} - (\mathbf{a} \cdot \mathbf{b})\mathbf{c}$$

and this is certainly not the same as

$$(\mathbf{a} \times \mathbf{b}) \times \mathbf{c} = (\mathbf{a} \cdot \mathbf{c})\mathbf{b} - (\mathbf{b} \cdot \mathbf{c})\mathbf{a}$$

If $\mathbf{r}$ is the position vector of a mass which is subject to a force $\mathbf{F}$, then the moment of this force about the origin is $\mathbf{r} \times \mathbf{F}$.

The rules of differentiation also carry over to vector variables so that, for example,

$$\frac{d}{dt}(\mathbf{a} + \mathbf{b}) = \frac{d\mathbf{a}}{dt} + \frac{d\mathbf{b}}{dt}$$

$$\frac{d}{dt}(\alpha\mathbf{a}) = \alpha\frac{d\mathbf{a}}{dt} + \frac{d\alpha}{dt}\mathbf{a}$$

$$\frac{d}{dt}(\mathbf{a} \cdot \mathbf{b}) = \frac{d\mathbf{a}}{dt} \cdot \mathbf{b} + \mathbf{a} \cdot \frac{d\mathbf{b}}{dt}$$

$$\frac{d}{dt}(\mathbf{a} \times \mathbf{b}) = \frac{d\mathbf{a}}{dt} \times \mathbf{b} + \mathbf{a} \times \frac{d\mathbf{b}}{dt}$$

Note that we *never* divide by a vector.

The gradient operator, ∇, is defined by

$$\nabla \equiv \left(\frac{\partial}{\partial x}, \frac{\partial}{\partial y}, \frac{\partial}{\partial z}\right)$$

Thus we can define $\nabla\phi$, where ϕ is a scalar, as

$$\nabla\phi = \hat{\mathbf{i}}\frac{\partial\phi}{\partial x} + \hat{\mathbf{j}}\frac{\partial\phi}{\partial y} + \hat{\mathbf{k}}\frac{\partial\phi}{\partial z}$$

The divergence operator $\nabla \cdot \mathbf{F}$ is defined by

$$\nabla \cdot \mathbf{F} = \frac{\partial F_1}{\partial x} + \frac{\partial F_2}{\partial y} + \frac{\partial F_3}{\partial z}$$

where $\mathbf{F} = F_1\hat{\mathbf{i}} + F_2\hat{\mathbf{j}} + F_3\hat{\mathbf{k}}$, so that the literal translation of $\nabla \cdot \mathbf{F}$ as the dot or scalar product of ∇ with $\mathbf{F}$ is justified.

Finally, we define $\nabla \times \mathbf{F}$ by

$$\nabla \times \mathbf{F} = \begin{vmatrix} \hat{\mathbf{i}} & \hat{\mathbf{j}} & \hat{\mathbf{k}} \\ \frac{\partial}{\partial x} & \frac{\partial}{\partial y} & \frac{\partial}{\partial z} \\ F_1 & F_2 & F_3 \end{vmatrix}$$

$$= \hat{\mathbf{i}}\left(\frac{\partial F_3}{\partial y} - \frac{\partial F_2}{\partial z}\right) + \hat{\mathbf{j}}\left(\frac{\partial F_1}{\partial z} - \frac{\partial F_3}{\partial x}\right) + \hat{\mathbf{k}}\left(\frac{\partial F_2}{\partial x} - \frac{\partial F_1}{\partial y}\right)$$

Vector integration is a little more tricky. The secret of all vector integration is to parametrise. The work done by a unit mass moving along a curve C subject to a force $\mathbf{F}$ is the line integtral

$$\int_C \mathbf{F} \cdot d\mathbf{r}$$

For example, suppose the force is given by

$$\mathbf{F} = yz\hat{\mathbf{i}} + zx\hat{\mathbf{j}} + xy\hat{\mathbf{k}}$$

and the curve C is the twisted cubic $x = t$, $y = t^2$, $z = t^3$ between $(0,0,0)$ and $(1,1,1)$. On C,

$$\mathbf{F} = t^5\hat{\mathbf{i}} + t^4\hat{\mathbf{j}} + t^3\hat{\mathbf{k}}$$

and

$$dr = \hat{i}dx + \hat{j}dy + \hat{k}dz$$

$$= \hat{i}dt + 2t\hat{j}dt + 3t^2\hat{k}dt$$

Hence

$$\mathbf{F} \cdot \mathbf{dr} = t^5dt + t^4 \cdot 2tdt + t^3 \cdot 3t^2dt = 6t^5dt$$

on the curve C. Finally, the extremes of C are given by $(0,0,0)$ $t = 0$ and $(1,1,1)$ $t = 1$, so that work done,

$$\int_C \mathbf{F} \cdot \mathbf{dr} = \int_0^1 6t^5dt = 1$$

If the force is conservative, then $\nabla \times \mathbf{F} = \mathbf{0}$. However, if C is a closed curve enclosing the surface S, we have the result

$$\int_C \mathbf{F} \cdot \mathbf{dr} = \int_S \nabla \times \mathbf{F} \cdot \mathbf{dS} \qquad \text{(Stokes' theorem)}.$$

Hence

$$\int_C \mathbf{F} \cdot \mathbf{dr} = 0$$

for a closed curve C and a conservative force $\mathbf{F}$.

Fuller, more complete treatments of vectors can be found in specialist texts, for example Bourne and Kendall (1977).

Appendix B: Differential Equations

By their very nature, the equations that arise from mechanics involve rates of change. The solution of differential equations is a very large topic in mathematics, larger perhaps than mechanics itself. In this appendix we can only briefly summarise some solution methods; we adopt three headings: first-order equations, second-order equations and numerical methods of solution.

B.1 First-order Equations

These are equations which have the general form

$$\frac{dx}{dt} = f(x, t) \tag{B1}$$

with one boundary condition, usually of the form $x = x_0$ when $t = t_0$. Let us look at special cases.

Case 1: If $f(x,t)$ is of the form $a(x)b(t)$, the equation is separable, and we can write

$$\int \frac{dx}{a(x)} = \int b(t)dt$$

This is the simplest case.

Case 2: If Equation (B1) is of the form

$$\frac{dx}{dt} + P(t)x = Q(t)$$

where P and Q are functions of t, then we have a linear equation of the integrating factor type. The factor $R(t) = \exp\left[\int P(t)dt\right]$ can be calculated and it is easily shown that

$$\frac{d}{dt}(xR(t)) = Q(t)R(t)$$

so that it is straightforward to integrate both sides with respect to t. $R(t)$ is called the integrating factor.

Case 3: If the function $f(x,t)$ can be rearranged so that it only depends on the ratio x/t, then Equation (B1) can be solved by separating variables. Some examples are given below:

(1)
$$t^2 \frac{dx}{dt} = xt + t^2 + x^2$$

which, with $u = x/t$ is

$$t\frac{du}{dt} = 1 + u^2$$

which is separable.

(2)
$$\frac{dx}{dt} = \sin\left(\frac{x}{t}\right)$$

becomes

$$t \frac{du}{dt} = \sin u - u$$

which is separable.

(3)

$$t^2 \frac{dx}{dt} = x^2 + t^2 \sin\left(\frac{x}{t}\right)$$

becomes

$$t \frac{du}{dt} = u^2 - u + \sin u$$

which is separable.

B.2 Second-order Equations

We restrict ourselves to considering the equation

$$a \frac{d^2 x}{dt^2} + b \frac{dx}{dt} + cx = A\sin\sigma t \qquad \text{(B2)}$$

where a, b, c, A and σ are constants. This equation occurs in mechanical oscillations, for example.

First of all, we examine the case for which $A = 0$, called the homogeneous case. The technique is to try solutions $x = e^{\lambda t}$ and obtain the equation

$$a\lambda^2 + b\lambda + c = 0$$

which is called the auxiliary equation. Call the roots of this equation λ_1 and λ_2. The three cases (real distinct roots, real coincident roots, complex conjugate roots) lead to the three types of solution to Equation (B2) (with $A = 0$).

If $b^2 > 4ac$: $\quad x = A_1 e^{\lambda_1 t} + B_1 e^{\lambda_2 t}$ (B3(a))

If $b^2 = 4ac$: $\quad x = (A_2 + B_2 t)e^{\lambda t} \quad (\lambda_1 = \lambda_2 = \lambda)$ (B3(b))

If $b^2 < 4ac$: $\quad x = e^{\alpha t}(A_3\cos\beta t + B_3\sin\beta t) \quad (\lambda_1, \lambda_2 = \alpha \pm i\beta)$ (B3(c))

where A_1, A_2, A_3, B_1, B_2, B_3 are arbitrary constants.

Of course, in vibration/oscillation problems the solution is usually sinusoidal in character. As far as Equation (B2) is concerned, these solutions apply only if $A = 0$ and are called the complementary functions. A particular solution to Equation (B2) may be found by elementary methods. (Either write the RHS as $-A i e^{i\sigma t}$ and look for $x = z e^{i\sigma t}$ as solution, then take the real part, or look for $x = k_1 \cos\sigma t + k_2 \sin\sigma t$ and equate coefficients of $\cos\sigma t$ and $\sin\sigma t$.) The particular solution so found is

$$x = \frac{-A\sigma b \cos\sigma t - A\sigma^2 a \sin\sigma t}{(c - a\sigma^2)^2 + b^2\sigma^2} \qquad \text{(B4)}$$

Hence the general solution will be one of Equation (B3) plus Equation (B4). An interesting case arises if $\sigma = \beta$. This is called resonance and causes $x \to \infty$ if $b = 0$.

If Equation (B2) is generalised and a function $f(t)$ is the RHS, Fourier decomposition can be employed to render this new equation into one amenable to similar analysis to the above.

Note that if a, b and c were replaced by vectors $\mathbf{a}$, $\mathbf{b}$ and $\mathbf{c}$, then the solutions (B3) would be as written, but with vector arbitrary constants. To solve the general non-homogeneous version of Equation (B2), however, would require slightly different matrix techniques based on eigenvalues and eigenvectors. For these and other methods of solving differential equations analytically, specialist texts should be consulted.

B.3 Numerical Methods for Solving Differential Equations

Most undergraduates will have become familiar with numerical solutions of differential equations. Therefore, only very brief notes are given here.

There are basically two types or classes of numerical method for solving an equation of the type (B1): single step methods or multi-step methods. Single step methods are exemplified by Euler's method, by which

$$\frac{dx}{dt} = f(x,\ t), \qquad x = x_0,\ t = t_0$$

is replaced by

$$x(t + \Delta t) = x(t) + \Delta t\, f(x(t),\ t)$$

That is dx/dt is replaced by $[x(t + \Delta t) - x(t)]/\Delta t$, the forward difference, and $f(x,t)$ is evaluated at the earlier (known) time. This method is inaccurate but easy to apply (cheap and cheerful). Various modifications of this method, whereby $f(x,t)$ is evaluated more accurately, for example the Runge–Kutta methods reduce the truncation error but increase computational complexity – the classic trade off. The multi-step approach is better if there is a certainty about the accuracy of several points of the solution, so that these can be used as the springboard to obtain later solution values. Two well-known multi-step methods are the Adams–Bashforth method:

$$y_{k+1} = y_k + \frac{h}{24}\left(-9f_{k-3} + 37f_{k-2} - 59f_{k-1} + 55f_k\right)$$

and the Milne method

$$y_{k+1} = y_{k-1} + \frac{h}{3}\left(f_{k-1} + 4f_k + f_{k+1}\right)$$

This latter is based on Simpson's rule for approximate integration.

Second-order equations can be reduced to a pair of first-order equations, as shown in Chapter 12. These then become amenable to solution by numerical means. However, multi-step methods become more difficult to apply.

Bibliography

Andronov, A. A. and Chaikin, C. E. (1949). *Theory of Oscillations*. Princeton University Press, Princeton.

Anton, H. and Rorres, C. (1987). *Elementary Linear Algebra with Applications*. John Wiley, Chichester.

Bourne, D. E. and Kendall, P. C. (1977). *Vector Analysis and Cartesian Tensors*. Nelson, London.

Chester, W. (1979). *Mechanics*. George Allen & Unwin, London.
  An excellent textbook covering all, and more, of the material in this book (except Poincaré maps).

Chorlton, F. (1977). *Textbook of Dynamics*. Van Nostrand, New York.
  Full of good examples; readable too. First published 1963, so perhaps a little dated.

Dyke, P. P. G. and Whitworth, R. W. (1992). *Guide to Mechanics*. Macmillan, Basingstoke.
  A modern, gently paced introduction. An ideal preliminary to this *Work Out*.

Jordan, D. W. and Smith, P. (1987). *Non-linear Ordinary Differential Equations*. Oxford University Press, Oxford.
  Ideal background for Chapter 12.

Lunn, M. (1991). *A First Course in Mechanics*. Oxford University Press, Oxford.
  Excellent vectorial treatment of mechanics. Particularly good for orbits.

McCluskey, S. W. (1959). *Introduction to Advanced Dynamics*. Addison-Wesley, Wokingham.

Quadling, D. A. and Ramsay, A. R. D. (1963). *Elementary Mechanics*. Bell, London.
  The text is now rather old, but the examples are worth examination. Good for Chapters 2 and 3.

Ramsay, A. S. (1954). *Dynamics*, Vols I & II. Cambridge University Press, Cambridge.
  Now old and out of print. Some classic questions, but they tend to be over-dependent on geometry. Still an excellent source book for problems.

Smith, P. and Smith, R. C. (1990). *Mechanics*. John Wiley, Chichester.
  Perhaps the best modern textbook on mechanics. Very readable.

Spiegel, M. R. (1967). *Theoretical Mechanics*. McGraw-Hill, New York.
  Now rather dated in approach; nevertheless a serious rival to the present text.

Synge, J. L. and Griffith, B. A. (1960). *Principles of Mechanics*. Dover, London.
  The classic text. Some material has dated, but it is still an extremely rich source-book. No vectors to speak of.

Thompson, J. M. T. and Stewart, H. B. (1986) *Nonlinear Dynamics and Chaos*. John Wiley, Chichester.
  A research text for further reading from Chapter 12.

Whitaker, E. T. (1960). *Analytical Dynamics of Particles and Rigid Bodies*. Cambridge University Press, Cambridge.
  An advanced text. The classical treatise for specialist final year courses. However, this is a non-vectorial treatment.

Woodhouse, N. M. J. (1987). *Introduction to Analytical Dynamics*, Oxford University Press, Oxford.
  Brief but excellent vectorial treatment that takes the material of Chapter 11 further. Recommended for final year undergraduates.

Index